Also by Marvin Brauer

POETRY

Rattler

Where the Redbud Grows

Wander

Leanin' In (with Suzanne Deshchidn, Charles Van Gorkom, Tim Riter, Mary E Demuth, Spencer Ridley, Wendy Ridley)

Southern Woman

Poet in Love

Brauer's Book of Hours

PROSE

Shall Die By the Sword

The Little Schoolhouse
by the River

The Little Schoolhouse by the River

A Young Teacher's Odyssey

MARVIN BRAUER

Raven Croaks Publishing

Raven Croaks Publishing, San Bernardino
ISBN 978-1-957743-02-8

Editor Julienne Brauer
Interior design by Ronald Brauer & Marvin Brauer
Cover by Mary Rumford

www.ravencroaks.com

For all the Children I'll never forget:

Mike
Ron
Doug
Kelli
Shon,
Danny
Carolyn
Steven
Heather
Roy
Cory
Chrissie
Angie
Chad
Heather
Wayne
Justin
Kimberley
Doyle
Katie
Misty

Book One: Summertime

CHAPTER 1

TAKE ME TO THE RIVER

The summer was drawing to a close and the dog days of August were upon me. My car had no air-conditioning and the heat had been mounting ever since Vail. Behind the driver's seat, my silver Corolla was stuffed with clothes, shoes, books, records, my stereo, a sleeping bag, and a pillow, in other words, the essence of my possessions. It was 1981 and I was alone in my car.

I was steering with my right hand. My left rested on the open window. Out the window was the Colorado River. Its muddy, virescent waters soothed my worries like a balm. Whenever chance allowed, whenever the winding, two lane road permitted, I kept stealing glances at the river.

In the depths of the Glenwood Canyon the highway had an abundance of twists and turns, so I could not look often, but I kept wanting to sneak peeks. The river was quiescent here, backed up as it was by a small power dam. And on either side of my little car the steep walls of the canyon rose sharply. Down at the bottom, where the road was, it was a shadowed patchwork.

I had spent my summer working in the aspen enchanted mountains at Glacier View Ranch. The crispness of the Colorado

Rockies, the mountain air, the sweep of the breezes over the tarn, the aromas of the Ponderosa pine, had as always enthralled me, but that was over. This morning, with a packed car I had driven away from my parent's Westminster home; followed the road over the mountains and through the newly constructed Eisenhower tunnel.

Less than three months had passed since I had donned the graduation regalia, marched across the stage, and had my tassel flipped. With an education degree in hand, I was now headed for my first teaching assignment. I took in a deep breath and slowly exhaled. Though I looked forward to it, I did have significant trepidations. For the moment, however, my eyes needed to remain focused forward. In 1981 Interstate Seventy, I-70 for short, had not yet been finished. It would be another decade before the freeway through the canyon would be completed. They still had a lot of complex engineering, environmental studies, and politics to be argued out. I was young. My journals were plastered with Greenpeace stickers. Whatever was best for the environment was good for me.

And then I was through the canyon and the interstate resumed. The prevailing speed limit was fifty-five miles per hour. We were a country keenly aware of our increasing dependence on foreign oil. Before leaving office, Jimmy Carter had instituted a nationwide speed limit. The eighty-miles-an-hour speed limit was history. I tried to be a good citizen and was mostly compliant.

Glenwood Springs passed by quickly. I had but a moment to glance at the historic inn and hot springs, but a moment to recall memories of swimming there whenever my father had had preaching assignments in the area.

The valley opened up and the tiny towns of New Castle and Silt slipped by drawing nary a look. The biggest town in the area, Rifle, with a population of approximately thirty-five hundred, was next. Roll on. Then the interstate crossed the river and the Colorado flowed on my left.

My destiny lay before me. I was headed to an unincorporated area of Garfield County called Rulison. A humble, two room, church school lay empty. In one week, I would be the teacher.

Majoring in elementary education, minoring in history, I had graduated from Union College, an Adventist school, in Lincoln, Nebraska in May. I had received multiple job offers from Minnesota, Kansas, Nebraska, and Colorado. But the small one-teacher-school in Colorado won out.

Initially, at the interview in the spring, the school board had projected five grades and ten maybe twelve students. Even though my training had emphasized multi-grade classrooms and I knew the theory—how in this environment one had to be more adaptive, more efficient and adjust quicker—still multi-grade classrooms were more difficult. Everyone agreed. But since for me, schoolwork came easy, I had downplayed it. My Achilles heel, my vulnerability, was my conceitedness and it had been amply fertilized. The roots of my pride were deep. Now, as I was driving to the school I was ruminating. I was having second thoughts. I was rueing my flaw.

For the spring interview Mr. Rice had driven me over the mountains. We had met at the conference office in Englewood. I knew that building well. My father had worked there. My mother still did. Mr. Rice was the education supervisor for the Rocky Mountain Conference of Seventh Day Adventists. He had also been the one to initially sound me out on the job. Intelligent, well-spoken, somewhere in his late fifties, with a well-established male pattern baldness, Bob Rice impressed me. My departmental chair at Union also highly esteemed him along with his two associates. She believed the Rocky Mountain Conference Education Department was the best in the Mid-America Union. If I got a job offer from Colorado, she recommended that I jump on it. In any case, I already favored Colorado. I had lived there a number of years, and my parents were living in Westminster near Boulder. Furthermore, Colorado had the mountains. It was beautiful. But that had been March, now I was coming to Rulison by myself.

Over the summer, news kept rolling in, enrollment was increasing. From the five grades and ten students initially forecasted, they were now talking about seven grades and sixteen students. It was becoming overwhelming. I had qualms of failure and did not want to disappoint everyone.

The exit approached and I slowed down. Looking across the river, there was no town, no gas station, no stores, just an exit without a discernable purpose. I drove under the interstate and then over a bridge. The road went over the river and up the hill. Surrounded by fields of green alfalfa and hay, I continued up the county road and turned east on County Road 309. The school was a few hundred yards past the turn. Being August, the grounds were, of course, empty. I expected nothing else. I pulled into the driveway and turned off the engine. This was my school. Apparently, there would be a herd of kids, a flock, a bevy, a swarm, like a school of fish. Right, a school of kids.

But for now, I wanted to wander, amble, pause, imbibe the atmosphere, let it settle like water in these dry lands, slowly sink in. This was my school, my school, and I would be the only teacher. Mine. And I was excited.

Slowly I got out of the car and with one hand on the roof of my car, I made a three-hundred-and-sixty-degree survey of the school and property. Drawing the keys out of my pocket I walked up the short dirt driveway. To my eye it was all beautiful.

The schoolhouse, painted a quaint pale-yellow trimmed with aqua, was situated at the rear of the property. The roofing was tar patch and green. (There was a second structure at the front, but since it was in no condition of occupancy, and was rarely used except as an excellent place for hide and seek, it will get little mention.) A simple staircase led to the foyer. To the west of the schoolhouse was a small cement playground for children's games: dodgeball, four-square, jacks, and even basketball with a backboard and net. Above the driveway, the land was a dry lawn. Below, it was patchy bunchgrass, gravel, and dirt. There were two large poplar trees that shaded the slide, the swing, the merry go round, and the teeter totter. The grounds were enclosed by

4

fencing stapled to rough cut pine posts. All in all, the grounds were not larger than any ordinary housing parcel along the road.

Midway and just to the right of the driveway stood the flagpole. It was constructed of two overlapping slender tree trunks spliced together. It was nearly perpendicular and spoke volumes about the industry and self-dependence of the community. No need to buy a metal pole when a perfectly serviceable flagpole could be made with local talent. The air was still, and the rope hung limp.

To the left of the staircase, on the southern wall, the second set of steps led down to the cellar, which was the coal room. It was dark. I found the string that hung from the bare lightbulb in the center of the room and gave it a yank. With the light on, the bin along the wall was visible. It overflowed with locally mined bituminous coal. A black cast iron coal stove took up the central position of the room. It was the school's only heat source.

When winter came — and winter always came to Colorado — my duties would include keeping the coal stove, shoveling coal into it in the morning, lighting the fire, refilling it on snowy days. I had been warned on cold days I should expect to arrive early.

"On cold days you will need to allow time for the stove to heat the classroom."

They had discussed it at the interview, along with assurances that it was not complicated. Yes, there were a few tricks, which they would teach me when I returned. Most importantly I needed to make sure when it was cold, even on weekends or holidays, not to let the fire completely go out. Frozen pipes were a disaster.

"Keep some coals simmering Mr. Brauer." I had nodded then, during the interview, but for the present it was August in Colorado, and it was hot and dry.

Back outside, I climbed the stairs to the front door. At the entrance I turned around again to view the grounds. Sliding the key into the lock I turned it and pulled the door open. There was a water fountain in the foyer. I took a drink. It was well water — good, cold, and refreshing. To the left were two bathrooms: boys and girls. To the right were the classrooms. The one on the north

5

was the main room. When I had been here before, it had been at the end of winter, and we had arrived in the darkness.

Now it was late afternoon, and the view looking out of the big bank of windows on the outside wall was breathtaking. The sun shone brightly on the Book Cliffs.

The Book Cliffs, the south-facing cliffs that so abruptly terminated the buttes north of the river; the desert mesas of Western Colorado and Utah; these plateau-shaped mountains rising in near vertical ascents. The valley floor here was at about five thousand feet. The Book Cliffs rose to maybe seven thousand feet of cretaceous sandstone topped with a mesa. Early settlers had thought they looked like a bookcase, hence their name.

As a boy of Colorado, the mountains reassured me. Their endurance, their persistence, their silent observance, how they towered above the valley, so motionless at least to our transient human ears, though I had recently read that they did make sounds which could be recorded, a slow grinding of rock on rock, but not in a way that we could intuit.

At the front of the room was a big, oak, teacher's desk. I took a seat and looked out over the empty metal desks in rows before me. I sat back and gave a little attention to the drawers on either side. It struck me as quite the thing, this was my desk. I opened the drawers with a newfound ownership. They were for the most part empty. The top one had some miscellany: yellow Dixon #2 unsharpened pencils, red pencils, erasers, and rulers. The other drawers were empty. No magical talisman left to bestow gifts upon me. No magic wand. Too bad.

I spread my hands and ran my palms over the tabletop. It had numerous gashes and cuts, but since it was made of solid wood it was resilient, and the wounds were absorbed. If anything, the blemishes, the defects enhanced the desk's aesthetics with a well-earned patina. Pressing down on the desk I leaned over. Here it was. With this battle-scarred warrior at my command, how could I fail? I would be the teacher. They would be my pupils. I felt my pulse quicken, and suddenly a wave of panic hit. God help me!

6

My attention returned to the windows. They were mesmerizing. Unlatching one, I drew it open. The fields of sage that surrounded the school exuded a musky-mint aroma, and there was a milk cow, in the neighboring field, not more than twenty yards away; a fawn colored, wide-eyed Jersey, lying on the ground chewing her cud and looking at me. Her name, I would learn, was Bessie. She belonged to the Massey's who owned the fields above and behind us. Over the following year, she spent a lot of time chewing her cud and in turn being studiously observed by young eager children.

A second exit, at the front of the classroom drew my curiosity. It opened directly onto the lawn, which was long and dry. Small grasshoppers jumped before each of my steps. I wandered onto the grounds. A seasonal stream bed, currently dry, ran across the school yard. To the east, a big willow tree in the neighbor's yard rustled with a summer zephyr. A ladder stile connected the properties and I climbed three steps to the top stair and stopped. In the neighbor's yard, a picturesque wooden bridge crossed the dry stream bed.

I looked around a little more then returned to my car.

CHAPTER TWO

OUT IN THE COUNTRY

Satisfied with my reconnoiter of the school, I dug some notes out of my pocket. They were the scribbled directions to the Mitchell's house. Examining them, I wished I had been more precise in my notations. They were hardly readable. I should have taken more care, written them on a good surface. Nor did it escape my self-observation that I was soon to teach pupils the art of penmanship. Well, if I put my mind to it, I could a write a respectable hand. But now to decipher these hieroglyphics. How hard could it be to find their house? Mrs. Mitchell had said it was just up from the school, not far. I looked around. Rulison was quite rural. There were few houses. But I navigated well. I prided myself on it. This should not be difficult.

I will point out this was 1981. There were no smart phones with built-in navigation. Cellphones were decades away. I would need to find my way through the maze of country roads by reading signs, and I wanted to get there before dark.

Needless to say, I got lost. I went up wrong roads; retraced my path; tried other roads. I was clueless as to where their house was. I returned to the school and did a very unmanly thing. I called and asked for directions — I apologize to men everywhere. In specific I called the Mitchell's. Tina had given me their number. I went into the schoolhouse and called; Danny answered the phone. He would be one of my students.

He was very excited. "It's Mr. Brauer!" I could hear him call out. A moment later Tina Mitchell was on the phone. Tina was Danny's mother.

"Mr. Brauer where are you?"

"I'm at the school. I tried to find your house and got lost." It was late afternoon by now.

"I was getting worried about you. I'll send Mitch down to get you."

Mitch was Danny's father, Ron Mitchell. Mitch was the nickname his wife and most of his friends called him. I took a seat on the hood of my car and waited. A few minutes later his Volkswagen Rabbit drove into the driveway. It had the distinctive sound of a diesel. Diesel cars were very en vogue at the time. Those in the know, with resources, were buying diesel.
Danny popped out.

"Hello!" he yelled. He was grinning all over as he jumped out of the car and ran a few steps toward me, then stopped. Danny was going to be in fifth grade. He was a bonny lad, with a slight build, dark sandy hair cut a little over the ears of his narrow face, and a smile that seemed to rise with the sun and lingered long after all daylight had passed. He saw all things and held goodwill to all. He loved to laugh, and always appreciated a good joke, or actually any joke.

"Just follow me," he said. "Tina is just about to set supper. You are in for a treat, Marvin. My wife is an excellent cook." He gave me the smile of a satisfied man, then turned to Danny. "Why don't you ride with Mr. Brauer."

Danny did not need to be told twice. As I cleaned off the passenger seat, he jumped in and fastened his seat belt. His grin made me chuckle.

Up, up, up we went, my car following Mr. Mitchell's along the narrow country roads. They were a full thousand feet above the school.

In early winter or late spring, it was not uncommon for it to be snowing at their house, while down at the school it rained. We turned left onto their private road, crossed the bridge over their year-round mountain fed creek, then inclined steeply to the top of the hill. At the top we had entered a new mesa, and it steadily ascended in fields of pasture. Their house was firmly grounded above the embankment. It was a large house with a big picture window and a great stone fireplace.

Turning around and around the views everywhere were spectacular. There were horses in the fields above the house, and beyond the mountains just kept rising. To the east, in the distance, the river flowed through the valley. And across the valley the Book Cliffs! Three hundred and sixty degrees of awe-inspiring scenery.

"You have a nice piece of property, Mr. Mitchell, really nice!" I said as I shook my head.

He appreciated the wonder in my voice and told me to call him Mitch; everybody did. No one stood on ceremony here in the Western Slope. I tried. I tried to get my voice around that, I tried to say, Mitch, rather than Mr. Mitchell, but it just did not feel right. I could not do it. My upbringing would not let me make that leap. He was Mr. Mitchell to me.

He paused and looked around. "We have a hundred and sixty acres. We've been here a couple years. God has been good."

Danny ushered me into the house. Tina came out of the kitchen into the great room. "Danny has been so excited." She wiped her hands on a towel and gave me a hug. "I'm so glad you will be staying with us for a few days."

Tina Mitchell was short of stature and vibrant. She loved people, especially young people. She loved to entertain and had a gift for making everyone feel comfortable. She was world class in her hospitality gifts, and quickly made me feel at home.

Mr. Mitchell pointed to a couch, and I took a seat. Two couches formed an L shape around a 25" inch wooden television console. There was a T.V. guide on top. I sat down and noted the magazines on the side tables: *Newsweek, National Geographic, The Review and Herald, Popular Mechanics, and Seventeen.* Seventeen was a concession for which Mr. Mitchell apologized.

From my seat, I gazed out the large picture window onto the Colorado ranch. To my left was a magnificent rock fireplace, which was the focal point of the room. In the winter, it was unusual, especially in the evening, not to see a pine fire set and burning. On the hearth, neatly spaced, were wedding pictures and photos of each of the three children.

Behind the couches was the dining area and a large mahogany table. Tina was happiest when the table was full. On Saturday night, games were often played at this table: *Uno, Monopoly, Rook* (never poker!) *Clue,* and some 3M games.

The kitchen abutted the dining area, with a long deck and bar stools. I am a muggle in the kitchen and not adequate to describe it other than to say it was better equipped than any I had seen. For example, the stove had two ovens. Who had even heard of such a thing? But my mother had taught me how to clean up, and I often helped Tina and Danny, or Valerie (when she was home) with the clean-up.

I spent a lot of time in their house over the following year. Mr. Mitchell had originally built it as part of a plan for a school for wayward boys, and it had seven or was it eight bedrooms. Unfortunately, the school idea had fallen through, but the Mitchells always had guests staying with them either up the stairs where there were four bedrooms, or down the split level to the family room where there were another three bedrooms.

For those first few days I stayed upstairs in the office/bedroom. It was a big room with windows extending across the entire eastern wall. As you can imagine the sunrise made sleeping in difficult, but no matter, I had always been an early riser.

11

At supper I met David, their oldest child who was a couple years younger than me. David was stout, profoundly stout, with long, straight, blond hair, and he oozed charisma. Apparently, he had been at Union College last fall. He had been a freshman and had not lasted long before running into disciplinary problems. Thus, he had been expelled. He liked his alcohol, and Union College as an Adventist school was adamantly prohibitionist. I did not remember meeting him.

Tina would later confide in me that David had been a driving reason why Mr. Mitchell bought the ranch. David was the prototypical wayward boy, and Mr. Mitchell had hoped a boy's school, where they could work outside would be the tonic to turn David around. She also confessed that her husband and David were often at odds with each other. She blamed it on Vietnam. Her husband had worked in a MASH unit when David was a baby, thus she explained they had not properly bonded. But as you would have it the school idea had fallen apart.

However, that may be, David and I got along great. We had a mutual sense of what was funny, and we both liked history.

The Mitchell's middle child was not there. Valerie was away at a boarding school, Campion Academy along the Front Range. I knew her from my summers working at Glacier View Camp. She was a supple teenager with a disarming smile.

On one particular evening at the camp there had been a group hike-and-climb to the top of a large granite outcropping known as the Devil's Bathtub. As everyone was hanging out, sitting on the great granite boulder, enjoying the nightfall, she and another girl and I had fallen into conversation. I remembered it as being enjoyable, intelligent, and pleasantly serious. So, when it became knowledge that I would be teaching at the Rifle/Rulison school, she had prepped Danny: he was getting a great teacher. He should consider himself lucky.

While trying to resolve where I was going to live, the Mitchells had offered to put me up, which was extraordinarily kind of them.

Where I was going to live had been a dilemma for me all summer. My problem was that the salary for starting Adventist teachers was a pittance. Even being frugal, an apartment renting at three hundred dollars a month stretched me. Furthermore, the three-hundred-dollar units were depressing. On top of that, all the apartments were in Rifle, a twenty-minute drive away. I was under no false illusions. I knew I would be spending a lot of after-hours at the school. I knew I would be at my desk long into the evenings, grading papers, writing lesson plans, reviewing teacher's helps, writing tests, mimeographing papers, working on bulletin boards — I was a first-year teacher, for goodness' sake, and my class size was increasing. The extra hours did not disturb me, nor was I intimidated by the work. I could outstudy my peers and had regularly proved that. But how could I live twenty minutes away and still put in the after-hours. It was logistically impossible.

One of the options I considered was an unoccupied house about a half-mile below the school, close enough that I could walk to and fro. Over the summer, my dad and I had sought out the landlord at his house in Denver. We had talked to him while walking through his gardens. He gave it some thought, but he was asking three hundred and fifty dollars a month. I did not see how I could make that balance. So, we had looked at apartments in town. They were small, drab, and depressing. They sucked all the joy out of me. After looking at them, I decided I would have to make the three hundred and fifty dollars a month for the house, work. But the landlord had changed his mind. He no longer wanted to rent. Thus, it would be town for me. I just needed to finish up the paperwork.

CHAPTER THREE

ROCKY MOUNTAIN HIGH

The next day was Sabbath, and I followed the Mitchells on a back road to the church in Rifle. It was a new structure on the south side of the river, in a good location with ample parking. The congregation was proud of it. For one thing, they had paid off the final debt note in May. That was big.

To my eye, despite its architectural blandness, I thought it was a fine church. The sanctuary had a traditional rectangular design with golden carpet and golden pew cushions. There was a stained-glass window behind the baptistry, and plenty of light from the surrounding windows. Moreover, the sanctuary was attached to an annex with plenty of Sabbath School rooms, and a large fellowship room for potlucks and Saturday night activities. Also as I would hear on numerous occasions, the kitchen was well designed and equipped. The potlucks there would be spectacular. These observations came instinctually to me, almost as a birthright.

I was a fourth-generation Adventist. (My oldest brother claims we are sixth generation.) My great grandfather had been a pastor. Both sets of grandparents had been missionaries. My grandmother, as a baby, had been babysat at Elmshaven in the home of Adventist pioneer Ellen White. I, too, had grown up in the mission fields of Egypt and Lebanon. My father had worked there as a Pastor and then had been promoted to the division office in Beirut.

When we returned to the States on permanent return, he worked in the Colorado Conference, where he traveled almost every weekend preaching in the Colorado churches. My two older brothers had been too old to go with him on those travels, but Ron and I did. Dad now pastored a church in north Denver. My mother worked as an executive assistant for the president of what was now the Rocky Mountain Conference, Elder Bill Hatch.

As an aside, when there had been some squabbles among the permanent staff at Glacier View Ranch last summer, Elder Hatch had personally asked me to talk to him. He wanted to get my assessment on the matter. Later in talking with my mother, he had complimented me on my perception and then had added. "You know, Alice, I noted something about Marvin in my visit with him. He really has a lovely smile, just so broad and warm."

And I also want to add my mother was a genuinely gifted executive assistant. She had an amazing ability to remember everybody's story: how they were related, which elders were at the church, where pastors had been, which families were squabbling, who paid their tithe, and their children. Once she heard their story, even if it was secondhand from Bill Hatch or another departmental man, it just dropped into place in her relational database. She had told me about all the major players at Rifle before I arrived.

But I have strayed from the topic—my bona fides—how I intuitively could size up a church facility. I would also note that my two oldest brothers were now pastors as well. Bob was in Duluth, Minnesota. Jim had just recently moved to Lincoln to be an associate pastor at the college church. So yes, I indeed had had plenty of opportunities to assess church aesthetics and amenities discriminately. It was a frequent topic of conversation in my family. And the Rifle church had a lot of excellent features.

As I was standing in the fellowship hall, several members gathered around welcoming me. I complimented the church facility. Dr. McElvain Sr. was glad to point out extras they had added. One of the older men, Mr. Dix, folded his arms and rested his chin on his palm. He gave me a good inspection top to bottom. He had a ruddy face thickened with lines of someone who had spent his life working outdoors.

"So, you're the new teacher, eh."

I nodded. Wondering where this was going, but being a preacher's kid, that is to say, a PK, I had experience with such questioning. I had been in this predicament often enough.

"Well, I just want to say you have chosen a difficult path. I could never do it." The other older men nodded.

"My wife is on the school board." He continued, "She was there when you interviewed. She thinks you're awfully young." Then, he stopped and gave me another long look.

This was getting uncomfortable. Just because I had a lot of experience being grilled after church did not mean I relished it.

"Well, all I can say is you're in the frying pan now, eh? Good luck, give it a try, huh?"

The other men had a good chuckle.

"Okay, Okay, yea, well, I'm going to try."

"Good." And then there was a long awkward silence. Or at least it was awkward for me, although I think the men were comfortable just standing there looking at me.

Thus, I was pleased when Bill Holderbaum gave me a clap on the back and joined the circle. I had met Dr. William Holderbaum twice before. First, in the spring when I had interviewed—he had been the school board chairman at that time. Then again, we had met over the summer at Glacier View. He and his wife Bonnie had driven over on a weekend to see their two children.

Dr. Holderbaum was a dentist in town, over six-foot-tall, solidly built, with a strong chin. He was ebullient, confident, outgoing, and Bill and I had hit it off from the start. Our friendship had begun during the interview. After some introductory remarks by Mr. Rice and some questions about my theory on discipline, Dr. Holderbaum—and I will have to say it was hard not to call him Bill. He so much wanted me to call him Bill—but after some of the preliminaries in the interview, Dr. Holderbaum—okay, you know what, I will call him Bill. I guess it's time—Bill stopped the interview, sat back in his chair, and presented the following scenario to me.

"Marvin, I want you to think about this carefully. We have had for some time a program here on Thursdays—or some years on Fridays—where we take the children skiing. A ski slope supplies ski instructions, and we have felt since we don't have a fancy gym, like the larger schools, this was a way to get some more formal physical education. Could you be supportive of that?"

That had taken me back. I sat there for a moment, looking at all the board members.

"Seriously?" And I paused. Were they putting me on? "So, you're saying on Fridays in the winter, the children go skiing," I responded.

"And I'm assuming the teacher goes as well?" Several of the board nodded.

"And you want to know if I can support this?" I stopped and shook my head in bafflement. What was I missing? I rephrased it.

"That is, you'll pay me to go skiing every Friday with the children."

Bill was sitting back in his chair. He nodded and answered, "That sums it up."

I mirrored Bill's position. I leaned back in my chair and crossed my legs.

"Yeah...yeah. I'm on board with that. I can do that." And I gave a smile that the conference president would have approved, and laughed, and added. "You just sold me on Rifle. If you want me, you got yourself a teacher."

Bill sat there looking at me, nodding and smiling. That was definitely the start of our friendship.

Anyway, after clapping me on the back and relieving me from the awkward silence after church, Bill took over introducing me

17

to various people at the potluck. Then since I was the new teacher, I was the guest of honor; he guided me to the front of the potluck line.

Let us take a moment to discuss Adventist potlucks, particularly during the late seventies and early eighties. You see, Adventists are all about health. They do not smoke. They do not drink, not even socially. Or at least, they will certainly never admit to it. And Adventists (And while I am talking a little about Adventists, let me add the best way to tell if someone is an Adventist is how they pronounce the word. The press and non-Adventists pronounce it ad-VEN'-tist. So, if you were to say ad-VEN'tist, I would know for sure you were not an AD'ven-tist, and the last two syllables are said quickly. Okay, back to the potluck.)

The other thing is that Adventists have long advocated for a vegetarian diet. And it was understood, especially in the '70s and '80s, that at an Adventist potluck, all the dishes would be lacto-ovo-vegetarian.

And let me tell you I loved potlucks: potato salad, gluten steaks, cottage cheese loaf, coleslaw, macaroni and cheese, broccoli casserole, taco salads, deviled eggs. O man, I just salivated to see all this good food. And cakes, pies, okay, not everything was healthy, but O was it scrumptious, delicious, and just plain yummy. And since I was also a fourth-generation vegetarian—had only eaten a little meat during a rebellious teen period—I loved potlucks.

I followed Bill to a table, and then these two blond children came timidly, hesitatingly, the boy prodding his older sister in front of him, came over to our table. Bill saw them and smiled. He stuck out an arm, which gave them confidence.

"Hello Carolyn, Chad. Have you met your new teacher yet?"

They shook their heads and gave me furtive glances.

"Marvin, this is Carolyn and Chad Schlisner. Carolyn is in fifth grade with my son. Chad you're in third grade this year?"

Chad nodded his assent.

"Hello, Carolyn. Hello, Chad. I'm Mr. Brauer." I made a point of calling myself Mr. Brauer. I had been taught that was important in my education classes. "What have you two been doing this summer?"

Carolyn started talking about all the books she had been reading.

She was a little bookworm — that made sense. I had been given access to the test scores of the students. These two had scored high on the Iowa Basics Test. Carolyn had scored very high, the highest in the school. She was of a slight build, with straight, thin, blonde hair, burnt umber eyebrows, and dark oval eyes that took it all in.

She was sizing me up. It seemed, at least at the moment, I was given an initial pass. But the final judgment was far from certain.

I've been riding my bicycle," Chad blurted.

"O yes, he rides his bicycle all the time. I ride with him, some," Carolyn was apologizing for her brother. She knew, of course, that when you met a new teacher, the proper thing to say was how much you enjoyed reading, and maybe adding that you had been doing some math problems for fun in the evening.

"She rides with me a lot," Chad corrected her. I had asked them what they had been doing on their summer break. He wanted to tell the truth, that they were on their bikes most of the day. I believed him. He was a fine-looking boy, a towhead, an easy smile, and an athletic walk. He had no summer, sitting around fat. He was quick-witted and would have one of the best dispositions in the classroom. They talked to me for a little bit and then went back to their parents.

I had now met seven of my children. I had met four of them at camp over the summer, plus Danny and now Carolyn and Chad. And I was surprised. I figured I must have accidentally entered Lake Woebegone, where to paraphrase Garrison Keillor, all the children pretty good-looking because so far, they were all handsome children. What were the odds?

I mentioned to Bill that I had stayed with the Mitchell's the night before and was impressed with the views from their house, and I mentioned the rock fireplace.

Clare Livingood, sitting beside me, cleared his throat and then said, "You know 'round here rock fireplaces, well... they're not always a good idea. You must be careful. There was the man who built his own house, laid his own rock fireplace with shale. And when winter came, he lit a fire, and the whole fireplace, the rocks burst into flames. His wife and children burned up. Lots of shale in these parts, and it burns like dry pine. Rock fireplaces, I don't take to em. You never know what type of rock you have."

I was astounded—rock burning. I had never heard the like. It was beyond the scope of my experience. But I could see it in my mind's eye, and I could imagine the terror to watch the rocks of your fireplace burst into flame. Later, others would corroborate the story as true, or at least it was widely believed, and that the family had all escaped. Also, and most left this detail out, it had happened in the 1890's. Furthermore, any modern contractor worth his salt knew better than to use shale.

Still, it stuck in my mind, and I said, "Wow, rocks burning, that's almost biblical, 'even the rocks will burn.'"

The older men nodded sagaciously. They respected a biblical reference on the Sabbath.

Bill also nodded and then turned the subject away.

"Do you like horses, Marvin?"

"I love horses," I was quick to reply.

I did. During my five summers working at camp, two in Virginia and the last three up at Glacier View, I rode whenever I could. I often coordinated with another staff member on my day off, and we would take a ride during the campers' naptime.

I knew how to saddle my own horse and often found myself down at the barn just chatting with the wranglers or helping them with their chores. I even enjoyed the slower guided tours with the campers. I liked the paints, the chestnuts, the appaloosas, the bays, the sorrels, the greys, the whites, the blacks, and of course the palominos.

One of the first things I did at the start of each summer was to learn the names of the horses, their temperaments, which ones were fast, which ones were stubborn, and any little tidbits of history the wranglers might want to pass on. That was how I won most every Friday barrel race my three summers.

Most of the staff chose the acknowledged speedster Santana. On a straight course, Santana was undoubtedly the best, but one of the wranglers had told me that Valentine, a couple of hands shorter, seemed to have some experience in the ring. She had great acceleration.

So, in short, yes, I loved horses. Riding in the Colorado mountains, the warmth of the horse beneath me, the fresh air, the groves of Ponderosa pine, looking up at the salient peaks, silver-tipped with snow, Sawtooth Mountain and Longs Peak that was a great joy.

"We have a couple horses," Bill said. "You should come over this afternoon. Bonnie and the kids are away. We'll take a ride up the mountain. There is a superb grove of aspen up Cache Creek. It is an old grove."

He stopped and shook his head, almost as if he were a little choked up. "It's more beautiful than any European cathedral. Yes, it is an aspen cathedral. You can't get closer to get God than amid his natural works."

I resonated with that, both the appreciation of nature and the willingness in a man to be affected by piety.

After potluck, I changed and followed him to his house. It was just up the road from the school, tucked behind a small thicket of juniper, a ranch with a modern layout. He gave me a little tour, and then we stood outside. He was an unreserved and candid fellow, and he thought we had a lot in common. Yes, he was a little taller. I was just under six feet. I guessed he was six feet two, and he was better looking.

In my late teens when my hair was down to my shoulders and parted in the middle people often said I looked like John Lennon. Later, when I cut my hair, people would often stop me and ask me if I knew who I resembled. I heard this so many times that I would stop and wait for it, and it was always the same.

"You look like Robin Williams." And I would nod and say people had said that.

21

Now I'm just going to add, and this is from a later period, that I recently clicked on one of those Facebook quizzes to discover which movie star you look like. The three that I matched with were Chris Pratt, Chris Hemsworth, and a 97% match, yes, a 97% match with Chris Evans, you know Captain America! Pause, so dear reader, when you imagine the hero of this book, I want you to imagine him being a doppelganger of Chris Evans. That is what I want you to see in your mind's eye, and if you would please make sure to include the muscles!

But in any case, Bill thought we had a lot in common, and he was right: team sports, scholastics, and expressive personalities. And I want to add, despite the difficulties the year would bring; Bill was always in my corner.

He told me the miracle story of how he had found the house, how he had prayed for it, and it had fallen in his lap, with acreage that extended almost to the river. It did, however, have one defect; despite multiple drillings, they had not been able to prove a well, and he was miles and miles away from any city water connections.

Personally, he discounted that problem. It was not insurmountable. They had a cistern, and a water truck regularly filled it. And if perchance they ran dry, he had a fifty-gallon tank on the back of his truck, and he could drive down to the schoolhouse and fill it with a hose. He did acknowledge that Bonnie was less confident the house was a miracle.

He told me about this as we saddled their two horses, the Appaloosa, named Hopi, who he said was a little stubborn, so he would ride him, and their older quarter horse, Bullet. He might have been a bullet in his younger years. But, he was a steady trail horse now.

Bill had two children, Kelli and Shon. I had met both at camp. Kelli was going to be in sixth grade, and Shon would be in fifth grade. At camp, as soon Kelli discovered that I would be her teacher, she had latched onto me, walking, and talking to me all the time, telling everyone that Mr. Brauer was going to be her teacher. It was adorable.

Then we rode, up the road, off the trail, always up. Looking back, we could see the valley falling away, stretching behind us. Occasionally the sunshine reflected off the silver river as it ran its course. The hills, the mountains rose before us. In the late summer, a panorama of wildflowers, patches of red Indian paintbrush, and tracts filled with purple Columbine arrayed the slopes. White cloud ribbons broke up the blue skies and then slid over the peaks. I inhaled the clean air deeply while listening to the clump of the horse hooves on the trail. We went up and up. Finally, having started about one o'clock, we achieved the aspen grove near four.

We dismounted. For most of the ride, we had kept up a lengthy commentary. We had both talked. Bill had filled me in on Rifle, the church and school politics, and personalities. But now, amid this ancient grove, we were silent.

If you live in Colorado and have any sensitivity to nature at all, you love the quaking aspen. The way their heart-shaped leaves crackle like paper in the wind, the freshness of their white bark, and how they space themselves so that you can indeed walk through them in reverence. In those years, we were not aware of how aspen groves are a community, if not one giant organism, how the root systems entangle and allow the mature trees to divert nutrients to the smaller saplings. But what we did appreciate that afternoon was the quietness and the coolness of the air at eight thousand feet.

And as we turned around, we had a different vantage of the Book Cliffs across the valley, their seemingly infinite horizontal lines stretching to the vanishing point, the spectrum of colors from crimson to somber hues of brown, these products of weathering and disintegrated rock, smashed down in layers.

"I had a guy in my office recently. He is a climber." Bill said as we stood by our horses and looked back over the valley. "You know there are a lot of people who come to Rifle for the climbing. They say the limestone makes great climbing.

"Anyway, this one guy started talking about the geology of this area. This whole area from here into Utah is called the

Colorado Plateau. He said this had been one of the most stable regions in the world. There has been no great cataclysmic event in the Colorado Plateau in the past five hundred million years. While the mountains of the Front Range were rising, this area has been stable." At that, Bill looked at me with a conspiratorial wink. As Adventists, we both 'knew' the world was only six thousand years old, fossil evidence ... be darned. (The worst word a good Adventist would say. My mother used it a lot.)

"Nonetheless, it is still interesting that we have all this limestone. You see, when water dwelling microorganisms precipitate calcium, this creates limestone. The dying shells accumulate on the sea floor, moraine lake bottoms, get buried, and cement into limestone. So, for us to have limestone, that means this area had to have been at one time a large, clear, warm, shallow lake. That's how limestone forms."

I wondered where he was going with this. I had an excellent Adventist education, which meant that I had taken no geology, and rigorously ignored evolution. Noah's flood solved all the conundrums of the geological column. Layers of fossil evidence, abracadabra, "Noah's flood." Carbon dating measures uranium's decay into lead, or isotopes of potassium into argon, abracadabra, "Noah's flood." Cambrian, Pennsylvanian, Permian, Triassic, Jurassic. These names I had heard, but they meant nothing to me. We could plot out the history of the world using the recorded evidence of the Bible, and I was not in any hurry to upset my belief system.

"So, it just goes to show that the flood explains everything." He said after a pause. My discomfort was relieved, and we were back on safe theological grounds. "A big lake here, though, interesting to think about, isn't it? How this area was once all underwater, just like the Bible says."

CHAPTER FOUR

ALL THOSE YEARS AGO

In 1981 Ronald Reagan was in the first year of his presidency. I had not voted for Reagan on his first run, though I would on his reelection. Jimmy Carter, the good Baptist, peanut farmer from Georgia, had lost. In large part, he had been unable to negotiate the Iranian hostage crisis, which hurt his ratings. Reagan, after his inauguration, quickly solved it. Reagan was handsome and charming. And while I was an advocate of a larger defense, many thought he was excessive, especially as it came with a decision that the federal budget did not have to be balanced. That way, he did not have to upset his supporters by raising taxes.

When he had been shot in March by John Hinckley, we were all stunned. This was the second assassination attempt in three presidencies; of course, Squeaky Fromme of the Charles Manson cult had attempted to shoot Gerald Ford in 1975. So, now, two presidents in less than six years had been shot at.

But what had upset me more was the fatal shooting of John Lennon, just three months before Reagan. He, too, had been shot by a crazy man. At the time of Lennon's death, many conservative Christians were blatantly unperturbed. John had, after all, once said he was more popular than Jesus Christ, so this was his comeuppance; this was his judgment. Many of my Adventist classmates in college espoused these thoughts, but not me. I had been a Beatles fan since I was seven. And while at the time I did not understand how the world could be a better place if we imagined there was no religion, nevertheless I loved Lennon, and I had joined the candlelight vigil organized on the day of his funeral. At Union College, ten or twelve students, including myself, had stood there around the clocktower and silently endured religious scorning as other students gave us a wide berth. They wanted to make it clear they were not taking part in a vigil for the atheist, John Lennon.

Okay full disclosure. I was conflicted. I have always loved music, all kinds of music: pop, jazz (learned that from my conflicted pastor father), symphonic, bluegrass, organ music, hymns, but most of all rock and roll! O how I loved rock music: the Beatles, of course, The Beach Boys, Chicago, Stevie Wonder, Marvin Gaye, yes, and even The Rolling Stones and Led Zeppelin, even with the subliminal messages being played to me when you spun the record backward.

The conflict was 'the church' did not approve of rock music. In fact, it vigorously vilified the odious genre. They had sho made their livings going around to conservative schools exposing the wickedness of the stars.

I had been to several 'burn the vinyl parties.' I had listened and felt guilty. Not quite guilty enough to burn my Santana albums, even though he did sing about an *Evil Woman*. But I wanted to conform, to fit in. I very much wanted to be a good Adventist. So, instead of burning my albums, I made resolutions. I even wrote them in my journal. I was going to stop listening to rock music.

But how in the world could you possibly avoid listening to the radio. (And just a sidenote, in 1981, you listened to music either on vinyl, cassette, or radio—eight-track was dead by eighty-one—preferably FM. There was no internet, no Spotify, or Apple play.) But back to my point, how did you possibly avoid listening to the radio when the Police were in their prime with: *Roxanne, Don't Stand So Close to Me* or the impossibly creepy *Every Breath You Take*. And they would put out *Every Little Thing She Does Is Magic* in the fall. That indeed was magic.

And how did you not roll down the window and harmonize with Blondie in a *Tide is High* or feel exactly what Fleetwood Mac meant when they sang over and over and over *Hold Me* I was young and single and when Foreigner sang *Waiting for a Girl Like You*, let me tell you, it resonated. In 1981 Linda Ronstadt was in the midst of her record-breaking career, platinum record after record, and O my, her voice, just slew me. Seriously, it was not uncommon for my voice to choke up when I was listening to her, and I was not the only young man in the States taken with her. So, for the most part, when I was driving that year, despite my good intentions, I was listening to the radio, waiting for the hits I liked. And then at night making new resolutions in my journal.

CHAPTER FIVE

COME TOGETHER

When I sat down at my desk in the schoolhouse the following morning, my rear end was numb. I was entirely unconditioned to six hours in the saddle, and my bum was feeling it. Notwithstanding, I was down at the school early, real early. They had scheduled an old-fashioned work-bee for today, and I wanted to be prepared. I made lists and outlined projects. I broke them up into manageable tasks. I had had some mentoring the year before on project management by the college president. He had presented a daylong seminar to the oncoming student body officers on organization and planning. As president, I had avidly soaked up his ideas. They were a fine model on how to organize complex tasks.

When the church members, the parents, the older men, and the older women, started arriving, everyone just launched into the tasks they saw that needed completion. The women took over the inside of the building, straightening up, cleaning windows, cleaning bathrooms, scrubbing out the desks, floors, cobwebs. No one was in charge. It was like a beehive where everyone knew what to do. They did treat me with respect, making sure to ask my opinion when I happened to be near, smiling at my lists.

"How were you planning to line up the desks?" Or "Do you want the teacher's desk back to the window?"

I looked at my notes. Organizing the desks was not on the list. "Umm, uh, yes, we could...."

"Well. What if we put your desk up here? That way you are close to the backdoor? You have this chalkboard behind you, and it is the better chalkboard."

"Yes, um, okay, that looks good."

And then Mrs. Forshee, who had been going through the closets, called out, "I found the chalk. You will have to order some more, Mr. Brauer. It is getting low, but this will get you through the first couple of weeks."

"Well, great, that's wonderful. But um, I'm going to see what's happening outside."

"That's fine, Mr. Brauer. We got it here."

I went into the foyer and stopped. The women were talking about me.

"He's so young."

"Yes, but he seems nice."

"The conference was very high on him."

"Yes, I heard that, but teaching is very hard, especially when you have no experience."

"Then we will have to support him, won't we?"

I descended the stairs. One man was mowing. A couple of men were checking and tightening the connections on the playground equipment: the merry-go-round, the swings, the slides, the teeter-totter.

After arriving in his truck, Dr. Holderbaum began putting up a new basketball net. I went over to help. Roy Leatherman gravitated beneath the net.

I had met Roy earlier in the morning. He had come with his mother, Linda, and his siblings Bobo (who halfway through the year decided he did not want to be called by his middle name anymore, and we should call him by his first name, Wayne.) and Katie.

When he arrived, I had tried to talk to Roy, introduced myself, asked him some questions, but he would not have it. He did not see any reason why a conversation with another new teacher would be to his advantage. His attitude had elicited a short rebuke from his mother, and he had then perfunctorily answered my questions. Roy was going to be in fourth grade. He was too old to need his teachers to tell him what to do, and he certainly was not looking for a friend. Roy had a reddish-blond mop of hair and freckles. He was a regular Norman Rockwell-looking kid and earnest. Confidentially, his mother had said that Roy took life too seriously since his father was rarely in the picture. I nodded, understanding a little more.

I was standing on the back of Dr. Holderbaum's truck when Roy came over. His attitude of nonchalance was fading quickly. It was clear he liked basketball.

"You want to help?" I asked.

"Can I?" He scrambled up. I showed him how to attach the net to the rim. Roy was in fourth grade, but he was already tall. He was a big kid. Only Ron in seventh grade would be taller.

After he finished the last part of the net, he turned to me. I could see him formulating his question, almost afraid to ask, afraid where it might lead. But then he mustered his courage and asked, "Do you like basketball, Mr. Brauer?"

"I do."

And it was like a distant rain coming across the mountains, the way his smile just spread across his face and then filled him, and that serious young man began to almost jiggle. He was so pleased.

"I love basketball," he gushed.

"How about football, do you like football too?" I asked.

"O yeah, I like to play receiver."

"Great, I played quarterback in college."

And he just stood there smiling.

"In fact, the next thing we are going to do today is to build a field up there in the Massey's land."

The rest of the day, Roy hung around me talking about basketball or just digging in and helping. I had a little posse that tagged around with me all day: Roy, Bobo, Katie, Kim, Doyle, and Danny.

To clarify—I am afraid I might have given the wrong impression—when I mentioned playing quarterback in college, I suspect a few of you conjured these images of me on the gridiron in shoulder pads, knee pads, a white uniform, hard white helmet, a large black number 19 on the back. You imagined me under center, calling out the signals. As I take the snap and then drop it back into the pocket, it starts to collapse. I sense the All-American, two-hundred-and-fifty-pound defensive end has escaped my left tackle and is charging, ready to sack me. I scramble out to the right on that lush green turf. His heavy steps are closing, but my attention is downfield.

My star-wide receiver is getting some space. I air out the pigskin, and it sails in a beautiful spiral into the blue skies dotted by cumulus clouds in a perfect Nebraska fall afternoon. I let it fly fifty yards in the air. And it looks like I might have overthrown him, but my favorite receiver, Eric Robinette, has some jets. Man, can he fly! He catches the ball with his fingertips, arms fully extended. He is going so fast; however, though he catches it on the two-yard line, the momentum carries him out of bounds just after getting his feet down. The defensive lineman hits me, and I watch the reception from the ground. The crowd erupts in thunderous cheers.

But, no, no, you would be wrong. I played intramural flag football. Union College had no varsity teams since no Adventist colleges or high schools had varsity teams. Adventists were uniformly against competition, especially college versus college. Competition stirred up the wrong passions, passions that did not ennoble the young man. So, I just wanted to clarify. I did not want you to get the wrong impression.

Dr. Ron McElvain came over and asked me if I could come up to look over the proposed playfield with him. We went up. I had already, by this time, dropped all my detailed plans for the day in a trash bag.

Creating a field for the children to play games at recess was one of the things they had questioned me about on my interview. The question had been to discuss my philosophy of physical education. Everything in teaching is a philosophy. You do not just say you want the children to learn to read, do the math, and play outside. That is not how it is done. No, it is a philosophy. "My philosophy of education is that children need to utilize the physical as well as the mental." That comes across so much better. They wanted to know whether I would be a hands-on teacher.

"We've found it is important for the teacher to be involved in the physical education as well as the academic learning. How do you see yourself, Mr. Brauer?" They had asked. And that was when I wondered what type of field they had for sports, such as soccer, football, softball, and tag. They confessed they had limited school grounds for games, but my comments promoted many discussions. The neighbors above the school, the Massey's, were church members. They were the owners of Bessie, the Jersey cow, and they had a field just above Bessie, which was not in use. They offered it to the school. It was overgrown with sage, but that could be tilled down. With some work, we could make it into a field to play on. That was going to be the biggest project of the day.

I went with Dr. McElvain and several of the other men. We climbed the wooden stile and cut through the back corner of Massey's land. How much of the field did I think was necessary? The east end was flatter. Maybe we could clean out the top half and leave the bottom in sage. Although not ideal for softball, it would work well for most elementary children's games. Indeed, as a boy, I had played in less-than-ideal situations. Half the field meant half the work, which pleased the men. They had a tractor till what it could, and we put our backs to the rest. We put a chain around the larger sage bushes and pulled them out. We stacked them up. All the sage piled up made an impressive bundle, which of course, the kids jumped in.

About that time, we had a most unfortunate event. Clare and Mabel Livingood lived behind the school. They were brother and sister. She was a retired nurse, and he was extremely handy with projects, etc. They had both been there from the beginning of the day, helping out. He had been working on getting all the playground equipment tightened up and safe. Somehow a metal clamp had snapped and severed his finger. It was barely hanging on by some skin. His sister quickly wrapped his hand in some gauze with the first-aid kit that she had replenished just that day. They rushed him to the hospital. If we had been living in Denver, a hand surgeon might have saved the finger. But we did not live in Denver, and in 1981 Rifle did not have a helipad to transport him.

CHAPTER SIX

COUNTRY ROAD

The injury put a damper on the mood. We were worried about Mr. Livingood, but there was still work to do. Also, it had been a hot day.

In the middle of the afternoon, I was back down at the schoolhouse, helping to haul out trash bags. The ladies had cleaned out a lot. I grabbed two at a time and walked them out to Mr. Boggs's truck. He would take them into town. He and the Schlisners had a carpet store with a large trash bin.

Amid this work, another car pulled into the school driveway, an old Plymouth, which had long lost its luster. A lean, somewhat unkempt man probably in his late thirties stepped out. He had shoulder-length, curly black hair and a full beard. He looked around awkwardly. His face seemed familiar to me, though I could not place him. He asked a couple of the parents who would be the teacher this year. They pointed to me. The stranger ambled over. Now I remembered him. It was Mr. McQueary.

"Don't mean to disturb you..." he looked around at all the people doing their work. "You all are very busy...." His conversation style was soft and full of pauses.

"Do you remember me? We met this summer." He sniffed and turned around to cough. "I have to stop the cigarettes. I'm determined this time."

"Yes, I do," I answered and thought to myself the aroma might not have been tobacco. "You're Mr. McQueary, right. You own the little house down on the corner."

"Yeah, well about that...." He paused again and looked around. "Wow, look at all these people, getting it all ready for the little ones, righteous. I mean, that's heavy. All these people coming together for the children."

I smiled and looked at all the help. We probably had thirty adults all working together. It was indeed amazing.

"Well, anyway. I don't know if you took some other lease in town, but if not...." He juggled his hands as if throwing a ball back and forth. "I know I said I had decided against renting it, but uh," And he dipped his head toward the house as if the head signal meant words were not necessary.

"Yeah, I haven't finalized anything," I said, jumping into the space he had left. "I would be interested." I was excited, but I tried to hide my emotions, probably not so well.

"Would two hundred and thirty-five a month be, okay?"

O my! O my! Two hundred and thirty-five a month and I would live close to the school. I had been looking at three hundred dollars for a small apartment in town. I would get a house in the country for much less.

"Yes, yes, I'll take it. Thank you very much."

We worked out the details of when I could move in. I asked about pets. He said a cat was okay, but no dogs, which was a little disappointing. I had wanted to get a puppy, but a cat would work. I liked cats, as long as I could have a pet of some sort.

And then he shuffled back to his car, stopped, looked around at everyone working. "All of these wonderful people working for the kiddies, right on man, right on." And he drove away.

I told Ron McElvain my exciting news. He was pleased as he knew how much I wanted to be close to the school. Things were beginning to wind down; Ron and I walked around the grounds.

We could see the repainted flagpole, the spotless windows, and the freshly mowed grass. The field was ready, not perfect, but children did not need perfect for running and playing. I felt moved. This would be my school, and many people had put so much energy into it.

Ron got into his car as I stood at the door. "I'm going to go in and check on Mr. Livingood," he said as he looked around one more time. "We got a lot done." He paused. "Well, I'll see you tomorrow at registration."

CHAPTER SEVEN

BE LOYAL TO YOUR SCHOOL

Wes Peterson from the Rocky Mountain Conference was out the next day. He was tall with sandy, curly, thinning hair that was beginning to accumulate some grey. In his early fifties, Mr. Peterson was well on the way to developing a midlife spare. Loquacious, sunny, and always encouraging, he was one of the three education supervisors for the conference, and he was here to support me. The education supervisors: Mr. Rice, Mr. Peterson, and Miss Archambeau, had been worried about the projected student numbers. Sixteen students with six grades exceeded any of their recommendations, even for a seasoned teacher, and I was a rookie.

I knew Mr. Peterson on two accounts. First, I knew him because he worked with my mother at the conference office, and I had met him on several occasions when I dropped by to see her. And secondly, his daughter, Kristin, had graduated with me. She, too, was an elementary education major. She had taken a job in Missouri. I had a lot of respect for her and by transference her father.

When Mr. Peterson came into the classroom, I brought out the conference checklists and showed him how I was getting everything in the school ready. He nodded approvingly and then quickly put together a table and organized it for the registration; got the forms that needed to be signed, financial contracts, permission slips from the parents, etcetera.

Dr. McElvain arrived about an hour before registration. Since this was his first year as school board chairman, he too was grateful for Mr. Peterson's presence.

The parents came in groups and intervals. The Schlisners came with Carolyn, fifth grade, and Chad, third. Bill Holderbaum registered his children: Kelli and Shon, sixth and fifth grade, though they were still in Spain and would miss the first couple weeks. That had not been his idea, but he did not dwell on it. Dr. McElvain registered Kim, first grade. The Forshees registered Misty in first grade. The Mitchell's came down with Danny, who would be in fifth. The Boggs brought Steven, fifth, and Heather, fourth. Mrs. Leatherman had three children: Roy, Bobo, and Katie, fourth, second, and first, respectively. The Sisk's brought Doug, sixth grade. And the Opitz's brought Doyle, first. Fourteen children in six grades. Down from the rumored sixteen, the numbers were still considerably up from the ten to twelve they had promised me at the interview.

When we finished registration, the sun was setting down the valley, and the desert coolness was settling in with the twilight. Mr. Peterson walked behind the schoolhouse with Dr. McElvain for a few minutes. When he returned, he went to his car as he had a long trip back to Denver. Mr. Peterson gave us both a handshake and wished us a successful year. He promised to check back in with me in a couple of weeks.

"You will have a lot of questions for me then." And then, turning to Dr. McElvain, repeated a refrain that I had heard several times. "You are going to be very satisfied with Mr. Brauer. He comes from a good family, and everyone at the conference has high confidence in him. Of course, he will need help, but I'm sure you will provide it. The Rifle school has good credit in Denver."

He got into his car, rolled down his window, and added, "Someone told me today that this school has been here since 1917, is that right?"

Dr. McElvain confirmed it, and then Mr. Peterson drove off on the empty country road.

After Mr. Peterson left, Ron and I stood by his car, and we talked for almost another hour. He relayed that Mr. Peterson had told him that the conference would insist on me having an aide at fourteen students.

Dr. Ron McElvain was an optometrist in Rifle. He was in practice with his father, Dr. Paul McElvain. His father had been in Rifle for decades and had been the head elder at the church for an equally long time. Ron and Connie had lived in Rifle for just under a decade. He was tall and slender with a large sloping forehead, and his dark hair parted on the side. He did not have the charisma of a Bill Holderbaum nor the gravitas of Mr. Mitchell. Ron approached problems, conversations, life by systematically reducing it to its components and working each step one after the next. In my dealings over the summer with him, that had been initially somewhat frustrating. I wanted quick decisions. He was thorough, assessing each problem to make sure it was appropriate. However, by the end of the year, Ron would easily be my best friend at Rifle.

We talked about the students who were registered. He gave me a background on the families. He said that hiring an aide might be difficult, convincing the board and then finding one. Where would they find an aide? But he would try. We talked about the numbers; how fourteen was better than sixteen, way better, but I sensed regret. Not that he said that. On the contrary, he mentioned several times how much better fourteen was than sixteen, but then he would list some other child who had not registered. He mentioned the Cloningers who lived just a couple of houses from where I would be living. I had not met them yet, but I remembered her. She had taught my brother seventh grade. He said they had two children, and the oldest was the same age as his girl. He had thought they were going to enroll him.

39

Although maybe they had decided on homeschooling. There was also another first-grader, Justin, who he had been told was sure to register. That would have been sixteen, too many.

"Well, fourteen in six grades is still going to give me a challenge."

He took a big breath and looked at the half-moon straight over our head. "Yes, you are right. Well, sleep well. I'll see you tomorrow."

The next morning, I ate breakfast at the Mitchell's. I had my habitual bowl of Wheaties. Danny volunteered to come down and help me at the school. I accepted. Danny was my little buddy. Always eager to help, as well as to hang out. We checked all the books to ensure we had the right books for the right students. He was a good assistant and made the day more enjoyable.

In the evening, the school board came to the school. We all sat around the table in the second classroom. Dr. McElvain passed out the agenda. He was very thorough. We spent a great deal of time and considerable discussion on each issue: would they give me a petty cash fund to buy supplies; the flag is in bad repair, shall we move to buy a new one; the issue of Mr. Brauer's residence has been resolved as he had been offered the house around the corner. That was unfathomable to me. How could there be any discussion? But there was. Finally, at the end of the meeting the issue of an aide as recommended by the conference was brought up. The registration was fourteen students in six grades. And the conference policy mandated an aide in those circumstances. To which they turned to me to see if I felt that with only fourteen students rather than the sixteen they had been hearing, if I still felt I needed one. To which much to Dr. McElvain's credit, he thought that line of questioning was unfair.

"Mr. Brauer is a brand-new teacher. And Mr. Peterson told me that even his most experienced teachers would need an aide in those circumstances." Again, there were many opinions, though 'of course' Mr. Brauer, especially since he was so young and inexperienced, 'of course' they would need to hire an aide. But that would be much easier said than done. How were they to find an aide among the women of the church? It was not even a consideration that the aide would come from someone outside the church. That was an absolute. To be fair, I agreed. The whole point of paying money to send your child to a church school was to educate the child on the values of your church. I understood this and totally agreed. The decision was that Dr. McElvain would talk to some of the mothers who were not working. In 1981 there were still a lot of mothers who did not work. Probably in my classroom, fifty percent of the mothers did not work outside of the home.

It was nine-thirty before the meeting had ended. It took two and a half hours. We could have been done in under an hour, but Dr. McElvain had guided everything through to the answers we needed.

CHAPTER EIGHT

EDGING CLOSE TO SEVENTEEN

Since I was single, the idea of being alone every night weighed on me. Plus, I have always loved animals; hence when the Mitchells heard of a litter of adoptable kittens, I put everything else aside and picked out the tiniest little ball of yellow fur. He was so small. I christened him Mittens after a runaway cat of my childhood. But since I was still living with the Mitchells, and because they had a dog named Sugar, who they could not vouch would be safe with the kitten, I thought it would be best for him to sleep in my car at night. Poor little thing, meowing pitifully.

The Blehms lived in the house below the Mitchells. Mr. Blehm had been the man with the dream of a school for wayward boys. A couple days before I got the kitten, the Blehms had found and rescued an orphan fawn. On the day following my adoption, after putting in a good day's work at the school, I was back up at the Mitchell's for supper. While Tina was applying the finishing touches for the meal, Danny and I were outside watching Mittens exploring. To our enchantment, the fawn wandered into the yard, and the two little innocents were curious of each other. The fawn's size, however, scared Mittens. He was so big. Mittens scurried and jumped into a plastic butter dish. He was so small the walls of the dish nearly ensconced him. The fawn approached cautiously, spread his legs, and put his black nose down to touch Mitten's pink one. Danny ran inside and got his mother, and the three of us stood outside for a few minutes while the two youngsters, neither of them more than a couple of months old, made friends. I felt like I was in a Disney movie.

A couple of weeks later, when caring for the fawn became more than the Blehms wanted to provide, the Holderbaums adopted him.

I worked hard that week writing lesson plans. Since I was a brand-new teacher, the conference required me to write more complete lesson plans with the same detail I learned in college. These requirements included listing all my objectives, detailing all of my methods to reach the goals, and describing how I would be assessing the students' mastery of the objective. And by writing out my lesson plan, I mean, I was literally writing them in pencil in a big lesson planning book, each class for each grade, for each subject: mathematics, penmanship, language arts, reading, Bible, social studies, science, art, spelling, physical education. I put a piece of carbon paper under my lesson book and pressed it down hard enough to make the copy legible. Then, I was to mail them to the conference office each week, who would review them carefully to assure the students were getting a quality education.

I worked from early morning to late night each day on this. I was also preordering films that I would be showing the children to provide a variety of teaching modalities. And again, in 1980, if you were going to show an educational film, you went through the academic catalog, and filled out a requisition for an actual 16-millimeter film which, when it came, I would show using a film projector or filmstrips. I remember ordering films from the embassy of Czechoslovakia on the country's geography for a social studies section.

Apart from math, I also had to write tests for each subject, think up the questions, type them up, write a key, mimeograph off the tests. We did not have a Xerox machine in the school. That was too expensive for a small church school. So, we used the more primitive mimeograph where you hand-cranked the copies using a stencil master. The cost per page was one-twentieth that of a

Xerox machine. But the process was tedious and laborious. Then I filed them to be ready for the day.

So, I was working hard on this. And I was frustrated knowing that with fourteen students and six grades, I could not spend nearly enough time to try to be creative, make up fun skits, role play. I had too much to do.

On Thursday afternoon Ron McElvain called me. He was pleased to say that the Hesses, with their three children, would be joining the school. The oldest was a boy named Ron, who would be in seventh grade. They had two girls, Chrissie and Angie. They would be in fourth grade and third grade. Ring it up. It was now seventeen students in seven grades.

Breathe in. Breathe out. Okay, I would have to get to the school earlier. Stay later, think quicker, concentrate more. Write faster. Under no circumstances would I be able to lean back in the chair and daydream or worry, worry, worry—no time for that. I lectured myself that I was going to have to work harder. "Come on, Brauer, suck it up! You wimp! You're going to have step it up there, boy! Come on! Come on!"

"O yes also," Ron was still talking on the phone, "Justin's mother had meant to bring him for registration. He will be joining the first-grade class. Five in first grade! Isn't that amazing? That is such a good omen to have five students in first grade. It's been a long time since this school was this large, maybe never. I'm going to be honest; the parents are talking to each other. A lot of this is because of you. You've made an excellent impression. Yes, indeed an excellent impression."

Eighteen students!

I was in shock, and since I could see I was not going to be able to get my mind cleared, I got in my car and drove into Rifle. I had to pick up some things at the City Market.

CHAPTER NINE

THE BOYS ARE BACK

The city of Rifle got its name from an early settler who found a Winchester rifle on the banks of a creek. As a result, the creek was named Rifle Creek. The town formed around the stream as it merged into the Colorado River. Settled in the 1880's, it was, for a time, the stopping point of the westward-bound railroad. For decades, Rifle was a ranching town and was the supply source for the surrounding cattle and sheep ranches, which was its principal economy. But, more importantly, it was a river town, a Colorado River town. Rifle existed because of the river.

The importance of the Colorado River cannot be underestimated, not just for Rifle but for the whole southwest. Without the river, the west would be vastly different. Without the life-giving water flowing through this arid land, much of what we recognize of that region would be impossible. Most people know the Colorado as the ancient river that carved out the Grand Canyon, but it is so much more. The river's headwaters, found in the high country of the Rocky Mountains, is located at La Poudre Pass Lake. From there, it gathers tributary rivers as it makes its way down; Fraser, Eagle, Gunnison, Green, San Juan, to name just a few, all augmented its flow. Flowing down from the mountains — much of its source is the snowfall from Colorado, Wyoming, and Utah — through the Glenwood Canyon. It bisected Rifle.

Then onward, the river flows through the Colorado National Monument and Arches National Park. In Canyonland National Park, it joins with the equally impressive Green River and continues to wind through the deserts of Utah and Arizona. It defines the boundaries of Arizona and California before eventually emptying into the Sea of Cortez. The volume reaches 100,000 cubic feet per second in the summer — much less in the winter. Since the 1960's, the river has been completely depleted before reaching the Sea of Cortez. In addition to its economic properties, a river, water amidst an arid land is also a source of beauty and comfort.

For decades Rifle had coexisted beside the river as a small town. In 1981, however, Rifle was in a boom. Oil!

With the shortages of oil that followed the formation of the Middle Eastern OPEC cartel, the United States was keenly energy insecure. You might even say panicked. The Roan Plateau, which extended north and west of Rifle, had long been known to have a vast untapped fuel source. The sediments of shale, in other words, rocks, were the source. The problem in the past was that the cost of extracting the oil had been prohibitive. Now, however, with escalating gas prices it seemed economically profitable.

Exxon was the largest global company and they saw an opportunity. That fall, they were opening a major plant in Parachute, just beyond Rulison. Money and people were pouring in.

The population in Rifle that had held at about two thousand people for a couple decades had bumped almost overnight to thirty-five hundred. The town was in rapid expansion. The hospital had a general surgeon for the first time, which meant Mr. Mitchell as an anesthetist, was busier. Contractors, like Doug Sisk's father, were building houses. And with new homes came carpet. Bob Schlisner had grown up laying carpet. The Schlisners had partnered with the Boggs to open a carpet store in town. Bob had quickly taught John the trade. Their business was booming. Everyone in town was busier.

The town grocery store, the City Market, had been renovated. I needed to pick up groceries and staples for the house: a bowl and plate, some silverware, and food. My parents were sending over an extra set of dishware, but it would not be here for another week. I also needed to do my laundry. The distraction was helpful to my frame of mind.

On the drive home with the windows cranked down — remember I had no air conditioning — I turned up the radio. It had felt good to get out. I had enjoyed the feeling of being grown up, picking out the food I needed. I knew I had to be frugal, so I had avoided deserts, but after looking at all the varied options, I splurged on a small block of cheddar cheese. I was feeling good about that. So, when the Police came on the radio with their song, *Doo, Doo, Doo, De, Dah, Dah* I started singing with their nonsensical lyrics. Eighteen students. It was going to be crazy.

I took my exit off the interstate and pulled to a stop just before the river. I got out and walked to the middle of the bridge. I looked upstream. The Colorado River was a deepening blue in the early evening as I stood there and watched the water flow. The river was both constant and ever-changing. I found it soothing. Turning around I looked downstream and saw an enormous cottonwood tree on the north bank. The girth of the trunk was impressive.

I drove back up to the Mitchell's.

On Saturday night, the Boggs had invited me to play some table games with them. They also asked Danny and David Mitchell to join us. The Boggs had three children: an older son, John Jr., David's age, and Steven and Heather, also enrolled at the school. David and John Jr. were a riot together.

I had met both Steven and Heather at summer camp. I had been the boy's director, and one of my jobs was to register all the new boys as they came in on Sunday morning. We would set up a table just beyond a small grove of aspen trees in front of the

47

cafeteria. On Sundays, all the staff wore the staff uniform—a white collared polo with the Glacier View logo, a staff designation, and blue jeans.

So, I had been seated at the registration table on just another beautiful Colorado mountain day. The Boggs had arrived about eleven a.m. after we had already processed the Denver and Front Range crowd. Steven had come up to the table first. Steven had black hair, cut in the style of the early Beatles, round cheeks and prominent front teeth. I looked at his registration form. I was always curious where the students came from.

"Are you from Rifle, Steven?" I asked with some enthusiasm and gave him a deeper inspection. He was a well-built boy who handled himself well and had the appearance of quickness and agility.

He nodded. He was quiet, a quality I would be grateful for in the coming year.

"And you will be going to the church school there in Rifle?"

"It's in Rulison, not Rifle." And he gave another perfunctory nod.

"Well then…" I stood up and put out my hand. "I'm going to be your teacher." This took him by surprise, and he hesitated for just a moment.

"You're Mr. Brauer!" The young girl next to him burst into the conversation. "I'm Heather!" She put her arm on Steven's shoulder, claiming him. She had just started to register with Deanna Bragaw, the girl's director. "He's my brother!"

Everything was an exclamation mark with Heather. While Steven was taciturn, Heather was effusive, verbal, talkative. She was like a guard in basketball that needed to have a lot of ball time to be effective. Heather had blue eyes and long flaxen hair. She sparkled. No one ever mistakenly labeled Heather as reticent or shy. She had a zero quotient of bashfulness. She was a force to be reckoned with and could not be intimidated. When the upper-grade boys tried to shut her up, she would not listen. No sir, that was not Heather's style, deferring to someone just because they were older, not her mojo. Until suddenly, almost mercurially, she would be devastated and deeply wounded. Why did they make such snide comments? "Why do they hate me, Mr. Brauer?" And she would be depressed, which might even last the rest of the day. Heather was also empathetic and maternal. She was keenly aware of the younger children in school, watching out for their needs. Heather had a very high upside. She would be in fourth grade.

Steven had stepped back, watching his sister and me. He did not smile a lot, say in contrast to Danny, and when he did, it was usually more subtle, a slight upturn of the lips. He had pulled out his knife and started whittling on a dead branch. I would learn that scholastics, book learning, was not his forte. He struggled at that but put something in his hand, and magic would appear. Spatial concepts, dimensions, how they all fit together, came naturally to him. He was going into fifth grade. I also want to say that overall, he had one of the most even dispositions in the classroom. He was a joy.

Heather turned around to a couple of kids, a boy, and a girl, just now approaching, "Kelli! This is Mr. Brauer!"

The boy had a full head of blonde hair and had spent the summer outside, very tanned. He moved with athletic symmetry. He stopped and looked at Steven. He, too, was not sure to do with the information. Were not teachers the enemy?

However, Kelli, his sister, displaying her three-way lightbulb smile, looked at me and beamed.

"Steven's my brother. I'm Heather. I'm going to be in fourth grade next year." Heather repeated herself. "And Kelli and Shon are also in your school."

"I'm Kelli," Kelli jumped in. Heather and Kelli started hugging each other as they talked to me. "I'll be in sixth grade." She wanted to lay some ground rules. Yes, she loved Heather. They were best friends, but she was in sixth grade, so there was that.

"That's my brother Shon." She pointed back to her brother, who was standing beside Steven. They continued to watch their sisters. They allowed themselves a slight smile, but they were not going to hug each other and jump up and down.

49

Mrs. Boggs came up to the table with the money and introduced herself. She had watched the histrionics with amusement. She said she had heard good things about me and that she would be the Home and School leader this year. Everyone was looking forward to me coming.

I shook all their hands and got the boys registered.

After they left, Deanna gave me a big smile. Deanna and her husband Paul were elementary education majors one year behind me; I had played on football and basketball teams with Paul. He loved the Dallas Cowboys. And since this was the era of Tony Dorsett, Randy White, Too Tall Jones, he like most other Cowboy fans in that time period could be rather obnoxious. I liked him much better after Dallas lost to Joe Montana in the Super Bowl at the end of the year. It was Montana's first ring. I jest. Paul was a very good friend, and Deanna was his perfect complement. Anyway, Deanna was pleased that my first year as a teacher seemed to be starting so auspiciously.

Heather and Kelli hung around a lot that week, especially on the long Sabbath afternoon hike. They felt like I belonged to them. The boys were usually near, but not as extroverted as their sisters. For instance, Kelli and Heather bragged to all the other campers that Marvin (I went by Marvin at camp, and Mr. Brauer when I became their teacher) was going to be their teacher. That gave them status. I found it endearing.

But that had been at camp, now school was about to start, and that Saturday night, I went to the Boggs's house for games. I enjoyed getting to know everyone in the community. Everybody was friendly.

The next day at lunch with the Mitchells, David told an intriguing story from the night before. He had asked John Jr. when he was going to get married. John Jr. had a girlfriend but had been noncommittal, was not in any hurry.

David had then turned to Heather. "So, Heather, when are you going to get married?"

Everyone had laughed. Heather was ten. But Heather knew her mind. She sat up and said most seriously.

"I will get married when I get older, and when Marvin asks me."

When I heard that the next day at lunch, I choked on my mashed potatoes, buried my head in my hands, and laughed, and laughed, and laughed. The rest of the family: Mitch, Tina, Danny, David all laughed with me. It was adorable.

CHAPTER TEN

MY HOUSE

In the afternoon, I loaded up my car with possessions. I was able to get everything in the back of my Corolla. Unfortunately, my furniture would not arrive until Wednesday. I wanted to leave the Mitchell's before I wore out my welcome, not that they had been dropping any hints. Still, this was Sunday. School started the next day, and I felt it was important to be in my house with my new tiny little kitten. We were the family now.

It was not much of a drive from the Mitchell's to my house, maybe seven minutes, but this was an important step. Finished with my schooling, this was my first house.

I pulled into the driveway. The house was a one-bedroom clapboard house, and I rarely used the front entrance. Instead, I came in the back through the mudroom into a small kitchen, with a fifty's era, faux-marbled, heavily chipped, Formica deck. There was a stove, an oven, and a small sink looking over some grass in the backyard. Okay, I said one-bedroom, though there was a small room which apparently could convert into a second bedroom. It, however, even to me, a man just out of college, seemed tiny. This other bedroom also had no heat source. Then there was a small combination living room/dining room.

The bathroom was at the junction of the kitchen and dining room. The bathroom had a deep, antique pedestal, porcelain bathtub, but no shower, and a small sink, mirror, and commode. The bathtub was nice. It might have been the one thing salvaged from the house in a later era. It would have been an excellent addition to a much fancier bathroom. I liked it, but I would have preferred a shower. I was not really a bath man.

The bedroom, off the living room on the right, could fit a double bed and a dresser. Mine, which I had bought cheap, would be coming soon. I needed the dresser. But I was only too aware I did not require a double bed. I was very much single. My parents, however, were more optimistic.

When the furniture did come, I would also have a second-hand dining room table with metal legs, three chairs, and an oversized brown hideaway couch. The couch was the best piece of furniture I owned. It was new and quite comfortable. When I was at home, I spent a lot of time sitting on it. The couch was the only piece of furniture in the house that did not fit in with the décor theme I was striving for, Early American Poverty. The light bulbs hanging from the ceiling, on the other hand, fit the décor, as did the relatively small wooden windows.

There was a rotary phone on the wall of the dining room. It had a party line. I had heard of such things but did not know they still existed. Etiquette was if a neighbor was talking, the polite thing was to hang up and try again. I was not a big talker. This was not going to be a problem.

Despite a rather flat family critical acclaim that I would receive later, I loved my house. I loved the two large white poplar trees in the front yard and the small patch of grass beneath them. The grass was too long; nevertheless, it felt good to walk barefoot in the summer. I loved that Mr. McQueary's fruit orchard with apple, mulberry, apricot and Bing cherry trees was within a few feet of the backdoor. And at the back of the property was an apiary and a functioning irrigation ditch. I had always lived in cities, most of them quite large: Cairo, Beirut, Denver. The idea that I was living in a house with an irrigation ditch filled with the water from the Colorado was bucolic. And I was enamored by the surreal quietness. Seriously, a car passed by my house, at most every half hour. In the mornings, at the peak time as I walked to work, I might see two or three in that same half-hour. I also loved all the birds that flitted in and out of the trees. I once had a whole flock of evening grosbeak in the trees and bushes around the house. And I loved the wide-open spaces, walking out my door and looking up at the Book Cliffs.

That night I placed my camping pad and sleeping bag on the worn rug in the living room. I wound up the alarm clock and set it for six a.m. I turned out the lights, and Mittens curled up with me on my pillow. Tomorrow was going to be a big day. I had worked hard, but eighteen children in seven grades; it was just beyond everything.

CHAPTER ELEVEN

A BEAUTIFUL DAY

I slept poorly, a combination of a hard floor, anxiety over the day to come, and an internal clock that did not rely on my external clock. There was no way I was going to be late. Finally, the alarm did go off, and I started developing my morning routines. First off, since the water pressure was slow, I started the water for my bath first. While the tub was filling, I made my lunch, a sandwich, and some fruit. On the first day, it was an apple. That seemed apropos. You might even say poetic, an apple for the teacher. Okay, sandwich and fruit done, put them in the brown bag. By then, the water was full enough for a quick bath, never more than two minutes — seriously, how long did one need. After dressing, I would check on Mittens and ensure he had food and his litter box looked good. For the first couple of months, I did not leave him outside. And then I drove up to the school. I planned on most occasions to walk, but on the first day, I was too anxious. What if I had forgotten something?

I arrived at my desk at seven-thirty, an hour before school started. I opened all the windows and took a seat at my desk. After laying open my Bible, I read a couple chapters and then prayed. In my life, I have had a number of times where I really felt the need for prayer. This was one of those times. True, I had been a good student in college, and I had worked hard getting ready. I knew the children, and I liked them. Their parents, too, I could not have asked for a more supportive bunch. But I had eighteen students in seven grades, and I had never been on my own before. I had never encountered anything remotely as difficult as this in my student teaching practicums. My first two practicums had been in one-grade classrooms. The third one, the last one, had been in Union College's experimental multi-grade George Stone school. They had all eight grades in that school. But there, they had two absolute master teachers with four grades each and no more than ten students per teacher. I was a rookie with eighteen students and seven grades.

The children came in groups and found their desks. Everyone was all a jitter, talking excitedly. Some of the parents, particularly for the lower grades, had come in as well and were helping their children set up their desks, arranging the pencils, the paper, the textbooks and notebooks, scissors, Elmer's glue, and a brand-new box of Crayola Crayons, either the square forty-eight size box, or the luxury sixty-four rectangular box. Finally, at eight-thirty, we began.

"Good morning, everyone. Please take your seats." Since this was the first day, everyone was on their best behavior and promptly did as I asked.

"I am Mr. Brauer." And as I said this, I went to the chalkboard and printed my name on the board. I had a moment of self-realization as the sound of the chalk against the board registered. I was aware that my handwriting was not as elegant and graceful as my favorite teachers'. Did this disqualify me? Would the students see through my thin disguise and realize I did not belong with my chicken scratch scribble on the board.

Apparently, not. There was no revolt. We carried on. I took the roll, calling out the names. As anticipated, Kelli and Shon were not there and would not be for a couple of weeks. I called out the name of the Hess children: Ron, Christina, and Angela. (For the record, Ron had a different last name, Borden) They seemed like friendly children. They had only recently moved to Rifle and did not know any of the other children yet. And Justin was not there. He was the new first grader. We pledged allegiance to the flag, and then I started to tell them a story.

It was a story I had first heard in a camp meeting tent when I had probably been in fifth grade. It was about some skinny drummer boy named Willie who was in a Civil War troop of hardened veterans. There had been a breach of conduct among the platoon, some serious offense for which the punishment was to be a cat o' nine tails whipping. The captain had called the platoon into formation and demanded that the offender step forward to take the whipping.

When none of the veterans stepped forward, Little Willie did. Of course, it was a parable of substitutionary salvation, a Christ story, and as I was telling this story, walking up and down the aisle looking at my students—my students!—I was feeling an overwhelming love for the little cherubs. We were coming to the heart-breaking conclusion of the story when…

A woman came into the classroom. She said she was Justin's babysitter, and Justin was on the front steps and would not enter. I stopped the story and went out to coax him.

Justin was a pixie of a squirt, with dark brown hair, nicely cut, a real boy's boy. He was well dressed in a clean shirt and new jeans. Overall, Justin had good self-worth and would be well liked by all his boy and girl classmates.

But this morning, he was standing at the bottom of the step with a quivering lip. I introduced myself to him and told him he had a desk with his name on it and I was happy to see him. Wouldn't he come inside? He just shook his head.

When I tried to take his hand to help him into the room, he quickly released his hand. He was not running away, but he was not coming in either. I tried telling him about the other students in his grade. There were four other first graders. Didn't he want to meet them? No luck.

The lady who had been babysitting him and had driven him here tried to prod him. That didn't help. After several attempts, I felt I needed to check on the class. I went up the stairs.

"Well, Justin is outside, but he won't come in." I threw up my hands.

Heather jumped up and came to the door. "I'll get him," she volunteered.

I stepped aside. I was ready for any help. Fifteen seconds later, Heather walked into the classroom holding Justin's hand. She guided him to his seat. And Justin sat down and then looked all around on his first day of school.

"We are glad to have you, Justin." And then I looked back at Heather, "Thank you, Heather, that was amazing."

Heather beamed but added, "Actually, not so amazing. Justin and I are friends, aren't we, Justin?"

Justin nodded vigorously. Now he was beaming.

As we started into the routine, I gave assignments. My anxieties dissipated. I realized I could not possibly be in two places simultaneously, so no reason to think I could. The first graders' arithmetic books had not yet arrived. Therefore, there was no arithmetic for the first graders. There was no reason to stress over what I could not control.

My professors had on innumerable occasions discussed disciplinary styles. How you ran the classroom was so crucial for a nurturing environment. While they noted there were alternative approaches for managing the classroom, still, they felt— especially for new teachers—that a stricter discipline was preferred. Loss of control of the students was disastrous and the most common reason for failure. It was better to start tough and then loosen up. I wholeheartedly agreed and was determined to hold a short rein in my classroom. I had studied this and had several methods ready to roll out.

Within fifteen minutes, maybe a half-hour, certainly no more than an hour into my first day of teaching, my first day ever as a teacher, which is the definition of a novice. Still, I consciously realized it would be constitutionally impossible for me to be a martinet. I could not carry the whip, nor the ruler—metaphorically, of course—it was just not in me.

I found all the little comments of my students displayed such ingenuity, such creativity. It was their remarks, observations, little witticisms, jokes, even their complaints, which allowed me to see inside them and get to know them. And I really wanted to understand them and know them, intuitively, as individuals. I also realized I wanted my classroom to be alive.

Yes, we would carve out periods of silence, and there would be structure. It was a necessity, but for the school to be a thriving community of young minds rapidly expanding, I needed to give it oxygen. I needed to let the little aspen grove expand and reach for the sun. So, I made the decision not to worry about that either.

Unfortunately, one of my favorite students, Kim McElvain, got too much oxygen on her first day at school.

On my first day of school, I have this vague memory that Stevie Wilmot had turned around and told me a joke, to which I had laughed. And since my laughter had been out loud, my teacher punished me. She told me to put my nose in a circle on the chalkboard. I thought this was monstrously unjust. (It was, by the way, not the last time a teacher disciplined me for finding things funny.) Still, my first day at school had not turned out well. And poor little Kimmy had been so excited about her first day.

At the school cleanup, she had told me how excited she was to start school. Kim McElvain was Ron and Connie's oldest child. She had sandy blonde hair in a long Dutch boy cut and parted on the side, high cheekbones, and a tremendous desire to do the right thing and be part of the classroom. She was first grade, which meant she was now a big girl in school. She was pleased that she already knew her ABCs. (In 1981, children often did not attend kindergarten, and their first school experience was first grade.)

But in the over-stimulation of her first day, she decided she would throw an eraser while I was not looking. Except she was a first grader and so was not as coy as maybe an experienced fifth-grade chalk eraser thrower would be. I caught her and wrote her name on the board. While mortified, it was still too much for her, and just before lunch, I saw her throw another eraser. I sent her to the next room and told her to wait a couple of minutes until I could talk to her. Again, the older students were amazed at her pluck. You did not get caught for the same offense twice in a single morning. Not cool.

When I went into the room, Kim was standing in the middle of the room with tears streaming down her face, sobbing. I sat down on a small chair to be at her level.

"Do you understand what you did wrong?"

She nodded vigorously.

"And you're never going to do this again?"

She again nodded vigorously and then broke out weeping. I put my hand on her head.

"Okay, as long as you're never going to do this again. Then that is it."

And she looked at me with such gratitude and then rushed forward and hugged me.

I had minimal problems with Kim for the rest of the year. She was smart and really enjoyed learning.

CHAPTER TWELVE

AND ANOTHER ONE

On Tuesday after school, I got two calls. Ron McElvain was the first. He called and asked if I would go out and see the Grants. They lived just a few miles south of the school in the brand-new community, Battlement Mesa. Exxon had seen they would need housing and had contracted to build a large development. They had worked fast, installing water, underground electric wiring, paved roads, cement gutters, sidewalks. It was something. Houses and trailers were rapidly filling the development. Workers were flocking to their plant, the Grants among them. Since he was a welder and having heard of the massive work happening at Parachute, they had moved and had quickly gotten a job that paid well. They were Adventist, and more relevant to me, they had a fourth-grader. They were thinking about placing him in the school but wanted to know about the teacher. Would I go out and see them?

Okay, sometimes… hold that… I often have an exaggerated belief in my abilities. It is not hard to strike oil when drilling into my ego. If eighteen students were too many, nineteen would fix that problem, wouldn't it? Also, both Ron and I loved the idea of growing the school. It was flattering. I had been here a week or two, and the word was out, 'Bring your children to the Rifle (Rulison, the names were frequently interchanged) school. There is a bright new teacher there.' And since it had only been two days, my teaching career had a legacy that did not include any deficiencies. It was all potential, like a new dam built on the Colorado River, like a new football season with the Denver Bronco's (This was pre-John Elway. He came in 'eighty-three'), like the Exxon shale boom, like a Ponzi scheme. You gotta get a piece of this action.

So, I said yes, and drove out to meet the Grants. They had a new trailer home and invited me in. They were a lovely couple. He had dark curly hair and was articulate, intelligent, and highly motivated to provide a quality life to his family. She was quieter, letting him dictate the conversation. She brought me lemonade. Adopted from Korea as a baby, with wide-set black eyes and straight, black hair, Cory came out of the back bedroom and sat down in a chair. Within a moment, I could tell he was exceptionally bright. Mr. Grant quizzed me a little on my educational philosophy. He talked about some classics of literature: Tolstoy, Austen, Dickens. He wanted me to know; he was educated, though a welder. I had read them and could engage in the conversation. His wife wanted to know if there were any others in the fourth grade. I told them Cory would make four in his class. They were pleased and said they would enroll him tomorrow. They did not want him to get behind.

And I remember as I sat there talking to them, I just looked around and thought to myself, this is what I wanted. I wanted a home. I wanted a companion, a young woman beside me.

This emotional disarray made me incredibly thankful for the second call I had received before I had driven over to meet the Grants. It had been a call from Tina Mitchell. She had heard that I was sleeping on the floor and that my furniture had not come. She thought that was awful, and I should stay with them at least until my furniture came. I accepted. True, I did not like imposing myself, but the thought of a bed, a nice soft bed with a mattress and sheets, a bathroom with a shower, and her cooking — have I said before that she was a fabulous cook? I have. Well, get used to it. I'm going to say it a lot.

Here was another thing about me, on occasions like this, when people saw my trials and extended such exceptional kindness, well on those occasions I choked up, tears formed, and I often could not speak, I was so grateful.

So, on the way back, I stopped and picked up my little cat, gathered some essential items, and moved back into the Mitchells. In the evening, my little buddy Danny camped out in my room, reading and occasionally talking while I sat at a desk and went over lesson plans for the morrow.

The conference office was worried. It was not the fourteen students initially enrolled, nor the expanded eighteen. Now it was nineteen students. Was I drowning with the classroom in complete chaos? Were the children getting any education? And what about the aide the schoolboard had voted to hire? When was that going to happen? On Wednesday, they sent out Miss Archambeau.

Miss Archambeau was in her late fifties or early sixties. Although she was physically a small woman, her red hair was in a large beehive, making her seem taller. While Mr. Peterson was gabby and loved to talk, Miss Archambeau was breviloquent. Her sentences were well-formed, informative, and concise. Her vocabulary, diction, and precision of words were exemplary. Her movement was refined and spare. Her attire was tailored and professional.

She had taught for years and years. Nothing could phase her. She was also the one I had sent my lesson plans to for review and critique. She read them and commented. She had come to spend the day with me to observe, give ideas, and provide encouragement. I was confident that she would also privately commiserate with me. She would tell me how the conference would rectify this intolerable situation.

You do see the irony here, don't you? How could I be out recruiting a new student the evening before, and then the next day be full of the injustice of it all, be filled with self-pity as a martyr of historic proportions? How had I been allowed to be placed in this untenable situation? You do see it, right? Really, you don't see it? Neither did she.

At the end of the day, she had no words of pity for me. We did sit down to talk. Quite frankly, the day had gone pretty well; even with adding a new student, setting up a new desk, the day had gone well. The students had gotten their assignments. I quickly taught the concept, put them to work, and moved to the next grade, the next class. Hence, she made a few comments about techniques I could try. She said my lesson plans were good. As to the nineteen students in seven grades, she remarked that teaching was demanding. That was it. No pity. No outrage. No inside words to me about how the conference would have this resolved within a week or two at most. No, none of that.

She did want to talk about discipline. I prepared myself. She noted that I had an open classroom style with a more relaxed discipline than she had expected. It was quite unusual for a new teacher. She went into a little educational theory about some proponents of this style. They had published some compelling papers on how it gave more room for growth and expanded the mind. She added, however, that there were more papers against the open classroom discipline style. Among other issues, it was noted that when this discipline style backfired, it often descended rather rapidly into chaos. We were sitting at the front of the classroom when she talked to me. She was at the desk. I was in a folding chair seated before her. She looked me in the eye, shook her finger at me, though more as a means of emphasizing a point rather than in a pejorative manner. She was not a habitual smiler.

"I do not advocate an open style of classroom control for young teachers. It's a difficult style, and while I do personally side with the proponents—I think it provides a better learning environment—still, I rarely recommend it. I watched you and the children, Mr. Brauer. I watched your interactions with them. And their interactions with you." She paused.

64

"Frankly, I have no concerns about your discipline. None! For this to work, it must be clear who has the authority in the room, and as I watched, it was clear. Three days. The classroom is yours. The children are watching you."

She closed her notebook and began to pack up her things. I walked her to the door.

"Teaching is demanding," she repeated. And then, as she was going down the stairs, almost as a consolation, she added, "Your lesson plans are well done. Finish up the week with detailed lesson plans. I don't need to see a month of your plans."

CHAPTER THIRTEEN

I'D LIKE TO TELL YOU

On Sabbath after church, I saw Mike Duerhssen. We fell into conversation. He was home one last weekend before heading off to college. Mike and I had met at college and had often gone on long runs together. We had similar paces. He preferred longer distances, such as half-marathons. I liked five k's. Mike's mother was Sandra, and his stepfather was Jerald Sisk, the Family Practice doctor in town.

Mike's best friend, Davy Schneider (who looked like a Michelangelo statue come to life), was also visiting. I did not know Davy nearly as well. He may have had a physical defect. If so, it was not obvious. Sometime later, when I watched him interact with women, it was apparent, they too had not discovered the defect. I don't know, maybe his ankle had not been dipped in the River Styx.

If Davy was a Greek legend, then Mike with his blonde hair, light skin, firm square jaw, bright blue eyes, six-pack abdomen, and rippling quads, was from the ancient Norse tales. But while I didn't know Davy well. I did know Mike, and I knew him even better the following year. We were such good friends that when he broke up with a stunning, dark-haired beauty, she came to me for assistance. She knew Mike and I were close. She knew he had a lot of respect for me, so she pleaded her case and wondered whether I could help. Mike had talked to me when they broke up.

Mike was one of those rare men known as a 'good guy.' Some people say they do not exist. I can vouch they do. He told me she wanted to get too physical. He did not feel it was right. And so, he had broken up. He did not feel it was right to cross certain physical boundaries, even though the girl was stunning, and even if she wanted to. I knew a lot of guys who would not have taken that road. Of course, I did not tell the girl what I knew. I just sympathized with her and said I would talk to Mike. I will say Mike and I agreed on this. We both placed a high value on womanhood. I was twenty-three and had not gone farther than a kiss. We both endeavored to be virtuous men. It was just that Mike had more occasion to exercise virtue.

Mike mentioned that Davy and he were going out to Rifle Park in the afternoon. He said there was excellent limestone rock out there, very hard, and made for some superb climbing. They had extra gear. Would I be interested?

I was definitely on board. My brother Ron—yes, I am aware there are a lot of Ron's in this book—and I had done some bouldering. I had never worked with climbing gear before. Well, not much. I had done some repelling at camp. Still, we would have done it if Ron and I had had the right equipment. So, I jumped at the chance.

I drove my car to Mike's house and then rode with them past Rifle Dam to the falls. It was a narrow canyon with vertical cliffs on both sides. They started me out with some less technical climbs as they gave me instruction. Davy then set down the rope at the base of a much more challenging climb. Davy had no fear and on the rock was like a mountain goat. Mike was a little more cautious. Okay, to be clear, that was only in respect to Davy. When I saw what Davy did, the gymnastics it required, the shear strength needed in the ends of his fingers, and the tip of his toes, I just shook my head in wonder. I told them I would sit this one out. I took off my shoes, walked in the creek, reveled in its coolness, and noted that some leaves were beginning to fall into the stream, and then turned and watched the two of them climb to a place they could not navigate. They were at that time about thirty feet up. When they realized they had no way up, they unclipped and slid straight down, using their feet and hands as friction. I had never seen anything like it. I realized while I liked adventure; I enjoyed hiking up mountains and skiing more; I had had an off-road motorcycle and had enjoyed that; still I realized that Mike and Davy were in a completely different class than me. Their tolerance of fear, their desire for thrills far exceeded mine.

At the end of the day, Mike told me that he had a younger step-brother in California. His brother's name was also Mike. So, if I heard people talking about Big-Mike and Little-Mike, that was what they were talking about. I wished Mike a good year at school. He told me his class schedule. It sounded interesting and I was a little envious. We promised to get together to do some skiing at Christmas.

As for Little Mike, I would hear that name soon.

On Sunday, I moved back again into my little house. And I remember Tina bringing me a bowl of soup in a Tupper Ware dish that I could have for supper.

"You're always welcome here. You know that, don't you? I was telling Mitch last night; Marvin is just like having another older son."

I laughed and hugged her. "Thank you. I love it up here."

"Mitch doesn't say much about people, but he likes you."

I gave Danny a little punch on the shoulder. "See you tomorrow."

But I had to get ready.

CHAPTER FOURTEEN

I'M JUST FIXING A HOLE

On Monday Mrs. McElvain (Connie) would be helping me. She had volunteered to be the aide for the week. She had two children: Kimberley, in first grade, and Jon, a couple of years from attending school. Connie was warm-hearted, mature, and intelligent. She was probably in her early thirties at that time, which to my mind, was unimaginably old. Connie was of mid-height and wore her blonde hair in a teased bouffant. She had a good sense of humor and liked to laugh, though she was never the jokester. I had never met a less needy person; so constant, never too up, nor too down; Connie was so comfortable with who she was. Invariably, she had a smile, though I would learn there were subtle variations to the smile. Those variations represented a myriad of emotions. She understood people a lot better than I did. She was not wont to complain. Not to say she that she never did—I do not trust anyone who never complains—but it was uncommon. She did not like speaking badly about people unless, of course, they deserved it, and then it was always with a smile. As an aide, she saw what needed to be done and did it. Most of all, however, Connie represented the best of motherhood. She doted on her children without indulging them. Consequently, Kim had a depth of confidence, even in first grade, which was uncommon.

On Monday, as the parents dropped off the children, or at the end of the day when they were picking them up, several parents wanted to have a little talk with me. They wanted to fill me in about particular issues for their child.

First, on the list, Cory was likely to speed through his work, not as diligent in his math as he should be, made silly mistakes because he did not check his work, and all of this was so that he could get back to reading. My job as a teacher was to be certain he did not do that.

Carolyn tended to daydream. If I kept a close watch on her, I would soon be able to recognize when her mind was drifting off. It might not be easy at first, but I would learn the signs by paying attention.

Finally, Ron was prone to talk too much. The parents noted that these faults had festered for years and needed to stop, and they were counting on me to institute systems to correct them this first semester. "It's a new year, new teacher; this is the time to jump on it."

I listened as if I was a man drowning in a lake when a boat pulls up and the driver with his family all in the boat wonders which way to that nice little store where they have the ice cream; it's such a hot day. And I, in my distress, point them the right direction. And they instead of throwing me a line, they motor off. I resume my thrashing. And they comment among each other how polite that young man was.

What was bothering me was that apart from the first graders I had so little time to instruct. With the first graders I made time, particularly for reading, I took all five of them into the next room. And I listened to each of them read every day. It was the only time in the day that I penciled in dedicated time. I had so little time to instruct the other grades and their subjects, maybe at most five minutes. Five minutes with each grade level on language arts. How was I to properly teach language in five minutes? How was

70

I to get them enthused about words, expand their vocabulary? How was I to teach the value of a well-placed comma? (By the way, thank you to my editors for continuing to improve my comma usage.) With seven grades, nineteen children, and such rushed intervals, how was I to exchange ideas that were so fundamental to the teacher-pupil relationship?

And this has nothing to do with Mrs. McElvain's help as an aide. Her help was fabulous. She fit in seamlessly. Without a great deal of discussion, she knew which tasks to take on and which to leave alone. This assistance enabled me to spend at least some time with the students. But it was frustrating, and so when the parents brought up their issues, I nodded and tried to dismiss them from my mind.

Another thing that troubled me was the Iowa Basics Reading test results. I had administered them the week before, and some of the scores were abysmal. Some of the students had not even filled all the circles in with their number two pencil. Their scores were invalid and not adequate measures of their abilities, but others had tried and had still done poorly. My impression of the children did not match the test scores. They seemed clever to me. Nevertheless, I could not wholly discount the scores. That, too, was going to make my year harder.

Ron McElvain closed his office early on Tuesday and drove out to Rulison. He had called the school and talked to Connie. She told me Ron wanted to talk to me in person, but she did not know what about. Whatever it was, he did not feel like he could discuss it over the phone. That seemed odd and a little worrisome. I had not done anything wrong, had I? I could not think of anything. Still, it was disquieting.

After all the children had gone except Kim, who was drawing pictures on the chalkboard, Ron sat down on the edge of my desk. Connie was finishing up some tasks in the next room.

"We have an interesting situation developing." He stopped and scratched at his ear. And by his tone, I knew this was not about something I had done wrong. "I'm just not sure how to bring this up, Marvin. It's quite amazing. Who would have thought?" He stopped and looked around at the desks and then at the chalkboard. There was an arithmetic problem still on the chalkboard, a conversion of fractions to decimals that I had illustrated. He smiled. "It's been a long time since I was here. I attended this school in my seventh and eighth-grade years. Did I ever tell you that?" he asked. It was a rhetorical question. He was beating around the bush. "Decimals..." He stood up and walked to the window. There was a breeze blowing up the valley. I could see clouds beginning to form. It looked like we might be in for an afternoon shower. They could come on quickly.

"Do you know the Sisks?" He asked.

"Yes, Doug is in sixth grade." This was odd.

"O yes, of course, but no, I mean Cliff's brother, Jerald, the GP in town."

"A little, I know Mike, I think they call him Big Mike here, don't they?" I replied. This was an odd conversation. Why did Ron drive all this way out to talk to me in person? "Mike and I were friends at Union, but no, I have not met them. I think I shook their hands. Why?" I knew Sandy was Mike's mother and that Jerald and Sandy had a pair of twins in kindergarten. They would be in first grade next year.

"Sandy came by to talk to me at the office today," Ron took up the conversation.

"She came to the office?"

"Yes, I thought it was odd as well."

I had not said anything about it being odd.

"So, Jerald was married before Sandy. They had a son, Little Mike, and it seems he is in town. Little Mike has been living with his mother in Southern California,"

By now, Ron was pacing. He paused and gave me an intense look. "Sandy came to the office to ask if they could enroll him in school. The boy wants to stay with his father this year."

"Twenty students?" I snorted. "Twenty students."

"Twenty, yes, that would be twenty. I didn't give them an answer,"

Ron was now resting with his hand on the chalkboard. When I did not speak right away, he continued. "As I said, I did not give them an answer. I told them I would have to talk to you first, and I told them we already had nineteen students. Dr. Sisk has been a big supporter of the school."

I just sat there.

Ron let the silence linger for a few seconds and then added. "Sandy said that her son, Big Mike, knew you well at school, and he thought you were brilliant. He gave you high recommendations."

That should not have made any difference, but it did. Mike was praising me. That was nice. Okay, it made me feel better.

"Well, nineteen or twenty, what's one more student?" I gave a fatalistic laugh. I was standing before the firing squad. I was waving off the blindfold, but what the hell, since I was about to be shot, maybe I would have that cigarette. It was not like I was going to die of lung cancer.

"What you're doing is exceedingly difficult. It is certainly a lot more than we anticipated. But you know, I agree. We are already at nineteen. As you said, twenty is not that much more." And then he paused. "So, are we in agreement?"

I was sitting at my desk, looking up at him. I had a pile of work before me. But like every other night, I knew that I would be coming back after supper and not leaving until nine p.m. or later. So, I tapped my pencil on the desk a few times and then assented. "Okay, let's do twenty."

"Great. Great." Ron was pleased. How quickly the school had grown under his watch as chair. And, of course, everybody in the church would be tickled pink. They placed a very high priority on their church school and loved their children.

"Did I say?" Ron stopped halfway across the classroom. "Did I mention Little Mike is in eighth grade? I think I might not have brought that up. Did I tell you that?"

"Uh nope, I'm pretty certain you did not add that little factoid."

There would be twenty students in all eight grades.

When I was a freshman in high school, I had for one semester this nicely curved student teacher. She taught us English. Because she was beautiful, I had memorized a poem and recited it in front of the class. It was Tennyson's *Charge of the Light Brigade*. It came to mind on this occasion:

> *Cannon to right of them,*
> *Cannon to left of them,*
> *Cannon in front of them*
> *Volleyed and thundered;*
> *Stormed at with shot and shell,*
> *Boldly they rode and well,*
> *Into the jaws of Death,*
> *Into the mouth of hell*
> *Rode the six hundred.*

That was me. See that fool at the front waving his hat to draw attention from the cannons. Yeah, that's me—a stupid fool.

Sandy called me at the school that evening to thank me. I would get to know Sandy better through the year. She was thin with good bone structure, a finely shaped nose, and platinum hair. At the time, I thought the hair was striking. I had never known anyone with hair like hers. In a church with a fair number of optimists, she still stood at the front of the line. She quickly got involved, and when winter came, she took the lead, coordinating and organizing the school ski program. I did not have to do anything with it. And if the school needed a van for an activity. She would either loan or drive it. During the year, on her turns to pick up the children, she invariably stepped into the classroom to give me some words of encouragement. I considered her a good friend. For the most part, she was the spokesman for Dr. Jerald Sisk.

When she called, she told me how pleased Jerald was that Little Mike would be spending the year here in Rifle. Jerald was looking forward to taking his son elk hunting in the fall, and of course, skiing in the winter had also been a big draw. She also said that they would have never considered it before. Some of the previous teachers had not been that impressive. Little Mike was a very smart kid with high potential and would start next Monday.

"He's a great kid. Good heart, but he does have a bit of a smart mouth. I'm afraid Southern California has rubbed off on him. You know, the city and all. Don't put up with it."

I thanked her and was about to hang up when Jerald took the phone.

"It's me, Jerald." Some people carry such an aura of authority that even when they attempt to connect it is always as if they are leaning over to hand something to a child. That's how I always felt about Dr. Sisk. (Another one of the parents I could never call by their first name, and to be truthful, I do not remember him ever suggesting it.) "I appreciate this, Marvin. I know you have way too many students, but I appreciate you taking on Mike." That was the extent of his conversation. Despite his taciturn nature, I always had Dr. Sisk's support. I never doubted it.

Dr. Sisk was a small and wiry man. All the Sisk males were short of stature and rock hard like basalt, the black volcanic rock strewn on many a nearby field. They were all outdoorsmen who hunted and fished. They waterskied at Rifle Gap Dam and at Lake Powell in the summer. They were all athletic, and their prowess was legendary, slaloming, barefoot skiing, jumping off cliffs, doing flips into the water at Lake Powell. I saw this with my own eyes. They took their off-road motorcycles on ridiculously challenging trails. Dr. Sisk had his private plane and took me for a ride one time coming back from Lake Powell.

And to add to his legend, this was the year he had been invited to be the doctor for a mountain climbing team; Dr. Sisk was preparing for a late fall snow ascent of Mt. Denali. (It was called Mt. McKinley in those years.) Mt. Denali is over twenty-thousand feet. My father and I had climbed several of Colorado's fourteen thousand-foot peak mountains, including the highest, Mt. Elbert. However, a twenty-thousand-foot mountain like Dr. Sisk was planning to do, was a very different animal, not to mention climbing it in winter. Dr. Sisk was in training and had been at it all summer continuing into the fall.

CHAPTER FIFTEEN

NO CHAPEL OF LOVE

That weekend was Labor Day, and most of my family was coming in. My oldest brother Bob came with his wife Lesli and their two girls Julienne and Adrienne. They had been on vacation, camping in Colorado. They arrived and set up their tent camper on the back part of the driveway, near the orchard. Bob pastored a church in Duluth, Minnesota, on the cold shores of Lake Superior. Bob was the acclaimed genius in the family. His interests were broad and ever-expanding. He read prolifically and retained an incredible amount of what he read. And boy could he talk; he talked circles around the rest of us.

Ron was the closest brother in age to me. He was the third of the four boys. We were both mostly blonde in those years and often mistaken for twins. I was more outgoing, but many girls thought he was cuter. I never understood that. He and his wife, Nancy, were passing through on their way back to California. Nancy was taking physical therapy. Ron was working and finishing up his master's in physical education. I gave them my bed, and slept on the hideaway.

On Sunday, my parents came over, and I put my sleeping bag down in the tiny room. I gave the hideaway bed to Mom and Dad.

Only Jim and his family were unable to come. He was in Nebraska.

I fed my family pancakes. As the youngest of four boys, I was the last to set up house. And I had mastered the culinary arts of Aunt Jemima's pancakes, that is, pouring the mix, adding water, and an egg, beating it all together, and frying up the pancakes. I had a much better-than-average record of turning the pancake at an appropriate time. Clearly, I would be fine if I could handle this domestic task. For lunch, I served boiled potatoes with spaghetti and canned spinach. It was a decent meal — nothing to worry about here. I did not need a woman to cook for me. I was doing just fine. Sure, it would have been nice to have found a wife. But things had not turned out in that regard.

Lesli and Nancy took over the remaining meals for the weekend. Sure, it was a little better, but I liked my spaghetti, boiled potatoes, and spinach. I thought the key with the spaghetti was to make sure you had grated a good amount of cheddar to sprinkle on top.

There were questions; of course, there were always questions about my love life with my family. I said I was seeing a girl in Denver. We had met at camp. We had been on a couple of dates, and we were planning to get together the next time I went back over the mountains. She was pretty.

"Yeah, you're not convincing me," Ron said. We were only fifteen months apart. He had seen me with other girlfriends. When I fell in love, I fell hard. So, he brought up previous girlfriends. What about them? What was their status?

Bob thought the girl in Denver sounded nice. However, he felt my situation being alone in Rifle, Colorado eating potatoes, spaghetti, and spinach was untenable. I thought Bob was a little hard on me. Did he not consider the grated cheddar cheese a nice touch?

Nancy mentioned that her former roommate in college, whom I had taken on a couple of dates two years previously, was still single and had said to say hi to me. I remembered her roommate. She was pretty. Too bad she lived on the east coast. That would have been nice.

When Mom and Dad arrived, Dad's first comment was how the tiny house made him claustrophobic. He meant that as a joke, but I still felt bad and defended the little house. And the others did point out the advantage of the proximity to the school.

Dad was not done, "Well, if you can find a girl who will marry you after they see this house, you better take her."

That hurt and festered.

At the end of the weekend, they departed. Ron and Nancy gave me a portable black and white television they no longer needed. I fiddled with the antennas trying different positions. I got one station from Grand Junction with a lot of static. That was discouraging. Then I switched the knob from VHF to UHF, and suddenly I got three Denver channels, including ABC. I was delighted; and superstitious, afraid that if I moved anything, I would lose it all. Picking up ABC meant watching Monday Night Football with Keith Jackson, Don Meredith, and Howard Cosell. Life was better with football.

CHAPTER SIXTEEN

MONEY

In the 1980's Forbes would start listing its top four hundred wealthiest persons. Daniel Ludwig was the lead person on the first ever list with two billion dollars. No one on that list would even qualify for the list today.

I grew up hearing about Jean Paul Getty as the richest man with wealth around a half a billion. In five years, Bill Gates and Paul Allen would take Microsoft public and add three more billionaires and twelve thousand millionaires. The eighties, the age of wealth accumulation, was beginning. The marginal taxes on the rich were going away, and the evolution of the inegalitarian distribution of assets was escalating. The decade of greed is good was ramping up.

In September, Reagan would nominate, and the Senate would approve Sandra Day O'Connor as the first female Supreme Court justice, and the Anglican church would vote to allow women to be ordained. Meanwhile, the Adventist church was successfully sued for the unequal pay of women. Men had received a head of the household bonus, but women were not eligible for this. When the case settled, my mother had been pleased. However, my dad worried about how the conferences would manage their budgets. He feared that they would have to let some pastors go to pay women a comparable wage.

In 1981 the United States successfully launched the first space shuttle, and the first stealth fighter rolled off the line.

In 1981 the CDC first reported of a series of unusual cases of pneumonia in homosexual males and the development of extremely rare infections in these patients. However, they had not identified the source. It would be another three years before Doctors Gallo and Montagnier discovered the HIV virus as the cause of the AIDS epidemic and before Doctor Fauci and his research team at the NIH made their substantial advances.

In 1981 Muhammad Ali had his last fight; China reached one billion in population; the first test-tube baby was born; the first documented use of crack was reported; and Natalie Woods drowned.

CHAPTER SEVENTEEN

CALL ME

On Monday, Labor Day, the family left before noon; I walked up to the school. I had a lot of work to do. I needed to look through the catalogues and order books for eighth grade. I had to integrate eighth grade into the rotation of classes. I was sedulous at my desk late into the night.

As I was seated there, the phone rang. I got up and went into the foyer.

"Rifle Adventist School, this is Mr. Brauer."

There was a stillness on the other end, and then bashfully, I heard a child's voice, "Hello Mr. Brauer, this is Kelli. I'm going to be in sixth grade, Kelli Holderbaum."

I chuckled, "I remember you, Kelli. How are you?"

She was delighted that I remembered her, and the bashfulness receded like any ordinary wave at the beach. "Am I taking you away from your work? We are back, Shon and I, and we will be in school tomorrow."

"Yes, I heard you were in Spain. I'm glad to have you back."

"We were in Spain with Mommy." She had not been listening to my part of the conversation. "I didn't want to go. I would have so much rather been in school! But Mommy insisted. She said it would be good for us to expand our minds. I told her my mind would have been better expanded if I were in school where I was supposed to be." She emphasized the last statement emphatically. Kelli was in full Kelli mode--quick, enthusiastic, sharp, and emotive.

I laughed. Kelli Holderbaum, how do you describe Kelli? She was complicated.

Let me start with Shon. He was a little easier. Shon was a handsome blonde boy, who the girls simplified to 'cute.' Just by watching him walk, you knew that at any game at recess, any sport, he would be the first pick. And it was true that despite being younger, only fifth grade, Shon was always at least the second-best athlete on the field in all the sports we played that year. If you were to adjust for age, he was the best. This was not to discount the athleticism of a number of the children that year. It was just an accurate assessment of his physical prowess. Shon was also bright. There was nothing wrong with his brain, no problem with his intelligence. It was just getting him to do his work. We had to concentrate on that. His issue at school was that he did not want to be inside, and the boy could be pervicacious. It would be a challenging year for him for reasons outside of the classroom, and he periodically had downswings. Shon was much quieter than his sister. He was quite content not to be the focus of the whole classroom, much different than his sister.

So now to describe Kelli. To say Kelli had personality was to sell it short. She was a force of nature, full of energy, full of ideas, full of joy unless, of course, she awoke feeling gloomy, in which case it was the end of days. Fortunately, this was not often. Also, Kelli had that rare gift of being able to see herself. She could laugh at herself. She could, amid being an absolute pain in the classroom, with a short-directed conversation, she could adjust. Let me tell you, that was uncommon. Kelli was also extremely bright and loved school. She wanted to be there and wanted to learn. Kelli was the oldest girl, and there was no doubt she was the classroom princess. For most of the year, she was a kind and benevolent princess.

In appearance, she had broad set eyes that were quite at her command in conveying the whole spectrum of human emotion. Her cheeks were full and surrounded by freckles. Her sandy hair fell just a little over her ears. Other than Ron, she was the tallest student and the tallest girl in the classroom, probably five foot six, only slightly shorter than Ron. Kelli and Roy were probably similar in height that year. She was somewhere between skinny and slender. Emotionally, she started the year more as a child, but the moodiness of adolescence was fast arriving.

Kelli loved to laugh.

I previously mentioned that I had met Kelli and Shon at camp. On the Sabbath afternoon hike, at one point as we were hiking with a group of probably thirty campers and staff, Kelli had caught up to walk beside me. I usually led the trail hikes trying to keep up a good pace. The objective was for the kids to have a fabulous time out amidst the ponderosa pines and aspen groves, doing some elementary bouldering up the granite rocks and returning tired. A camper with too much energy on Saturday night meant no one was getting any sleep.

So anyway, Kelli had picked up her pace to walk beside me. She wanted to tell me something,

"Sometimes I am bashful." She had just jumped into the conversation. She did not know how long she had before other people caught up to us. This was very typical Kelli: self-analyzing, trying to improve, and at the same time open with her faults.

I nodded. I had noted it. Kelli was the type of person who, even when feeling shy, would not allow her timidity to prevail but would push through.

"The reason I have been," and she blushed. "I have a lisp." She did. Not much of one, but she did have a lisp. She looked at me, wondering if that admission would forever discount my opinion of her.

I patted her on the head, "I had one when I was young. You can still hear it sometimes when I am tired."

Kelli stared at me dumbfounded. And it was as if at that moment she decided that she and I were out of adversity forever bonded, a mutual bond that non-lispers never could understand. They might try, but they had never lisped. Only Mr. Brauer and she had faced this brand of suffering.

On Tuesday, we resumed class. Sandy Forshee had volunteered to be my aide that week. The Forshees had a ranch west of town. They ran cattle. Frank was tall with a muscular physique built up with physical labor, solid biceps, muscular shoulders, and a broad chest. He had a square chin and deep-set blue eyes, basically Kennedy good-looks. Sandy was smart, pleasant, tall with wavy brunette hair — she was an eyeful. In my interactions with the Forshees that year, I do not believe I heard Frank say more than a couple of words. The communication came through Sandy.

Their daughter, Misty, was seven and in first grade. Misty had coal black, straight hair, very pale coloring and was a little pixie. She had a more retiring personality and was intimidated by the rambunctious older students. Nevertheless, she and Kimmy quickly became good friends. In that third week, they started coming up to my desk frequently to ask questions, and then they would stay standing at my desk. As first-graders, they were still short enough to stand at my desk and write without having to bend over. It was comfortable for them. And it seemed to them to be efficient to do their work right beside me; that way, they could get answers quickly.

"Is this right, Mr. Brauer? What does this word mean, Mr. Brauer? What should I do now, Mr. Brauer?" Their voices had not completely phased out of the early child tones, and I could not help but smile at them.

At first, they stood on the opposite side of the desk, and then they slowly moved to the sides. It was a large desk. Each time they had to return to their desk to get a new book, to sharpen their pencil, or grab their scissors, each time when they returned, they moved a little closer. I don't remember who was first, Kim or

Misty, who started leaning up against my chair, and then clambered up onto a leg to sit and write.

I think it was Kim, and when she was sitting on my lap doing her work, I looked over at Sandy. I leaned back and pointed to the first-grader sitting on my lap. Mrs. Forshee nodded and laughed softly. It was charming. Misty saw her mother's amused expression and quickly perched herself on my other leg. But, of course, I was too busy moving around the classroom and teaching all the grades to stay in one position for very long, especially now that I had eight grades and Little Mike.

I do want to say that Sandy was an excellent assistant, and I never had anything but support from her.

CHAPTER EIGHTEEN

THE NEW KID IN TOWN

Accordingly, Tuesday had a lot of changes. As noted, Sandy was the aide. In addition, it was Shon and Kelli's first day at school. Also, it was Little Mike's first day.

He came in that morning with his step-mom, the other Sandy. (This story would have been much easier to tell if everybody had had their own unique first name: one Sandy, one Ron, one Mike.) He stopped at the back of the classroom, looked around, and took in a big breath. He exchanged looks with his step-mom. It was clear he was having second thoughts. He had never been in a multi-grade classroom before, and there were a lot of younger children in the room. At the front of the room, they were very young. I had organized the desks so that the first graders were in the front two rows, closest to my desk. The second and third graders were just behind them. As always, the room was a little chaotic before the opening bell. He gave Sandy another look and shook his head. I was already up and headed back to him. Sandy was relieved.

"Hello, Mike. I'm Mr. Brauer." I tempered any enthusiasm. I did not imagine an eight-grader would want me to gush over them. So instead, I pointed to a desk on the back row, near the window.

He ambled over to it in no hurry at all. I sensed he was fighting an instinct to bolt. Probably, wondering what the heck he had agreed to. This was so different than his large school in Southern California.

Mike fit the model of the Sisk men, short, lean, muscular. He had an angled jaw and curly sandy hair. He sat down and started to arrange his desk. His cousin, Doug, in sixth grade, came in behind him. Doug was delighted to see Mike and pleased that I had arranged their desks side-by-side.

"This is going to be so much fun! I am so glad you're here!" And you could see that Doug wanted to be even more eager. Doug also had the Sisk male physique.

But Mike's nonchalant, "Yea, good to see you, Doug," toned down Doug's zeal.

Mike stopped and looked at the first graders at the front of the room. "Are they always this noisy?" But the way he said it, I could see that beneath his eighth-grader — I am the epitome of cool, I am the Mike Sisk — beneath that attitude, I could hear in the way he said it that he was intrigued and a little amused. But, of course, he would have to bury that as much as possible because the most important thing right now was to be sure that everyone knew he was here. Mike was here.

I laughed and replied, "Pretty much, Mike, pretty much."

He groaned. And then looked at me and almost smiled.

Just then, Kelli came running into the classroom full of vibrancy. "Good morning, Mr. Brauer!" She said with zest.

"Welcome, Kelli."

And then Kelli saw Mike and instantly became more restrained. I pointed to her seat on the far wall beside Carolyn's. She went forward with her items, occasionally looking back from her desk to Mike and wondering what changes Mike would bring to the school.

Shon came in much quieter but burst into a smile when he saw Mike. "Are you here this year?" Shon was incredulous.

Mike nodded and relaxed even more.

"That is so neat," Shon added.

I pointed Shon to his desk beside Danny. He was disappointed it was not closer to Mike's.

Both Doug and Mike were good students. I rarely had to get after them to get their work done, and they both quickly understood their assignments, particularly math. Doug had darker straight hair cut halfway over the ears. When I did have to pull rank on them, Doug was much more willing to accept it. Mike, not so much.

And then it was time for the opening bell, which was a hand-bell that I would take to the front door and ring several times. If there were children outside, this was their signal to come in. I say I rang it, though to be honest, after the first week, I rarely rang it. Ringing the bell was a highly sought privilege. "Mr. Brauer, can I ring the bell today, please, please?"

"Sure, Cory, you can ring it." I usually assigned it to the first person who asked, only varying the assent if there were two contestants, in which case I would choose one and promise the other child they could ring it the following day.

So now all of the students that I would teach were here. (Well, almost, but that story comes much later.)

First Grade: Kim, Misty, Justin, Doyle, Katie
Second Grade: Wayne (alias Bobo)
Third Grade: Chad, Angie
Fourth Grade: Heather, Roy, Chrissie, Cory
Fifth Grade: Steven, Danny, Shon, Carolyn
Sixth Grade: Doug, Kelli
Seventh Grade: Ron
Eighth Grade: Mike

They called an emergency school board meeting for that night. Twenty students in all eight grades had triggered widespread apprehension. The school board members gathered at the school at 7:30 p.m. I was, of course, already there. It was just a matter of arising from my desk and moving to the next room. We all sat around the table.

I was tired, and I had a lot on my mind, so I did not contribute much to the discussion. The first day with all eight grades had been exhausting. After school, I tried to strategize on how to improve efficiency. Plus, there was a fair amount of simple grunt-work, preparation that still needed to be done for tomorrow. In any case, the numbers spoke for themselves. What else did I need to say? Twenty students. Eight grades. Did they need me to repeat that? I could. Twenty students. Eight grades. Do you want it one more time? Sure. Twenty Students! All Eight Grades! What part of that was escaping their comprehension? I knew that condescending attitude would not have gone well. (At least I had the self-awareness to know I was tired and cranky.) Thus, I thought it would be best if I kept quiet.

The meeting took a long time. All the members wanted to have their say. They needed to say their piece, even if what they said was only slightly different than what the person before them had stated with such prolixity. They also needed to pass on the information they heard from the parents, who were talking. Of course, they were delighted the little school had swelled so abundantly. This was God's doing, and O how He was blessing us. Twenty students! Eight grades! Unheard of. Marvelous.

Ron McElvain, as chairman, brought the conversation around. Of course, the conference was delighted, but more importantly, they were seriously alarmed.

"O, and by the way, Marvin, Wes Peterson told me he planned to drop by later this week, Thursday, I believe, on his way to Grand Junction."

And then Ron laid out the conference's options. At the beginning of the year when we had started with, fourteen students and six grades, they said I needed an aide, but now with twenty students in all eight grades, an aide was insufficient. They recommended the school find a second teacher. And then, the board began discussing possibilities.

It seemed the pastor's wife was the best option. Would she work part-time? She was a retired secondary teacher, so it would make sense to give her the upper grades. Maybe she would work in the mornings, and in the afternoons, I would have all eight grades. I had met Mrs. Kungel. She was nice enough. Though I hated giving up the older students, it was a workable plan. Mary Dix knew Mrs. Kungel well and agreed to sound her out.

CHAPTER NINETEEN

A GOOD DAY FOR SUNSHINE

In the morning when we had our first recess of the day I was never in a hurry. When I stepped out into the nearly constant sunshine, I enjoyed the little path behind the school. I took in the warmth of the sun on my skin as it rose over the mountains and cascaded its beams on the valley. I tried to remind myself to pay attention to the scents of the sage that permeated the air, and I would tell my students to breathe it in as if it was the first time they had ever smelled it. In the fall, we often caught the aroma of newly cut alfalfa. Or as we crossed the little bridge, if there had been a rain, we might stop to watch the stream flow beneath the willow. The children especially the younger children frequently stopped to pick some grass to feed Bessie through the fence. After spending much of my life in the city I tried to catalogue it all in my visual and olfactory memory bank.

And then we would be on the fields. Today it was football.

In college, my teachers frequently commended me for my willingness to get out and play with the students at recess. My professors had noted that being involved in recess was an excellent way to develop rapport. Oftentimes deep bonds were formed when the teacher played with the students. I agreed. Since it was an eight-grade school, there was an even wider variety of skill levels than usual.

The first graders were not playing quarterback, but they could provide the two-hand touch when they stayed in a mob. And those bonds deepened as I would give little on the spot training: showing Chad how to catch the ball with his hands — even at third grade, he was quite athletic; or using the body to catch it; or teaching Shon how to make an over the shoulder catch at full speed; or telling everyone this ball is going to Doyle, the little first grader; and then I would come up close to the line of scrimmage and underhand lob it to Doyle while the older students gave him room, and they would cheer when he caught it, and then of course quickly tag him.

Or equally as fun was to turn and hand the ball to Bobo and let him run. And we were all surprised to discover the little second grader had unanticipated speed. The kid had a motor. He got outside, and suddenly the older boys realized they had to accelerate to full speed to have any chance to catch him. As it turned out, Kelli was faster than everybody except maybe Mike. She liked that. The boys did not.

But it was not always so tranquil. Though I almost always played, I tried to make sure the game was fun for everyone, but on one occasion, Shon had thrown a nice tight spiral to Danny in the endzone. It was a lulu of a pass. It would have given them the lead and probably the win. I had been covering Mike, who was running in the opposite direction, but I reached back with my left hand, tapped the football up into the air, then turned and intercepted it. When that happened, Cory, who was on my team, burst out laughing. On the opposite team, Roy did not find it amusing and started to pound on Cory. I broke it up and then turned to Shon.

"That was a beautiful pass, Shon." And I cringed, "Sorry."

Shon grunted, "Yes, it was. We would have won." And then, to his credit, reluctantly added, "You made a tough catch Mr. Brauer."

It was always strange that I was the one who had to enforce the recess. But, of course, I was now the teacher. I was the one who had to look at my watch, blow the whistle and herd everybody back inside the room. "Okay, get out your math books."

And when we came inside, I called Heather to my desk.

"Heather," I said with sotto voce. "You are behind four assignments. Two in math and one each in language and reading."

Heather bit her lip and hung her head. She did not like disappointing me. "I'll work on it, Mr. Brauer. I promise."

By the end of the day, she turned in five assignments. She had caught up and was a little head. She was pleased. So was I.

And I remember sitting at my desk that week on a couple of occasions, looking out over the classroom. There were, of course, too many students, too many grades, but I could not believe how overwhelmed I was by my love for them, all of them: the first graders, the older grades, the boys, the girls. I loved them all. I had long known I enjoyed working and interacting with children. But I had never anticipated, could never have fathomed, nor have imagined the immeasurable depths of my attachment to them. They were my children.

On Thursday, Wes Peterson did stop by. He observed the classroom for about an hour, and then while Sandy watched the classroom, we walked outside to his car.

"Here is what's happening, Marvin? We are coming down hard on the board. They have to get at least a halftime teacher. They have to do it. There has been resistance." Mr. Peterson was trying to decide what he could tell me and what he should not. "The problem, and believe me, I understand the issue; who do you get out here? You are in Rifle, which is in the boondocks. There are not a lot of unemployed teachers to pick from. There is Mrs. Cloninger down the road from you. She has a teacher's license."

"Yes, I know her," I interjected. "She taught my brother in grade school when we were at Mile High."

Mr. Peterson nodded, "Dr. McElvain and Bob Rice have both sounded her out. But unfortunately, she has no interest. And you are aware they have approached Mrs. Kungel." At this, he stopped and rubbed his hands together. "I have a good feeling about this, Marvin." And he gave me his best smile. "You would be okay with her taking the older grades?"

"Yes, yes, I would. I need help. Do I prefer the older grades? Maybe a little, but the little ones are so adorable."

At this, Mr. Peterson grinned. We were both teachers. We had a soft spot for children, and the little ones could be so endearing.

"But," I added in conclusion. "I'd take anything."

"Right. Right. Right." Mr. Peterson again rubbed his hands together. It was his most common mannerism when he felt satisfied. "Well, good." He shook my hand. "We will keep you informed."

He paused as if considering whether he should say it, then brought up his daughter.

"Kristin has four grades with eight students in Missouri."

I believe I have mentioned that his daughter and I had matriculated together.

He continued, "Also, in the Rocky Mountain Conference, there is no one new or experienced, nobody that has anywhere near the load you have. Not even close. We're praying for you, Marvin."

He got into his car and then rolled down his window and added, "If they can't find another teacher, we'll ask the board to list which students they are going to drop. We are praying for you, Marvin. Every morning Mr. Rice, Miss Archambeau, and I mention you at our staff meetings."

He backed out. That had been helpful. It was encouraging to know that they prayed for me. They were worried enough about me to name me specifically. They had not abandoned me. It felt good.

On Friday, all the upper grades were away at a Pathfinder Camporee. Only the first three grades were in school. Eight children were so much easier, so much less tension. The children were cooperative, and there was time for each of them. It was rewarding to concentrate on one student for a few minutes, understand their difficulty, and then find a pedagogical solution.

At recess, we played games of hide and seek around the schoolhouse. The little kids loved it. They did not say it — it would have been heretical to say it — but they enjoyed not having the older children dominate everything. At lunch, Chad and Wayne were outside throwing the football. They were trying to get the ball to fly like Mike and Shon did. They asked if I could teach them how to throw it with a spiral.

"Sure. Toss it to me."

Chad came close and lobbed me the ball.

I took the ball in my hands. It always felt good to have a football in my hands.

"So, you see, you balance it like this and make sure your fingertips are on the laces." I showed them my hand position. "And then it's like this." I demonstrated how you set your feet, rotate your arm, and let it go to get the necessary spin.

"You gotta make sure it has plenty of spin." I continued. "When you let it go just right. Ah, that is a beautiful thing. You know."

Chad and Wayne nodded at me and smiled. They were young, third grade and second grade, but they were both athletic and had already felt the joy of a ball. They were also lapping up this male bonding time.

"It's like when you shoot a basket and only get net," I was on a roll. "Or, when your bat hits the ball square, or getting the right spin with your racket on a tennis ball or kicking a soccer ball and having it curve."

They were looking at me in awe. I watched the two boys practice a little more and then went over to spin the merry-go-round for Katie and Angie.

CHAPTER TWENTY

HOW TO DISMANTLE A BOMB

Fridays were always a little shorter, and after school ended, I drove over to Parachute. There was a county school library where one of the ladies from church worked. She had invited me to come over and see what additional educational resources the county offered. I was interested. As I mentioned, some of the Iowa Basics test scores had been poor. In particular, I wanted to see what I could find for Steven.

In leafing through the previous end-of-the-year evaluations, the consensus was that he was a marginal student at best. They noted comments such as "cognitive diminishment," "poor educational skills," "difficulty paying attention," "disruptive." Some of the teachers had used more pejorative terms. I refuse to put those in print. Children were perceptive of adults' opinions, and his peers had absorbed the attitudes. Heather tried to protect him by telling me what Steven could not do. There had already been one fight in the classroom when someone had called him stupid. But I had done some work with children with disabilities. It was clear that Steven did not fit in the mold of the cognitively diminished. So first off, when the fight had occurred, I broke it up, and then I had stopped everything in the school, told everyone to put down their pencils and listen up.

"I'm not sure what you have heard in the past about Steven," I said, and frankly, I was mad. "I have heard little snide comments, and it must stop. First off, let me just put it out there. Steven is not stupid. Yes, I have read the comments of your previous teachers. Some of them even wrote that down. They were wrong. If anyone was stupid, it was your teachers. So, any further chatter like that will stop. But come on, guys. You know him. Outside of the schoolroom, isn't he full of ideas? Isn't his mind sharp? Doesn't he tell clever jokes? Let me tell you, if you had a problem with your bicycle, maybe the chain was off; I would advise you to ask Steven to fix it rather than me. I am not joking. I'm a mechanical idiot; it's true. We all have different areas in which we excel. Steven has a reading problem, and I will find help for him. There are names for reading difficulties, but that's my concern, not yours. Am I perfectly clear?"

We had no further problems with that in the year. And the real reason my speech was so effective was that all of Steven's classmates knew that to be true. They knew him well. He was bright, but his previous teachers had conditioned the children whether with good intent or not.

And so, I drove over to Parachute and arranged for Steven to have twice weekly specialized reading instruction from a reading specialist. So, I felt terrific about that.

Parachute—don't you love the Western Colorado town names—was a tiny little town just a few miles west of Rulison. And by tiny, I mean it had less than five hundred people during those years, and not much more today. The name had derived from the Ute word for twins, *pahchou*. The Utes who had lived in the area referred to the two mountains on either side of the stream. However, the white man thought they were saying Parachute, and it stuck. It was the only town in the world named Parachute. For several decades it was called Grand River, thinking that would attract settlers; however, in 1980, they voted to retake the name of Parachute.

The year I was there the city was getting a lot of attention from the Exxon plant. Even then, however, there was not much in town. It did have a bar where I dropped off a hitch hiker on one occasion and a gas station, but not much else, not even a grocery store.

While I am on this diversion, let's also discuss Rulison. There was no town of Rulison, no shops or businesses. It had some farms, ranches, and a few houses along the county road. That was it. Its only cause for fame, or rather notoriety, was that it was the site of an underground nuclear explosion in 1969.

The government had been trying to find nonmilitary uses for nuclear power. They initiated Operation Plowshare. The idea was to set off a nuclear explosion deep in the earth as a more efficient means of releasing natural gas.

So, they did it. Eight thousand feet beneath the surface, they set off a nuclear bomb. The test was successful — liberalizing a large amount of natural gas; however, they were never able to eliminate the radiation attached to the gas; and nobody had any interest in using natural gas for cooking that also emitted radiation. The government began the cleanup and erected a placard.

CHAPTER TWENTY-ONE

A SHORT HISTORY

While we are off the path, one more digression, I said the older students were away at a Pathfinder Camporee. What does that mean? Who are the Pathfinders? I have mentioned various beliefs about Adventism on several occasions, but I think a short history of Adventism could be useful. I emphasize a brief history. Of course, you could go to Wikipedia or buy a book. There are a lot of narratives written by authors with a more significant stake in the game. Anyway, here is my Short History of Adventism.

In the early 1800s, there was a religious awakening in America. Historians call it the Great Awakening. Out of this revival came a man in New England named William Miller. He was studying the prophecies of Daniel. He noted how the other visions of Daniel had come to pass just as Daniel predicted, so he was wondering about the vision in Daniel 8 of the twenty-three-hundred-days:

Unto two thousand and three hundred days; then shall the sanctuary be cleansed.

In his studies, he became convinced that the twenty-three-hundred-day prophecy indicated that Jesus would soon be returning. By calculating the time of the decree to rebuild Jerusalem, which was the starting point of the prophecy, and using the day for a year prophetic principle, he then plotted out that the Second Coming would be in 1843. He subsequently revised it to 1844.

In my Adventist education, I had had numerous lectures about William Miller. How he studied this and became convinced; how he had gone systematically through all of his notes many times and had come repeatedly to the same conclusion: Jesus was coming back in 1844. He knew he should be telling his neighbors, but he was not a preacher. Finally, he had prayed to God that if someone came and asked him, he would go. He would preach. If they came to his house and personally asked him to preach, then he would accept.

The story I heard was that:

> *As he was sitting at his dining room table, nary had his prayer left his lips before someone was at his door with a request for him to preach at their church.*

It made a compelling story. William Miller was convinced. The next day he began preaching the Advent message, and it had spread with enthusiasm and controversy. Churches began having acrimonious debates, and they disfellowshipped those who continued to believe in the Second Coming. (Most Adventists had come out of Methodist or Baptist churches.) On October 22, 1844, the day the prophecies had foretold, tens of thousands of people all over the northeastern United States went out into the fields. Many of them wore white ascension gowns. They gathered on the hilltops in small groups and sang and worshipped. Today they would be going to heaven. Many had been so confident that they had not even harvested their fields that year. Why should they? It would be a lack of faith to harvest when they were so soon to be translated like Elijah or Jesus on the Mount of Olives. They were going to heaven where there was food aplenty.

I am sure your understanding of history has already anticipated the plot twist: Jesus did not come on October 22. For the believers, it was a catastrophic letdown. To this day, Adventists everywhere call this *The Great Disappointment*. Most of the followers went back to their lives, but out of the movement, a small body of believers continued to study the Bible until they came up with an alternative understanding.

A certain man, Hiram Edson, was walking through a cornfield when he saw a vision of Jesus passing through the sanctuary of heaven, and they then realized that the prophecy was talking about the cleansing of the heavenly sanctuary. Jesus had gone into the Most Holy Place to determine which of the people through history and those still alive were to be saved. One thing was clear Adventism was saved. (Sanctuary: Fundamental Belief Twenty-Four)

Other doctrines followed, although to be clear, Adventists are adamant that they have no creed, and none of their twenty-seven fundamental beliefs should be interpreted as creed. (I'm sorry it is now twenty-eight, my mistake.) Still, even though before an immersion baptism (Baptism: Fundamental Belief Fifteen), you are still questioned whether you believe all of the doctrines, Adventists maintain they have no creed.

I never had a problem with the Adventist edifice, although I was always a little skeptical. Were we not eroding the pillar of Adventism, which is to say having no creed? But I digress.

Most of their beliefs were well within the norm of mainstream Christianity. They believed in the Trinity (Fundamental Belief Two), God the Father (Fundamental Belief Three), the Holy Spirit (Fundamental Belief Five), and that Jesus Christ was fully God. (Fundamental Belief Four) To be honest, this evolved. Early Adventists were more in line with Latter-Day Saints and Jehovah's Witnesses with an Arian belief in Jesus, which is to say that Jesus had been created and became God. But it did evolve

101

and later became indistinguishable from mainstream Protestant churches.

And I will say Adventists were always concerned about being differentiated from Latter-Day Saints and Jehovah's Witnesses since we were often grouped together. The three of us were the outliers, beliefs out of the mainstream.

For like Mormons, we had a prophet, Ellen G. White. (Fundamental Belief Eighteen) We tried to separate from Mormons by claiming that Adventists only took their doctrine from the Bible, which was a difficult position to hold because we loved Ellen White. We quoted from her in the pulpit, read from her in Sabbath School, memorized her in church school, talked about her in prayer meetings, and eulogized her on Sabbath afternoon walks. She had eighty books. We printed them and distributed them. Some have said that she has sold more books than any other 19th or 20th-century author. And much of Adventism had been stamped with approval by one of her visions. That made it difficult for the average Christian to see the difference between the Mormons and us.

"You have a prophet. They have a prophet, right?"

"Yes, but we take the Bible and the Bible only."

"Do you use Ellen White to help you understand difficult passages of the Bible?"

"Well, yes, but...."

"So that would be the Bible plus, right?"

"No, you just completely don't understand."

"Right, well, nice talking to you."

We also believed that they did not immediately go to heaven when someone died. Instead, they rested in their graves, a position now called Soul Sleep. (Fundamental Belief Twenty-six). It made no sense to believe in a resurrection if all the righteous had already, immediately gone to heaven when they died.

We continued to stress the soon return of Christ, though maybe not more than Evangelical Christians. (Fundamental Belief Twenty-Five), consequently our name, Adventist.

The other major difference was that early on, Adventists came to believe in a literal interpretation of the ten commandments and that when it said, "Six days shalt thou labor, but the Seventh is the Sabbath of thy God," it meant what it said. And when it said that he had created the earth in six days and then had rested and blessed the seventh day, that meant there was one special day. Adventists understood that the day God had blessed was the same as the Jewish Sabbath. All other Christian faiths agreed on a sabbath. Only Adventists, however, felt that keeping Saturday as the Sabbath was critical. (Fundamental Belief Twenty)

If Saturday was really to be observed, then all the activities of the rest of the world that fell on Friday night and Saturday had to be eschewed. Friday night dances, football games, graduations on Saturday, parties, most everything that occurred on the weekend involved the Sabbath and had to be avoided. And if you were going to bring up children to stay in your branch of Christianity, bring them up following these rigorous Sabbath rules, then it would be best to develop a parallel culture, your own schools, and your own scouting clubs. Scouting had many excellent features. Still, on Friday night, your children were going to be around non-Sabbath observers, other children who were not carefully watching the borders of the Sabbath. Ergo in the fifties, the Adventist church came up with Pathfinders, with uniforms, sashes, badges, marching, and camping. The leaders were all Adventist men and women, usually the parents. And the kids were able to get outside and have a good time.

CHAPTER TWENTY-TWO

CHANGES

That Sabbath, the church service was held in Rifle Park. They had reserved a group site. I arrived while they were still setting up and joined in carrying potted flowers and helping the ladies and older members with their folding chairs. Around ten a.m., John Boggs greeted everyone. He had his guitar in his left hand and started strumming familiar hymns. I migrated to the left side of the group and took a seat on a large boulder by the banks of Rifle Creek.

When I had been here last week with "Big Mike," the leaves, had only hinted at change, today they had progressed. Saffron yellow leaves covered the alder bushes growing along the banks, while the riparian boxelder trees had the hue of golden flax. And the waters themselves were beginning to fill with leaf boats. The sun had risen over the narrow canyon and shone on our little congregation as Pastor Kungel took over from Mr. Boggs.

The Leathermans arrived at the same time as the Opitzes. Linda was there with just Wayne and Katie. Like many of the other older children, Roy was still away at the camporee, but Doyle and Wayne seeing me sitting on a rock and not in a chair, came over and sat beside me.

Wayne (Bobo) was a solidly built second-grader, with thick light brown hair and a button nose. Wayne was smart as a whip.

He had a cheerful disposition, was curious, and did not let anything intimidate him. The older children sometimes mistook this brashness as a lack of respect for his elders. But that was not his intent. He just wanted to be a part of whatever was going on. And if they were offended, the older children, he just shook it off and moved on. He was not a sulker. He was a sweet kid.

Doyle had lighter hair. Being a first-grader, he was smaller. Doyle was quiet, much more willing to follow along with the plan than Wayne in a group. Doyle started his education with all the right tools of diligence, persistence, and a willingness to learn. Doyle made friends quickly because you could always count on him. He was just a first-grader, but I always figured Doyle would turn out just fine.

During church they sat beside me on the rock, picked up twigs, and drew in the dirt. After church, at the potluck, they loaded up their plates and ate with me. They had loaded their plates with the same order of things I had: potato salad, veggie wieners, coleslaw, potato chips, Hawaiian punch, Oreo cookies. They sat beside me and commented on the food, making exclamations about the same foods as I did.

And then while the parents were sitting around talking, the three of us took to exploring upstream, carefully jumping from rock to rock to get out to a little grassy island in the middle of the creek. This we declared was a separate country and we were the rulers. Then we had to search out for the right rocks to make a bridge to our island. And I told them how Alexander the Great had torn down Tyre and used the rubble from the city to make a causeway so he could conquer the resisting island city.

They stayed with me as we wandered farther upstream where the boxelder had formed a grove and placed the stream in a shadow. And we laid on the banks and watched a small brown trout mark time in a deep pool.

They stayed with me until Ron McElvain approached and said he needed to talk for a couple of minutes. By this time the food had been all cleared away, and most of the members were gathering their things.

"I don't want to discuss this today. We can talk about it in more detail tomorrow. I'll give you a call." There was an understanding that on Sabbath, conversations were to try as much as possible to stay on religious topics. Nature was always an accepted topic, as was theology. Health in general or compassion over another member's ailments were also acceptable. But discussion of business and the mundane details of life were to be avoided. Overall, it was not such a bad idea.

"I just wanted to let you know there'll not be a second teacher." Ron was visibly upset, which was why he had felt it so necessary to tell me. "Mrs. Kungel has turned it down. We have no one else.

"Also," he hated to add insult to injury. Being board chairman had lost its appeal. "The Forshees have threatened to pull out Misty unless we have a second teacher."

O no, not Misty, I thought. She was such a little darling.

"I don't know what we're going to do," Ron shook his head. "You hang in there, Marvin." He put out his hand to shake mine. "We'll figure something out. Will you be at the school tomorrow?"

"All day and into the night," I responded flatly.

Ron gave a slight smile, which was both I am sorry for you, and also, we sure did get the right guy for the job.

"Well, I'll call you sometime tomorrow."

I nodded and took a breath as he walked away. I could feel my throat tighten. I was in quicksand. It was so overwhelming all of these children, all of these grades. It was no comfort that none of the other teachers in the conference had a load nearly as bad as me. Nope, that was not in the least comforting. Also, I did not want to lose Misty.

I watched Ron catch up to Connie. Kim was just behind them. She turned her head and gave me a little smile. I waved at her, and she grinned.

Ron and I did talk on Sunday, and we came up with several changes. He spoke with the school board, and then on Monday, he called the conference to get their approval. They signed off. So somewhere midweek, I handed out a letter to the parents. We were going to change the school day. Since I was so tied up with the lower grades in the forenoon, we were going to extend the afternoon bell to 3:30, and we were going to release the first two grades at one-thirty. The indomitable workload necessitated these changes, which ensured the students' education did not suffer. I would have more teaching time with the older grades with these modifications. Overall, it was not that big of a change. But we were trying to adjust wherever we could, even if they were minor tweaks. We were looking for anything to maximize my teaching time.

A more meaningful change was that Tina Mitchell worked as the aide that week. Sandy Forshee and Connie McElvain had both been excellent as aides, but they had other younger children, and it was impossible for them to do it for more than an occasional week, which meant every week I had to be training in a new aide. Danny was Tina's youngest, and he was in school. This would work well. Furthermore, the children all liked her. There was nothing not to like about Tina. She had a calm, even manner. Also, having been a mother for a long time, she had experience in dealing with kids. She worked that week as an aide, and it was helpful.

The parents had been talking as well. They must have realized the weight on me because the parents had been going out of their way to make little positive comments when dropping off or picking up the children all week. They repeatedly told me how much their children enjoyed school, which was not always the case. And they also said how pleased they were that I was the teacher. Mrs. Forshee said she had talked to Misty, and she really wanted to keep coming. She also thought that the change to the schedule might make it doable, so they would not withdraw her. I was relieved. The Sisks, both Doug's parents and Mike's parents, went out of their way to express their pleasure. Doug's parents said he had not enjoyed school this much in some time. Mike's stepmom was amazed at how quickly Little Mike had settled in. He was always looking forward to school.

And so, the week went on. We realized that week that Carolyn was our little China doll. She was constantly bumping into something, twisting an ankle, falling at recess, and straining her wrist. It became common to see her holding a stack of brown wet wipes on her wrist, head, or ankle. She had her box of Band-Aids in her desk that she was frequently applying. I would see her sitting at her desk, putting a Band-Aid on her elbow. And when she saw me looking, she would show me a little abrasion on her elbow, and she would be smiling. As long as I was aware, she was satisfied.

And Angie had been at the fence that week watching Bessie, our mascot cow, when she had been stung by three hornets. So, I took her up two houses to Mrs. Livingood, a church member and a retired nurse. She had given her a little poultice to apply.

The parents had arranged carpools for delivering and picking up the children. On Wednesday, Connie McElvain, on her pick-up rotation, came inside to hurry Kim.

"You usually go into town on Thursdays to do your laundry, don't you?" She asked me.

"Yes, I do."

"Well, Ron and I were talking, why don't you come to our house tomorrow night. You can eat supper with us and do your laundry at our house." She said this as she was helping Kim pack her belongings in her backpack. She looked over at me as she put her hand on Kim's shoulder, guiding her to the door.

It floored me. I had not expected such generosity. This was above and beyond any reasonable expectation from the parents.

"Yeah...sure." And I sat there for a moment struck dumb. "Thank you."

She smiled and then grabbed Kim's hand. A moment later, Kim came running back into the room, "Mr. Brauer, my mother wants to know if you like manicotti?"

"Yes, yes, very much so," I said emphatically.

Consequently, the following day I brought my laundry in my car, and after school, I did a few necessary things around the school and then drove into Rifle. Connie showed me their washing machine, and I put in my laundry. I had, of course, brought my own soap. And then I had sat down at the table with Ron, Connie, Kim, and Kim's little brother Jon. Jon was quite excited to have Kim's teacher in his house. The food was delicious, and I was grateful. It far exceeded anything I prepared at home. But, of course, boxed meals and canned soup only go so far.

Connie asked how I had chosen elementary education.

I talked a little about my path towards elementary education, how I had grown up mainly thinking of medicine or the law, and then while in college, had drifted towards a career as a high school history teacher. That had veered sharply when I took a class from the chairman of the education department, Dr. Virginia Simmons. I completed a one-month observation in a fourth-grade classroom as part of her class. I had been astounded by how much I enjoyed that month. Dr. Simmons had requested me to schedule time to see her in her office. She wanted to give me feedback on my practicum. I liked Dr. Simmons immensely; everybody did. She was probably in her early sixties, tall with short, silver hair. And she had a bright all-encompassing mind and was warm and gregarious.

When I was comfortably seated across the desk from her, she pulled out the report from my supervising teacher. She looked at it, smiled, then pushed it across the desk.

"I respect Mrs. Ramirez a great deal," Dr. Simmons started the conversation. "She speaks very highly of you. Mrs. Ramirez is always a positive person. She speaks well of most of the college students, but not like this."

I had gotten along well with Mrs. Ramirez, a short, plump lady, probably of Philippine origins. Her children respected and liked her.

I quickly skimmed her evaluation, which was very complimentary. I liked Mrs. Ramirez even more.

"Marvin, you are currently a history major, thinking about teaching in secondary school, is that right?"

I nodded.

"Marvin, have you thought about elementary education? Not many have your rapport with children. And," She paused and looked over her glasses at me. "We need more men in elementary education."

I put my hand over my mouth in a common mannerism I had when I was thinking and paused. "Actually, Dr. Simmons, I had not considered it until this month. But I have to tell you it was so rewarding. I was blown away with how much I loved those kids, but well, I have wandered about a little in my college education, and I need to keep on track to graduate."

"Get me your transcripts."

"Excuse me," I was puzzled.

"Let me look at them. Then, I'll see what can be done."

"Thank you." I was taken aback by her encouragement. She spent another fifteen minutes talking with me about an assortment of issues related to elementary education and career paths that she thought would open to me. Finally, the conversation wound down, and I got up and opened the door.

"Mrs. Ramirez called me," Dr. Simmons said as I was exiting. I turned around. "She never calls, but she called me. She thinks you are one of the good ones."

"Mrs. Ramirez is an excellent teacher."

"Yes, she is."

I told this story to the McElvains, and how Dr. Simmons had then made some accommodations to keep me on track to graduate on time. Connie said her brother and I were a lot alike, similar in age, single, and so full of adventure.

After supper, while my clothes were drying, I sat on the couch in the living room. Kim changed into her pajamas and was cuddled up beside her mother while her mother read the Sabbath School lesson to her. And that whole domestic scene affected me. This was what I wanted; my desideratum was a family of my own. I wanted a daughter to snuggle up to me at night while reading to her. I could not imagine anything so fulfilling.

Thursday nights—or sometimes Wednesday—for the rest of the year were spent at the McElvain's. Except that from that week on, I would bring in my laundry in the morning, and Mrs. McElvain would pick it up and then have it all washed and folded by the time I arrived. Let me repeat that in case you were skimming through the page. Not only did the McElvains feed me every week, and it was usually a pasta dish, but in addition, Connie would do my laundry, and have it all folded when I arrived. And I would sit down with them at supper and have a pleasant conversation. Ron and Connie were both excellent storytellers. Occasionally, Ron would invite me to stay for a family board game such as monopoly. And Kimmy was always so pleased that her teacher came home to her house every week. No one else save for the Mitchell's could lay such claim. The bounty of my amazement and gratitude has not faded even these decades later.

The buzzer went off. I folded my laundry, thanked everyone, and drove home in the darkness. The Book Cliffs were towering on my right. The air at night was cool, and I could see the glimmer of the moon reflecting off of the Colorado on my drive. When Eric Carmen's *All By Myself* came on the radio, I rolled down the windows and joined with him on the chorus. I didn't want to live alone.

CHAPTER TWENTY-THREE

RAISE YOUR HANDS

On Fridays, I gave the children more time to catch up on their work. I was very much against giving the children homework at night. Seven hours in the classroom was long enough. When they left the school, I wanted them to go home and play. I did not want to tie up their remaining daylight hours with busywork. So, on Fridays, I scheduled time to catch up on some of the work they had fallen behind on. Also, it was a time when I could personally explain difficult concepts. If they had been struggling through the week, we could find some time on Friday.

Fridays were also a time to add extras into the curriculum. On Fridays, we did art projects and had a period for music. I might play them some classical music, or we sang. Mostly we sang songs. None of the children played instruments, so a band was not feasible. In the second semester, the conference organized a choir festival. On Fridays, we practiced the songs, and I would play the piano, unfortunately very poorly, but still, I would play.

On Fridays, I was a little laxer at enforcing the recess times, and if it was a nice day, I would often open the back door by my desk, prop it open and let the children take their book and sit out on the lawn.

At the end of every day, I always took a few minutes to summarize the day. On Friday, this comment period was longer. It was a chance to discuss the week.

This Friday, I was standing up front at the end of the day. We had talked about the week. I discussed the upcoming changes for the next week, i.e., the schedule changes, which thrilled no one. The first two grades did not want to leave early. They liked being a part of the program with the older children. The older grades did not like having to stay an extra half hour. I thanked everyone for being willing to help. Mike, Doug, Kelli, and particularly Ron had been very willing to help explain concepts to the lower grades. I discussed that there was a better than even chance that Tina Mitchell would turn in her resume and become the full-time aide. Everyone thought that was a good idea. The rotation of aides would stop, and the aide would now stay past lunch. The aide would leave when grades one and two left. They asked me my plans for the weekend, and I said I would drive over to Denver to see my parents. Mike asked me if I would see anybody else while I was over there. Everybody knew what he was angling for.

"Wouldn't you like to know? " I said and smiled at him.

He laughed.

The windows were open, and the sun was shining through on its way to the Book Cliffs. I was wearing a black crushed, fake velvet shirt with a v neck collar and a pair of khaki pants. I never wore a tie as they looked too old for my taste. I sat down on the front of my desk.

"Well, is there anything else before we have a closing prayer?"

Near the front over by the interior wall, Kelli raised her hand.

"Kelli." I recognized her.

She put down her hand and sat up very straight. She was wearing an orange Broncos shirt and blue jean overalls. She looked all around her and then pronounced, "I like my teacher."

I smiled and chuckled. "Thank you, Kelli."

Wayne's hand shot up. He was over by the window, and he was waving his hand desperately.

"Wayne."

He burst out, "I like my teacher too."

"You guys are sweet."

And several hands flew up, but Doug was waving his hand the hardest, so I called on him.

"Doug."

"A couple of mental cases up front, Mr. Brauer."

Now, that was funny. Mike, Shon, and Steven liked it, but the younger kids protested without waiting for me to call on them, they put their hands down, and there was a cacophony of, "I like you, Mr. Brauer."

Chrissie, however, thin petite blonde, fourth grade, cute as a button nose, quiet and unassuming little Chrissie in the midst pronounced seriously, "I don't like you, Mr. Brauer."

I looked at her and laughed. "Yes, you do, Chrissie." And I gave her an all-knowing gaze. And she blushed, and gave me a slight smile, and said nothing further.

I quieted everyone. "Alright, everyone, bow your heads."

After prayer, I went to the back of the classroom to say goodbye, and when Wayne hugged me, the younger children all rushed to surround me.

CHAPTER TWENTY-FOUR

BIRTHDAY

"Mr. Brauer! Mr. Brauer! Kelli is hurt." Danny cried as he came running into the school. It was Wednesday and lunch break. Mrs. Mitchell had submitted her resume, and the board had hired her as a full-time aide. She was outside supervising the students. I was at my desk reading *Of Human Bondage*. Over the weekend, while at my parents' house, I had picked up a paperback copy. I wanted to resume progress on my classical booklist. My reading had stalled. I was not far into the book, but I liked the writing and related to the protagonist.

I jumped up from my desk. Kelli was hurt, and from Danny's voice, it sounded serious. I ran out the back door, following him. He headed to the front of the Fellowship Hall. (That was the name given to the second building at the front of the property.) And then suddenly I slowed down. Okay, it was Kelli. If anyone was going to be in on something, it was Kelli, and it was my birthday. I rounded the corner, and no one was there, but the door was open into the hall. When I entered the building, all the students jumped up and yelled "Happy Birthday, Mr. Brauer!" And then Kelli and Heather added, "We love you, Mr. Brauer." It was delightful. They sang "Happy Birthday," and then Mrs. Mitchell cut the birthday cake. Everybody had a piece. It was a white cake. I had not remembered telling Tina that was my favorite, but I must have. I love a moist white cake and chocolate swirl ice cream. It was delicious, chased down with a cup of soda.

They wanted to know how old I was. I told them.

"Twenty-three!" Mike was astounded. "Seriously? Twenty-three. That is old. I'm surprised you can run at all. How are your knees?"

Doug and Steven took up the banter. They said if they had known I was twenty-three, they would have bought me a cane.

I took the ribbing. In my opinion, it was justified. I felt old. Twenty-three, and I did not have a serious girlfriend. How was that possible?

But mostly as I ate my cake and saw all the children eating theirs and laughing at the boys' jokes, and so delighted that they had completely surprised me, I once again felt my heart was replete, overflowing like the Colorado at the spring thaw.

In the evening Tina took me into town to a concert of Up With People. She picked me up at my house. We had some shop talk about the school and the children on the drive there. She said she had heard that Bonnie Holderbaum was upset about the new schedule.

"Yes, she called me. I talked to her for a while. I dropped by their house to talk."

"Really?" Tina was impressed.

Their house was close, just up the hill. It was close enough that Kelli and Shon walked to and from school every day, so I had dropped by. I had been aware of historical tensions between the Mitchells and the Holderbaums, and so when I heard the complaint, I went to their house.

Bonnie Holderbaum was probably in her mid to late thirties. She paid a lot more attention to her attire than most in the community. Obviously, she did not buy her clothes from the Ward's catalogue. Her clothes hung well on her. Her hair was cut in the popular mid-shaggy style that was gaining fashion. She was a blonde, though in the picture-stand on the side-table, when she and Bill were in college, in that picture she was a brunette.

116

Bonnie had an easy grace with me. Tina told me later that she was nicer to men than women. That seemed about right.

In any case, I explained the reasoning behind the schedule change and that we had run it by the conference. Bonnie said she just did not like the children in school for so long. We parted on good terms, and as we did, she went out of her way to tell me that her children liked me. They hoped I would stay at least another year.

That topic covered, Tina and I moved on. Tina was an engaging conversationalist. She could cover up blank space if required, but she could also listen, an uncommon gift.

We arrived at the auditorium and found our seats. When the performance started, and the young people came on stage, I was thunderstruck, bowled over, bedazzled.

Up With People is a non-profit organization based in Denver for young performers to travel and work with communities. They had performed at the Cotton Bowl, the White House, and a couple of Super Bowls. The group, noted for their upbeat, smiling, wholesome performances, performed well. They sang well, and they danced. What addled me, however, was the sight of young women my age, attractive young women my age. I had been so deprived. It was like a strong drink, just better.

On the way home Tina put in a Neil Diamond tape — she was a big fan of Neil Diamond — and started talking about her daughter. Valerie was coming home this weekend and was bringing a friend. Tina assured me that my invitation to come up still stood. Valerie had also reminded her mother that she and I had been friends. I was pleased Valerie phrased it that way. I remembered her and thought she was nice, although we had had at most two conversations. Tina then let slide that Valerie's last boyfriend had been twenty-five. I sat in the passenger seat and listened to Neil Diamond and watched the moon over the hills. I was in a receptive mood for listening to talk about attractive women.

She dropped me off, and I gathered my little cat and sat for a little while on the couch. I put side two of *Abbey Road* on the record player and read a few more pages *Of Human Bondage* before going to bed. I slept fitfully.

CHAPTER TWENTY-FIVE

I'M TRYING TO SEE BOTH SIDES NOW

At school, the honeymoon was waning. I had a more difficult time motivating Roy to keep up with his work, and Mike tested me. He got up from his desk on Thursday morning and told me he was going outside. I replied it was not recess yet, and could he please return to his seat.

"Who made you the boss?" He sniped.

"Actually, the school board. That's why they hired me. The common term for my position is… teacher."

He stared at me for a moment and then grunted, "Fine!" He plopped back down in his chair. The moves were all wildly exaggerated, letting me know that this battle for control had just begun.

For the issues with Roy, I called his mother — children love that. I knew Roy had a deep respect for his mother. We had a good conversation. She said she would talk to him.

For the larger issues of unrest amid the other pupils, their sniping, their ill-humor, and their petulance, I realized I needed to be creative. Morale was declining. Their cheerfulness was receding, and I wanted to arrest the deterioration. Part of me had hoped, however unrealistically, that the year would have been full of laughter and enthusiasm, children eagerly sitting at their desks for eight hours a day. That, of course, was fanciful thinking. Still, I had hoped it might be that way. It would have been wonderful. But in truth, I had anticipated the insurrection. No child, if given a choice, would choose this confinement. It was unnatural. Still, it was part and parcel of the discipline education needed. But if I was to continue to instill a love of knowledge, I needed to suppress this discontent. I needed to stop their sniping. I decided to add the Rulison Dollar.

After school, I drew up the currency on copy paper and then printed it on the mimeograph. Activities of citizenship earned it — I was a big proponent of positive discipline. You earned the Rulison Dollar by doing the expected things: your homework, getting in your chair quickly after recess, being quiet when requested, helping another student if they had a problem, or an act of kindness. Tina and I handed out the money after lunch and at the end of the day. But we would also give it, on occasion, without forewarning. The school embraced the system. Mike liked to spend his money to sit out on the front step. Doug became a currency mogul. He haggled and bargained. While most of the students had ten to fifteen dollars, Doug soon was sitting on over two hundred. Steven decided to increase his wealth by using the Xerox machine at his parent's business. But a Xerox produces a different look than a mimeograph, and the counterfeiting was ferreted out. I thought it was creative, but of course, it had to stop, and so I impounded all of his capital.

Saturday arrived, and after church, I went up to the Mitchell's. As I sat down on one of the sectionals, the aromas from the kitchen were wafting out to the living room. It smelled wonderful. Danny was up and down: from sitting on the couch beside me, to running to do an errand for his mother, to sitting back down, to jumping up for a task his sister requested of him. David was standing by the large picture window near where Valerie's friend, Ruth, sat. He was regaling us with a running stream of stories and humor. I felt the growing conviction that I was in the presence of a livelier mind than my own. And when we laughed, Tina would step out of the kitchen for a moment to have him repeat the joke. After that, she would usually contribute some embellishment, some further detail, then wiping her hands on her apron; she would return to the kitchen. She was delighted to have her family altogether.

At church, Tina had been certain to invite me again. "I must come. I was coming, wasn't I?" I had no intention of missing one of her meals. Besides, David and I always had a good time together. He was the only one anywhere near my age.

Also, there was the factor of two attractive girls, Valerie and Ruth. They were both young, pretty, and best friends. Ruth's hair was blonde, very long, and very straight. She was quieter than Valerie and more reserved. Her laughter was more restrained, and she was more comfortable observing rather than jumping into the fray. Then again, it was Valerie's home, so that might not have been a completely accurate assessment. They were both about the same height. Ruth was twiggy thin. Valerie was also blond, but she styled her hair in the Farrah Fawcett style with big curls and waves. She was also thin, although her curves were not limited to her hair. They were both seventeen and in high school.

Mr. Mitchell came down the stairs and sat on the opposite couch. He had taken off his coat and tie and put on more comfortable shoes. He nodded at me and smiled. It was apparent he was even happier now that his daughter was home. Valerie came out of the kitchen and told Danny to get a couple of eggs from their chicken coop. Danny asked me if I wanted to join him.

"He's in his suit pants," Valerie protested.

"I can be careful, I'm sure," I replied and got up to join Danny. I had helped Danny several times with chicken chores, and I found these country ways fascinating. The coop was up the hill to the east of the house, not far. We crossed the dust and scraggly weeds in front of the house. (This would be the front lawn when watering pipes were laid.) The sky was overcast. Like his mother and brother, Danny had no difficulty keeping up a conversation, and he too was delighted that Valerie was home. It was obvious he idolized her. We opened the door to the coop. There were cobwebs everywhere. We both looked at the webs and then at my clothes.

"Maybe you better wait outside," he offered.

"Yea, I think you're right."

So, I stepped back out and paused to savor the view of the valley and river. A life lived along the river brought a sense of magnitude, a tranquility that was difficult to measure by any of the usual metrics. There was a quietness, a calmness formed by the never-ending running, day and night of the waters—these waters that were impervious to the opinions of men. And it was this strength they lent to the folk who dwelt in their environs that I was doing everything I could to imbibe. I was consciously soaking in this serenity from the river.

From the sky, I was trying to learn the cycle of the clouds, trying to distinguish cumulus from cirrus, cirrus from nimbus, nimbus from stratus. It was stratus which blanketed the sky today.

I was also trying to be attentive to where the sun rose each morning, behind which nob it ascended, and in the evening how far down the Roan Plateau it folded into the earth.

Although, of course, I had not been there long enough to synchronize with these daily and perennial rhythms, still, I was trying. I was trying to absorb what I could, trying to slow my mind. And as I stood there just outside the chicken coop by slowing my mind, I became aware of the rustling of grasshoppers jumping amidst the autumn dry weeds, and I heard the melody of a meadowlark from a nearby fence post.

I loved this life: the children, the beauty of Western Colorado, the graciousness of all the church members, and if only somehow, I could figure out how to make a life here, I would be delighted to plant roots and stay.

It did not hurt the mood that Valerie and Ruth were in the house. They were both attractive—too young, of course, only high school. Still, they were not children.

After lunch, a massive lunch, in which we all ate way too much—Tina was a fantastic cook and delighted when we took

122

seconds and thirds. I was young with a high metabolism, and teaching burned up a lot of calories. I could eat a lot. Anyway, after lunch, Valerie persuaded her father to take everybody on a Sabbath afternoon drive—all seven of us in their Jeep Cherokee. Even with the bench seat in the front, and the fact that in 1981 mandatory seat belt laws were still several years away, still, seven was crowded. I tried to excuse myself. I was not family. I would go home and see them at the hayride tonight. Tina, Danny, and Valerie protested. Tina insisted I was indeed family. While everyone was getting ready and I was still wavering, David pulled me aside. "You need to come with us, man. I kind-a-like Ruth, but I'm gonna have a much better chance if you're around. That's how girls are, you know."

It was going to be a little while before they were ready. Tina suggested, if I wanted to change, they could pick me up at my house. That sounded good. That way, I could also check on my kitten.

On the drive, I sat in the backseat beside the left window. Danny was next to me, then Ruth, and on the other side David. It was tight. Mitch, Tina, and Valerie were up front. Mitch wound around some back roads up into the mountains to the south. Valerie turned halfway around and put her hand back for her best friend. They held hands often during the drive. Mitch gave us a travelogue as we coursed through the backroads. And I felt so incorporated, such a sense of belonging. The whole family was so inclusive. Finally, we arrived at the church near sunset, just in time for the hayride.

Mr. Johnson had a hay and alfalfa farm below the school. He brought his red tractor over to the church parking lot. He was rearranging the hay bales, giving them some final preparation. I went over to see if he needed assistance.

"Well then, Mr. Brauer," He was broad-shouldered with deep set eyes, rough hands, and short, grey hair. His hair was much shorter than city folk, like me.

"You need a hand?"

"Never turn down help." He showed me what he was doing. "Maybe, I'll catch the restroom once more."

He stepped off. I moved the bales around as he had outlined. When he came back. He nodded. "That'll do."

And when I jumped down and brushed off my jeans, he added, "I see you in the mornings…sometimes…walking up the road… you're keeping some early hours, young man."

Coming from a farmer, I knew that was a high compliment.

There was a good turnout, probably thirty to thirty-five people, half of my school, the Schlisners, the Holderbaums, the Mitchells, the Optizes, the Boggs, the McElvains, and the Cloningers just down the street. There had been some concern over the weather. It had been cloudy most of the day and had sprinkled off and on earlier in the afternoon. But now the rain seemed to have stopped, and as I looked down the valley the clouds were beginning to break up. That was a promising omen.

Everyone loaded up. Several of my children proceeded to claim me. Tonight, it was Doyle, Chad, and Carolyn. Carolyn insisted on sitting next to me.

A hayride, particularly among a group familiar and comfortable, has a unique charm and its own particular rhythm. First, there was the settling in as you left the parking lot, everyone adjusting their position, folding their blankets, or their jackets in little crooks, little gaps in the hay, trying to avoid leaning against one another, overcrowding, moving around a bit. Some children wanted to sit closer to a different friend or make room when someone else made imploring requests. And it was always more fun if the group was big enough that you had to crowd somewhat by necessity. Cozy was desired. And tonight, it was very cozy.

Initially, everyone was watching the road, watching the houses pass by. Then soon, we were rolling on a dirt road that skirted along the river, and we moved out of town into the countryside. The clouds did indeed disperse, and we began to see planets and stars, Venus and Mars. The moon would not arise in its waxing stages until the trip was nearly over. People told stories, and intermittently we sang.

Having worked at summer camps, I knew a lot of songs, and I was not bashful in getting them started. First, we sang gospel songs like *Do Lord, Glory, Glory,* and *Amazing Grace.* Then we transitioned to other folk favorites, *You Are My Sunshine, My Bonnie Lies Over the Ocean,* and *There's a Hole in the Bucket.* Finally, we sang rounds of *Row, Row, Row Your Boat.*

People adjusted their seating a little. In the beginning, Doyle was sitting on my lap. In the end, Chad was on my right, Kelli on my left, and Carolyn had perched herself on my lap. The Mitchell's daughter was directly behind me, and we ended up leaning back-to-back. There was a lot of laughter and people pointing out farms, telling me who lived where.

In between one of the songs, Kelli put her hand up to my ear and whispered, "Valerie thinks you're cute."

"What?" I remonstrated softly and glanced at Kelli. She was delighted.

Maybe I could not afford a house. Jesus never had a home. Did I have to make enough money to buy a house? Could I not learn to be satisfied with all of the wonderful things I did have? If only the finances would meet my limited expenses.

CHAPTER TWENTY-SIX

HISTORY IS REPEATING

Miss Archambeau from the conference was back out the following week, which now made the fourth visit the conference had made in the space of five weeks. This support was why my college chair, Dr. Simmons, had been pleased that I had picked Colorado. They supplied the best support in the union. The Mid America Union included: Minnesota, North and South Dakota, Iowa, Missouri, Kansas, Nebraska, Wyoming, and Colorado. "Some of the other conferences leave the new teachers to founder, but not Colorado," Dr. Simmons had said. And I felt that.

I knew they were trying, even though I had the worst load in the conference, likely the worst load in the union. I had never heard of any teacher having anywhere near what I was trying to do. Was it preposterous to suppose I had the largest teaching load in the country? On a whim, I pulled out the school's World Book encyclopedia and read the article on education. In one section, they discussed teaching in the pioneer days. In those early days on the prairies, they noted that a teacher might even have all eight grades. The idea was presented as an idea so preposterous the only way you could wrap your mind around it was to consider it in the frame of the hard, primitive, frontier days. As a caveat, they noted that the children were often not present. They were often absent from school during the planting or harvesting. The author pointed out that the student attended a little over fifty percent on average. I closed the book and let out a big sigh. It sounded like they had an easier caseload than me. It was distinctly possible I had the worst-case load in the history of these United States.

I will also say that these visits from the conference office never felt like an imposition. They did not make my day harder. I did not feel like my supervisors judged me, nor like I had to perform, which speaks volumes about the quality of my supervisors. On the contrary, I had only admiration for them.

We sat down at the end of the day's visit. She asked my opinion; wondered how I thought the day had gone. I assessed it as a decent day. I brought up some moments when I might have been more perceptive and handled things a little differently. I suggested ideas that I could have done differently in the reading class. Unfortunately, I had cut short a discussion that was beginning to expand because, alas, I had to move on.

"I have certainly had worse days. Overall, not a bad day."

She nodded. "Marvin, I completely agree. I am reassured."

Thursday and Friday that week, a number of the students were missing. The conference had a medical retreat at Glacier View. Thus, all the children of health professionals were absent. Danny's father was a nurse anesthetist, so he and Tina were gone. Mike's father was a Family Practice doctor. He was absent. Bill Holderbaum was a dentist, so Shon and Kelli were not there either. Finally, Ron McElvain was an optometrist thus, Kim was gone. Five students in total.

A big part of the identity of the Adventist church was its stress on the importance of the health message. Adventists had found a niche of value in the milieu as health workers. I had once heard an amusing comment that in Nigeria, there were only four professions acknowledged to the family: doctor, engineer, lawyer, or disgrace to the family. I thought that was amusing, and I understood it.

I knew to my core what I could do and could not do and be accepted. In the Adventist church, the professions that gained you status were minister, teacher, or doctor. If you were a woman and had to work, nurse, secretary, and teacher were all good.

The tension was always whether to give the minister or the doctor higher status. That was always pretty much a draw.

And the more you were indoctrinated into the Adventist culture, the more you accepted this unwritten dogma. As I said, my family was at least a fourth-generation Adventist. We were filling all the lanes. My father was a minister, my mother worked for the church, and my two oldest brothers were ministers. Ron, who was just a little older than me, was finishing up his master's to be a teacher. I was a teacher. Of course, most of my children had parents who were not in these 'favored' lines of work. But even though everyone understood, still, they lost status points.

I also want to point out that the children were absent based on their father's occupation. The mother was necessary, so critical, everyone agreed, of course, but everybody had their roles, their station in life. And the man was the man. We understood this.

All that aside, with five students gone, the last two days were so much quieter at school. Without the competition for oxygen from Mike and Kelli, Roy was much more verbal. For those two days, he kept filling me in on his progress. "Mr. Brauer, I finished my Bible worksheet, and now I am getting out my math. Mr. Brauer, I finished up page fifty-five of math. I think I'll go ahead and do page fifty-six, and then I'll be all caught up in math. Do you think I could redo my spelling test? I studied my words again." I had moved Roy up near the front to try and keep an eye on him. Also, he had broken his ankle at home and was using a crutch. On the front row, he could extend his long legs without bothering anyone and with less chance of someone accidentally bumping it.

Not to be outdone by Roy's play-by-play, Heather pulled her chair up to the side of my desk. She spread out her books and papers and proceeded to do her work right there. Heather was just as diligent and just as determined to catch up. Also, from that position, she could watch over the classroom. With Kelli being gone, she felt she had to assume the role of den mother.

And Chrissie and Angie, who were never behind in their schoolwork; and did not need to catch up, felt the quieter atmosphere. They were always near, standing close so that I could pat them on the back or tussle their hair. If I was helping the first graders, they were quick to volunteer. "I can show them, Mr. Brauer. Do you want me to?" Which, of course, would merit a thank you and a pat on the head. And they would help and then be right back by my side, so much so that I had to slow down when I turned around, almost like being aware that a little kitten might be under your feet if you turned too quickly.

Wayne in second grade wanted Angie to help him, which was not hard to see through. Angie and Chrissie were the cutest little waifs, slight build, shaggy blonde hair, thin faces. But Wayne was an intelligent kid; he quickly understood the material. He did not need more tutoring. Angie politely deferred.

With Mike gone, Ron, Chrissie and Angie's stepbrother, was now the oldest in the classroom. And with the classroom quieter, I had time to notice him more than just being the tallest in the school. He was witty, curious, talkative, and full of ideas. He had dishwater hair that started the day combed and ended the day disheveled. Being a seventh-grader, he was rarely picked on, but if someone did perchance make a joke about him, if it was a good joke, he loved it. His self-confidence was impressive.

Ron was my acolyte. He wanted to know if I was going to stay a teacher. And when I said I had not decided, all the classroom heard that.

"Are you going to be here next year, Mr. Brauer?" They all asked.

I told them I could not be sure. The decision involved a lot of things, but one thing was sure I enjoyed being their teacher. That satisfied them. Almost.

CHAPTER TWENTY-SEVEN

A MOONGLOW

On Friday night, I was home alone in my tiny house. Outside, it was drizzling. And the place was quiet. But, of course, one did not watch television on the Sabbath. I would sooner drive a nail into my hand than violate that commandment. And for some reason, my stereo was not working, or I might have put on Keith Green, or maybe since it was raining, *Brahms's Violin Concerto in D minor* with Isaac Sterns on violin. So instead, I sat on my brown couch in the stillness of the little house, petting my cat and remembering Friday nights at my parents' home. There I might have gotten out a book of piano music and played for a while or maybe started a fire in the fireplace. Or I would have sat opposite Mom and Dad, each of us with a copy of the Adventist Review and occasionally putting down the magazine to talk; and periodically being attracted to the snap and flames of the pine logs. Tonight, however, the only sounds were the patter of the rain, the purr of the kitten, and the hum of my refrigerator. I ran a bath, sat in the tub, and read back through old journals, picking out periods of life when I had also been alone. They were, unfortunately, not rare.

After church the following day, I decided to hike up the hill behind my house. It was a scrub oak, primitive forest, and in my imagination, it was like one of Tolkien's malignant, old forests. Was it with malintent trying to lead me onto strange paths? Were these small meadows of pretty yellow flowers seducing me to continue upward? My arms in short sleeves were getting scratched and poked by the sharp leaves and rough branches, and my little yellow cat scrambled through the thorns and entanglements, pitifully meowing when it was not sure where I had disappeared. I would call his name, and he would persistently meow until he was again rubbing against my leg.

After sun-down and with the Sabbath ended, I walked back up to the school and put in a couple of hours of work. It was disillusioning that my work was never done. Even on a Saturday night, I was at the school.

The following day, Sunday, I was back up there early. I spent all day writing lesson plans. Although, I could now write abbreviated lesson plans and not the detailed ones the conference had initially required, nevertheless, it was still tedious. But trying to teach a day without a plan would have been so chaotic, unimaginably stressful. Even the idea of a day unprepared was beyond my comprehension.

The rain continued, and I sometimes caught myself just watching the drops coalesce on the windows and make little rivers.

I walked home for lunch with the idea of treating myself to some football on my little black and white television. But at home, the power was out. So, I trudged back up to the school and stayed until nine. I drew out the lines, wrote in the plans, and tried to develop ways to make it enjoyable; break up the tedium for the kids.

When I finally left the schoolhouse, the rain had ceased, and the clouds had blown away. As I walked home, as I came out of the school yard, I became aware of how much difference the moon made. Here in the country, where there were no streetlamps, the moon's luminosity and phases made me aware of things I had never noticed in the city. Tonight, it was a full moon and how it shined, how it lightened the road and turned all the bushes into glimmering silver. And the beauty of that moonglow had an effect on my mood. My loneliness was replaced by a calm satisfaction of the simple life. And it was augmented by the contentment that came from knowing I had put in the work. Monday, however it turned out, even if it was one of those periodic days of mayhem—who could predict them—at least it was not because I was ill-prepared or lazy.

Monday went well, but Tuesday.

Mid-morning, Danny ran into the room waving a bra and shouting, "Carolyn wears a bra!" Of course, Carolyn was humiliated. Tina was chagrinned. She sat Danny down with a withering command and then led Carolyn out of the room. Chad jumped up to defend his sister and banged into Roy's casted foot. Roy screamed, cursed, and would have punched Chad if he had not been bent over holding his foot. The older boys cackling with great glee thought it was hilariously funny. Kelli and Heather were outraged. They stood up and told the boys to shut up and sit down. They were astounded at the boys' utter lack of couth. How could they be such beasts! The boys thought that made it even funnier. To Danny's credit, seeing how badly he had upset Carolyn —he was overall a good kid—he was repentant. He had just reacted without thinking. The idea that his classmate, whom he had grown up with, was maturing and now needed a bra seemed incongruous and funny. Humor can be cruel.

But that put everyone in a bad mood, and when at recess Heather picked dodgeball Doug, Mike, and Ron said that was for little kids. They were not going to play. I told them they could put their heads on their desks for recess. They gave me defiant looks, looked at each other, and put their heads down.

"All right, that works," I said. I was surprised Shon had not joined them. "By the way, you will also get dropped in the next rotation to pick recess."

That was too much for them, and they yielded.

Dodgeball was popular with the older boys. We delighted in trying to knock each other out of the circle. We divided into teams. Mike and Doug teamed up; they moved the ball quickly around the ring and caught me in a group of first graders where I had no escape route. Doug was exultant at applying the coup de gras. After that, they dispatched the others with alacrity. The teams traded sides. Mike and Doug and their team went into the circle. Roy and Steven on my team were able to get Danny and several of the younger graders out. Mike was hanging back on the far side, standing close to me. Steven tossed me the ball over Mike's head; I caught it and let it fly. Mike jumped behind Angie, and the ball hit her low in the calves and upended her. She fell and scraped her palms. Angie did not cry, but she looked like she was about to. I was upset with Mike. Against the lower grades, anybody other than the upper-grade boys I threw with much less velocity.

"What are you doing, Mike? Using Angie as a shield? Come on, Mike, you are better than that."

Mike's shoulders sagged. "I was just trying to get out of the way...." He looked at Angie, who was still sitting on the ground.

"I'm sorry, Angie," I said as I approached her and helped her to her feet.

"Are you okay?" Mike added. She nodded to him and stifled a sob.

Tina came over and took Angie into the bathroom to wash her hands, get the gravel out. I was thankful for Tina. A woman's presence was helpful.

I glared at Mike. "Not cool, man."

The mood for the day did not improve. I told Roy he had to include a legend on the maps when he turned in his geography assignment, which peeved him. He could be difficult when he was displeased. It also did not help that Cory squirted the girls with a water gun at lunch, including spraying Carolyn in the face. She plummeted back into self-pity. At lunch, I put my head in my hands. And Heather did none of her work that day.

After lunch, when I dismissed the first graders, Tina gave me an encouraging, hang-in-there smile as she was leaving. I walked the first graders out and gave them each a hug. I told them today they had been far more mature children than the older kids, and I would miss their sweet spirits.

"The older grades acted like babies, didn't they, Mr. Brauer?" Doyle said. I nodded and laughed.

I said it would be a free period for recess in the afternoon, no activity, but everyone should be outside. So, I went out and just walked around watching everyone. I jogged back into the classroom halfway through recess to grab a lesson book. I figured I could add up some numbers while I sat on the steps.

Chrissie in a light pink dress and Kelli in a blue jean dress were at the chalkboard inside the classroom, putting some curlicues around their drawings. They used colored chalk to beautify their creations and did not hear me come in. But, of course, they were supposed to be outside. I knew that. But they were not disturbing anybody, and I was in no mood to tell them. As I approached, however, they saw me and put their hands over their drawings.

"You were not supposed to come in yet, Mr. Brauer," they said, giggling.

I walked forward. They stepped back and looked at me anxiously. They had both drawn, decorated, and doodled large, colored hearts. Inside the heart, they had written, in cursive, much prettier than my cursive. They wrote, "I love my teacher." accented with exclamation marks.

"You guys are sweet," I said. "I needed that. Thank you." And I looked from their drawings to them and back. They squirmed and smiled.

After school, after the children had left, Bill Holderbaum stopped by. He was on his way home from the dental clinic. He walked into the classroom with a basketball under his arm.

"I heard you had a rough day," he said.

"You heard?"

He nodded. He held up the basketball. "Care for a game?"

That'd be grand."

We went out onto the small, cement, basketball court and worked up a sweat. He had a bigger body build and an inch or two in height. He used that to back me down and go for the layup. I was a better outside shooter, and when he came out to challenge me, I could drive past him. It was pretty evenly matched, though as I said he was taller, and in a one-on-one game between two otherwise equal players, height is the trump card. He won more often than me.

Still, it was great to work up a sweat and have a sounding board. He gave me advice while we played. He told me I should give the conference two weeks' notice. If they didn't get me a teacher, I should resign. I was not going to do that, but it felt good to have support.

"Well, I'm glad you're sticking it out. My kids like you." And then he went on to try to recruit me to work with him at Pathfinders. "I'd like you to be the boy's director."

I declined. "I do have all eight grades and twenty students, you remember."

He smiled and chuckled. We had finished our game of twenty-one and walked back to his truck. He had his water tank in the back and picked up the hose to fill it up. I went back inside.

In the evening, when I walked back up to the school for my second shift, intending to stay until eight, I got too involved in my lesson planning. Nevertheless, I enjoyed the quiet; I enjoyed figuring out what I would do, and I stayed until nearly nine-thirty.

So overall, it was a pretty good day.

CHAPTER TWENTY-EIGHT

THE SOUNDS OF SILENCE

But as the weeks accumulated, I found there were days when my energy lagged, and I wished for silence. Some days I had no enthusiasm for the commerce of social interaction. The prattle of children, the babble, the yackety-yack, which on most days I found amusing, would on occasion be something to which I was indifferent. I had long been a migraineur, and of course, on those days, all of the above negative feelings were accentuated. My teaching style had a playbook heavy on charisma. On some days, however, when I stepped into the pocket and reached for the charisma, it fell flat; there was nothing.

My supervisors had been giving me positive reinforcement, but it was not uncommon for me, at the end of the day, to reflect on my actions and judge my performance, and my self-evaluations were not as cheery as perhaps those of Mr. Petersen. When I had time to consider the day, I judged myself harsher. I found greater deficiencies. The students who had started the year with poor study habits still had not turned that around. If I were a better teacher, I would have found ways to motivate them. And I forgot things. I failed to follow up on assignments. The best teachers of my life had often written little encouraging comments at the top of my homework. I struggled to even get through them. I tried but did not have the time, or so I told myself. I knew it was a corruption in my character. I was lazy. Also, I became irritated at the incessant whining of a couple of the children and their pettiness. Sometimes I wondered what I was doing here at all. There were so many teachers who were better suited to deal with children. They had more patience than me.

On Thursday, I drove over to the McElvains. Ron was turning into the driveway when I arrived. I got out of my car, and we started talking. I followed him into his room, where he took off his shoes and put on his slippers. As he talked to me, I was impressed that he polished his shoes before putting them onto his closet floor, even though his shoes were already spotless. And his closet was immaculate.

The longer I knew him, the more I found him to be a man of varied interests. I had been talking about a small hawk that I had seen hovering above the grassy median of the interstate. I described it as best I could. But unfortunately, I had not had my binoculars with me. And as I was telling of this incident, I mentioned it because I found it interesting. I suppose it was also a way to place myself in a better light: not only am I an educated man as you already know but let me add to that and tell you how in tune I am with nature; I am even a birdwatcher. To my surprise, Ron knew at once what I was poorly describing.

He stood up and looked at me. "Well, the only hawk that fits that description would be the American Kestrel. Did it have a rufous back and a blue hood?"

I was not sure what rufous meant. Was that a color? If so, what color?

"I'm sorry I didn't get that a good look at it?" I replied.

"About the size of a robin, right?"

I nodded and thought to myself, "Wow."

He nodded. It had to be an American Kestrel. He then went on to talk about how he had spent several outings with a local raptor maven. I realized that Ron was much more of a birder than I was. I was just a novice.

The conversation carried on into supper.

"Last night at prayer meeting, the women were all talking," Connie said as she filled up my plate with a second serving of green beans. "They were saying they had not heard one negative comment from the children."

Connie looked at her husband to endorse the opinion. He nodded. "They were all pretty amazed." She handed me the plate, and I thanked her, feeling both astonished and humbled. How could that possibly be?

At the end of the evening, Connie went into her laundry room. She came out with a basket. My clothes were clean, dried, and neatly folded. I thanked her profusely and put the basket in the back of my car. Ron walked out with me. I got in and started the car when Connie came out in a hurry.

"O good, you have not already gone." She said and quickly came down the stairs. "Kim wanted me to give this to you. She bought it with her own money from the grocery store."

I had gotten back out of the car. Connie handed me the card. Inside, Kim had written in her first-grade, large block print. "I love you, Mr. Brauer."

I looked up at Connie with a tear glint in my eye.

"Goodnight, Mr. Brauer."

Ron and Connie waved at me as I backed out.

And as I drove home, I thought maybe, if I keep working on it, I could improve, maybe I could become a master teacher. But first, I needed to pay attention to my faults and figure out a plan to correct them.

CHAPTER TWENTY-NINE

A DAY IN THE LIFE

On October 12, 1981, I recorded my day in my journal in much more detailed intervals:

The alarm rings in the predawn gloom. I roll over and stumble into the bathroom. There I start the water in the tub. Banana toast is one of my favorite breakfasts. I go out to the kitchen and mash up some bananas, adding a little lemon juice, water, and sugar to them. I put a couple of slices of bread in the toaster. I get in the tub filled with hot water. I want to lie in the tub and relax for a good long while, but I don't have time. I quickly scrub and wash my hair.

A little before seven-thirty, I kiss my cat and start walking up to the school. The sun is shining on the top of the mesa, where it snowed overnight. Winter is coming. I stop off in the school's basement and shovel in some coal. I have learned that I can keep the fire going through the night by giving it a couple of extra shovelfuls in the evening and banking it down. That way, I do not have to restart it in the morning. I shovel in another two piles into the orange coals of the stove and crank the inlet valves wide open.

Upstairs, I take a seat at my desk. The smell of the burning coal begins to permeate the classroom, but it will take almost an hour to have the school up to a comfortable heat. So, I sit at my desk and read my Bible. I keep my hands warm in the pockets of my blue, down winter coat.

At ten minutes to eight, the Leathermans are the first to arrive. I tell them to play outside for now. The next big group arrives at eight-fifteen: Kim, Misty, Carolyn, Chad, and Justin. Everybody is rumbustious today.

Tina arrives with Danny. She gives me a sigh as we commiserate on how hyperactive everybody is.

At eight-thirty, Bobo rings the bell, and school starts. About one-half of the students are tardy. I have everyone stand up beside their desks and recite the pledge of allegiance. We sing some songs, and then the children gather in their prayer bands, four students to a group. Afterward, I assign Cory, Danny, and Angie to put up the flag. I make announcements about the field trip we are planning: a two-day excursion to Denver. Mrs. Mitchell walks through the room, handing out Rulison Dollars for good behavior.

For Bible class, we play-act Jesus' triumphal entry. Ron is the donkey, while Justin, the little first-grader, is Jesus. Mike, Doug, and Shon volunteer to be the priests ridiculing the crowd. Their portrayal of the cynical priests is spot on, almost like they had daily practice at it.

Then it is time for the first graders' reading class. We are reading a story about Sally and her cat Puff. I listen as they read and help with words as necessary. Some have caught on much faster than others. I take a few minutes to answer some questions for the reading assignments of the others. By the time I get to Bobo's reading class, I am behind schedule. He is doing well, and since he is the only second-grader, he gets one-on-one attention. He eats it up. He is the only student that gets that type of undivided attention.

By then, it is time for morning recess. I look at my book. Chrissie's turn to choose and she picks capture the flag. She does not say so, but I know she is picking it because it is her brother Ron's current favorite. We go up to the field. It is a little damp.

When we come back in, it is ten minutes to eleven. I move through the room, explaining language and math assignments for the other classes. I stop at the back window beside Mike's desk. He is progressing through algebra. I look at his assignment and then explain it to him. Fortunately, he is a bright kid. I remember when I was in eighth grade, the teacher had done three or four problems on the board before giving the assignments. Unfortunately, I do not have that luxury of time. Mike gets an abbreviated, shorthand instruction, and luckily, his aha moment comes quickly. Then he waves me off. "Yea, I get it. You can go, Mr. Brauer."

Despite his eight-grade demeanor, there is a large mutual admiration between us. Frankly, I find his attitude amusing. So often, when he is being super cool, he will look at me and see me smiling at him, and with the ability to stop and see himself, he will then chuckle, but it does not stop his act.

I continue moving through the room for the next hour, giving brief instructions. Then it is noon and time for PE. This one is up for a general vote, and they want to play capture the flag again. I play, but I try not to star. Instead, I work on organizing my team. Still, the joy of running in the sun when the air is cool and dry, dancing, cutting, dodging with the children laughing and trying to catch me always induces me to do more than I had intended, and my side wins.

Back in the classroom, the older boys start to rough house, and I warn them if I must talk to them again, it will cost them ten Rulisons. While they are eating, I get out the book I am reading to them. It is a story of a young lad with hound dogs in the west. A mountain lion has been killing sheep, and it is the story of his search. It is well written and seems appropriate to be reading in Western Colorado. Everybody is enjoying it.

At one o'clock, it is handwriting: printing for the lower grades, cursive for third and fourth grade, and a little free time for the higher grades. I walk up and down the aisles giving encouragement and passing out Rulisons based on the morning's performance.

Then the lower grades pack up and go home.

I teach the upper grades skills on how to work in a committee and then divide them into two groups. They are to decide on activities for our upcoming Denver field trip. I intervene and give them pointers when I see them getting distracted, showing them how to redirect, regain focus, and concentrate on achieving their goals. While they are working on that, I set up the film projector, and we pull down the shades over the big bank of windows. I showed two films I had ordered from the Czechoslovakia embassy before school had started. They were, unfortunately, boring. I had hoped they would have had more beautiful scenery, ala Disney, but alas.

For the afternoon recess, Doug picks football. We divide up. I again try to keep my team in a tie and purposely avoid scoring. We have no injuries. Everyone has a good time.

Then it is study period, and Mike pushes the envelope, constantly testing me. The kid has a lot of confidence.

We clean-up for ten minutes. Then the day is over, three-thirty. We have prayer. Several cars wait outside for the children, but Kelli and Carolyn hang around. Kelli is asking me if she is fat. She feels fat, and I assure her she is not fat. Kelli is a bean pole. She is sure she is getting fat.

When the children have gone, I get out the texts and look at tomorrow's lessons. I read over the teacher's copy of how to present the class and the goals for the day. Then I mimeograph some multiplication sheets to have the students work on. I stay until nearly six. Then I run home briefly, check on my cat, and head to the church for the Home and School meeting. I see that Mrs. Boggs, Steven, and Heather are in the car ahead of me. Phyllis Boggs is in charge of the home and school committee this year.

When I arrived, Heather and Carolyn hung around and on me. I get some punch, and when I come back out to the main room from the kitchen, Katie and Kim call out, "There is my teacher." They run over for hugs.

At seven we eat supper. And the food, as always, is plentiful, aromatic, and tasty. I fill up. There is a discussion that the Hesses are not there because their mother is in the hospital. She is having their fifth child.

They organize a game of musical chairs. I am quickly eliminated, not wanting to fight with Justin over an open seat. Then they embarrass me with too many kind words and superlatives, and an array of presents mostly boxed food, which even I think I can cook. I laugh and am very appreciative. I was getting tired of potatoes, spaghetti, and spinach.

I spy the moon on the top of the hill above the church on the drive home. Something is novel about it, so I stop the car and get out. There is a rainbow around the moon: a moon rainbow. I had never heard of such a thing. And at the end of this beautiful day, it seems auspicious.

CHAPTER THIRTY

LITTLE CRUSHES

The children liked Tina Mitchell as the aide. What was not to like? She was friendly, kind, and had a good sense of humor. She had known most of them for many years. Some of them, she had known all their lives. She was thus very comfortable in the room. She made my day possible. She answered questions when I was in the next room, working with first graders, or tied up teaching concepts to another grade level. She quieted minor disputes and helped keep order. All of this made it hard for me to dislike working with her, but I did. I was having a great deal of difficulty working with her.

I realized at the time I had no justification for my feelings. They were baseless. Still, there were times when the children would ask what we were going to be doing about this or that, and she would answer, telling them what the school's plans were. Was that her place? I thought she took on too much and was undermining me. I knew she was not trying to, but I felt threatened. She was, after all, older, wiser, and better known to the children. I would have preferred to have someone more like Connie McElvain. She had worked two weeks as an aide. Connie had never presumed to be the teacher or the final authority.

Furthermore, I had heard now on several occasions from Bonnie Holderbaum. She disapproved of Tina being there. She thought it unfair that her children had to take orders from Mrs. Mitchell. I suspected any complaints Kelli and Shon had with Tina; Bonnie amplified. She told them, "Mr. Brauer is the teacher, not Mrs. Mitchell." Kelli, who was mercurial, had now had a couple of moody weeks in a row. And when Kelli was moody, the whole classroom suffered. The issue with Mrs. Mitchell was not helping.

I struggled with these feelings. I knew that Tina had been the only one to volunteer to help. Nobody else had stepped up. Plus, outside of the school, I liked her. On weekends up at the Mitchell's house, I would often sit at the kitchen counter while she cooked, and we would talk. We talked about the children and the school. She would quiz me on how I was doing. She was easy to talk to. Away from school, the dynamics were so different.

But at school, when I would announce something. If the children were unsure about it, they would look to Mrs. Mitchell for confirmation. It was difficult.

On one occasion, I had announced the teams for softball. Doug had protested that the teams were unfair. And maybe they were a little unfair. It was nearly impossible to have completely equal teams with a wide variance of ages and athletic skills. Still, I did try to make sure if a child was on the lesser team one day, he would be on the better team the next. But Tina had agreed with Doug.

"I don't think they are fair either," she added.

I looked at her and thought, "What the heck! Come on, Tina. Don't undermine me. Not like this." But I kept my mouth shut and ignored her. "The team assignments stand," I declared.

We also had discipline issues that she did not ameliorate. In addition to the money system, I had started an alternative discipline system of green light, yellow light, red light. The Rulison Dollars were positive reinforcement. The colored light plan, when it was red, designated everyone to be in their seats and silent. It could be used as a punitive tactic if the classroom

145

veered toward chaos. However, it was primarily instituted as a safety for the easily distracted students like Danny to concentrate on their studies. I was always looking for techniques to get the children to do their work. This mandatory quiet time was supposed to support that, but Tina often subverted it. She allowed the children to talk when we were under the red light or modified the timeout I had ordered for a student's offense. It led me to ponder whether she, herself, had lax personal discipline.

It bothered me that I even had these thoughts. Tina was doing so much to support me. I could not possibly have done it without her. It was petty of me, and I knew that. I also knew it came out of my insecurity of being so young and inexperienced, but these lapses in her discipline made my day harder, not easier. I had, however, no idea how to confront her for the present.

For the rest of the week, Kelli spiraled downward. She was snide to the younger students. Kelli thought the new colored light system was dumb and resented when I called her out for talking during quiet time. She said she would rather have Mrs. Mitchell teaching her than me at Bible class. And if a younger student picked the recess, Kelli thought it was beneath her. She was, after all, in sixth grade and did not play those baby games anymore. It hurt since it came from Kelli, who the younger girls revered. Furthermore, she was sure that I was picking only on her.

Meanwhile, the children learned that Bobo had a crush on Angie. They began chanting the universal refrain, "Bobo loves Angie." Angie handled the teasing with aplomb. I was impressed. Nevertheless, I put a stop to that type of chirping.

To let them safely vent their gripes and feelings, I assigned, as part of their language class, for each of the children to keep a journal or diary, whatever they decided to call it. They could write down their honest feelings. Privately, I hoped it would give Kelli a way to vent on paper rather than in public. Maybe it would be enough. They wrote for the rest of the week. I collected them on Friday.

I also had them do another sociogram. It was a test that I found helpful. The one I used was simple. There were six circles

146

on the page,one circle in the middle, and five surrounding it. They were the center circle. In the five surrounding circles, they were to write the names of the students who were their friends, or whom they valued, liked, or respected, etc. This elegant, simple test allowed me to understand the social dynamics of my classroom. It was advantageous in identifying outliers. When I analyzed the results, I saw that Shon and Kelli remained the social leaders. I was a little surprised that even with Kelli's irritability, she had not dropped, even though other mid-grade students were telling her to be quiet; nevertheless, they all listed her.

On Friday at lunch, Chrissie came up to talk to me. She mentioned that she had written about me in her journal. I smiled and patted her hand. Then, after handwriting, as the younger children were getting ready to go, she asked again if I had read them. I shook my head, "Not yet, Chrissie."

When the first two grades had left, Tina gathered up her personal items. I was standing in the back of the room helping Steven with a math problem. As she passed by, she smiled and said she wanted to ask me a couple of things. I followed her outside.

"The Boggs are coming up on Saturday night for some games and a movie. We would love for you to come."

I, of course, had no other plans and was glad to accept.

"The other thing," she hesitated. "I noticed something as I was observing you this week." I knew she was speaking about my interactions with Kelli. It had been a trying week. "You are an excellent teacher."

"Well, coming from you, that means something."

She left. I went back inside and went up to my desk. Chrissie was staring at me intently.

"Okay, Chrissie, see, I am going to read it right now." And I sat down at my desk and opened her black and white composition journal. She started by describing the classroom, what grade she was in, and who was in fourth grade. Then she noted how her teacher wanted her to write a journal. She went on to say that her teacher was Mr. Brauer, and he had blonde hair and smiled a lot.

And then she wrote. "I like my school, but I love my teacher more." She went on to list why she liked me because I was kind, smart, and laughed a lot. In the end, she concluded. "Lots of people like my teacher, but they don't love him like I love him."

I looked up at her. She had her head down and was studiously avoiding me. I got up, went to her desk, and tussled her hair. She grinned and then worked even harder on the coloring she was doing.

CHAPTER THIRTY-ONE

JALAPENO PEPPERS

At church the following day, as I was walking in the hall, I saw Dr. Holderbaum walking with Kelli. When he saw me, he turned around and came over to me. He gave me a hearty handshake, a real man-to-man shake. We talked for a few moments. Then he noticed Kelli was standing back. He thought that was peculiar.

"Kelli, is there a problem with you and Mr. Brauer?"

She gave me an apprehensive glance. Was I going to rat her out? Was this going to be an adult-to-adult moment between her dad and me? She shook her head demurely.

"Well, good." Then he put his arm on her shoulder and guided her away. I could see he was talking to her. Obviously, her denial had not been believable.

After church, as I was standing in the lobby, he sought me out. Kelli was not with him.

"I talked to Kelli. She told me that you had to have several talks with her this week." Bill paused and threw up his hands in a gesture of resignation. "Bonnie has been gone for the last couple of weeks." He sighed and shook his head. "It has been hard on Kelli...and Shon."

I nodded slowly and repetitively. "That makes a lot of sense. Yea, wow, that is really hard when one parent isn't home."

"Yes, it is. Yes, it is. Bonnie has not been thrilled with living in Rifle. She went back to her parent's home in Chicago."

I spotted Kelli. She was watching us from a corner in the foyer. She was standing there uneasy, watching her dad and me, but too far to hear. I looked over at her with a sad smile. I felt such empathy for her. I wanted her to understand that her irritability had not changed my opinion. Our eyes met, and I could see her shoulders relax.

That evening I went to the Mitchell's. As I came in, David was in the kitchen. He had developed a hankering for a jalapeno-laced nacho cheese dip, and he was scrounging through the refrigerator. He found a block of cheddar cheese but could not find any peppers.

"Hey Mom, do you have any jalapenos?" He called out while pushing things around in the refrigerator. Looking over his shoulder, he added, "Don't you just love jalapenos?" He was in a vibrant mood and was delighted that I was there.

Tina came around the corner and said she did not think they had any peppers in the house.

"What! No peppers!" He exclaimed with a big smile and patted his mom on the shoulder. "Gotta have those peppers, Mom. Gotta have those peppers." Then turning to me, he asked, "Hey Brauer, you wanna come with me. Let's go into town and get some jalapenos. Tonight, is gonna be hot!" He held out his hand, and his mom gave him the keys to her car. She was smiling. David's energy was contagious.

I rode with him. He put in a tape of AC/DC and cranked it up.

"You like AC/DC?" He said as he accelerated on the two-lane road.

"Never was a big fan. I'm more a Beatles, Chicago, Stevie Wonder type of guy."

He looked at me and nodded. I was a little uncomfortable at how long his vision was distracted from the road, especially considering the speed with which he took the corners.

"Not into metal, huh?" He ejected the AC/DC tape. He tossed me several cassettes. "My mom likes Eddie Rabbit. Please tell me you're not an Eddie Rabbit fan?"

I laughed. "No, not a big Eddie Rabbit fan." I looked through his tapes. "I like Aerosmith," I said, holding up a *Toys in the Attic* tape.

"All right! We can still be friends," He lifted his head and laughed uproariously.

I punched in the cassette on side two, *Sweet Emotion*. We cranked down the windows and blasted out the sound. We drove into town. In City Market, he was talking to everyone. I followed behind him and was so amazed at his charm. He seemed to be like a smile machine. He walked by, he said something, and people smiled. And it was not just the young girls he talked with, but also the mothers and grandmothers who were in his purview. I did notice that he avoided men of his father's age. He circled them.

Back in produce he bought three large jalapenos. In the dairy section he bought another block of cheese, and then coming up the aisles he picked up another bag of chips. We went through check out and then headed home.

I realized long ago that Saturday nights at the Mitchell's were not about schedules. If they talked about games and a movie at seven-thirty, that was a guideline, quite different from my family.

Back in the kitchen, he grated down the entire block of cheese and cut an abundance of peppers. I helped and mistakenly touched my hands to my eyes.

"No, Brauer! You never touch your eyes when you're cutting the peppers." He exclaimed. "Mom, do we have any saline solution? Brauer got some jalapeno in his eye." He looked at me and smiled, "That's Mr. Brauer, right?"

Tina was quickly there. "O, dear. O, dear." She looked at me and then promptly went and borrowed a bottle of saline from Valerie. She always had a bottle in her bathroom. After that, Tina had me put my head over the sink while washing my eye. That helped a great deal, not completely, but much better.

In my family, we never ate hot peppers. We had no black pepper in our house. My mother never used it in any of her cooking; good Adventists did not. After all, Ellen White had spoken clearly against the consumption of pepper. I had heard the lectures at the Academy. I had read the messages in the "little red books." Pepper was corrosive on the stomach and, more importantly, stoked up, augmented the lower passions and should be eschewed. But tonight, I was in the mood for adventure. I had already listened to Aerosmith tonight; what more could a little hot pepper do?

So, I took a chip and dunked it in the dip. I made sure to get a healthy pepper slice. And the taste was ambrosia, like nothing I had ever had before. The flavor of the pepper was extravagant. But the heat! Unaccustomed to this flavor of fire, my mouth wept, and that not entirely with joy.

I took a drink of 7-Up and had another chip, this time staying away from the pepper. I was twenty-three and this was my first jalapeno.

The Boggs showed up. They consumed the cheese dip with relish.

David, of course, had to tell how I had gotten pepper in my eye and my reaction to the dip.

"You've not had jalapeno dip before?" Heather asked as she took a chip and made sure to include some pepper and then ate it with complete indifference to the heat.

Steven looked at me with fondness. He thought it was funny and endearing that I could know so much in school, be good at sports, and be such a pepper novice. How little I knew of the world if I had never eaten peppers.

Eventually, we got around to table games. We played a game of Acquire, a 3M game of hotel building. I knew that game and had played it often as a boy. Tonight, I won. Though to be sure, I won primarily because Danny, my little buddy, wanted me to win. On several occasions he played tiles that advantaged me at the expense of his brother. What a nice little buddy.

And everybody was having fun. The Boggs: John and Phyllis, and their children, Heather, Steven, and John Jr. The Mitchell's, Tina and Mitch were more animated than usual, which could only be because Valerie was home. She brought joy. Her smile was broad and beautiful, and her laughter, frequent. I also remembered what Kelli had whispered to me on the wagon-ride, that is that Valerie thought I was cute. It was always nice when the pretty girl thought I was good looking.

John and Phyllis went home after the game. Heather and Steven stayed to watch the Saturday night movie, *Wait Until Dark*. It was a psychological thriller with Audrey Hepburn about a blind woman set up by criminals, and to make the odds even, she busts all the lightbulbs in the house. It was intense; Danny and Heather came and sat close to me. Then, when it got terrifying, Heather climbed onto my lap.

CHAPTER THIRTY-TWO

TOUGH GUYS

In my education classes, they had emphasized the best way to know your students was to visit them in their homes. Therefore, they recommended at least once a year for the parent-teacher conference to be conducted at the child's house. Understanding my little friends was one of my fundamental drives. The Scottish use the word ken, as in *I ken that*, meaning a comprehensive insight, an overarching recognition that was deeply felt and known. That was what I wanted. I wanted to know how they ticked, their interests, and their weaknesses. I realized a vital asset in this school was a supportive group of parents. I wanted to maximize that bond.

It was not a novel concept that a home visit cemented bonds. We had known that since Biblical times. Did not Christ come in disguise to visit Abraham? Was he not fed in the patriarch's tent? I was symbolically leaving my domain and humbly entering theirs by going to their homes. I was the visitor. They were the host. And I was saying that while I was the teacher, I accepted that their role as a parent superseded mine. I also wanted the parents to know that I took this confidence they had entrusted in me: their faith in me of watching over their children, guarding them, guiding them, mentoring them, educating them; I took this confidence with great seriousness.

So, I made appointments for the following week. I made as many appointments as I could, as parents were willing. Most of the parents were delighted. A couple preferred to meet at the school. I accepted that.

On Monday, after school, it was back down to Battlement Mesa to see the Grants. I had been correct in recognizing Cory's intelligence. He was academically gifted. He quickly got through his lessons and then spent much of his time reading. He was an adept reader. His only issue was that he knew he was smart, and he had difficulty understanding why other students could not get the problems as quickly as him. He could be a little condescending, which did not endear him. Other than that, he was doing well. And once again, as I sat in the Grant's house and saw the comfortable dynamics of Mr. and Mrs. Grant, a husband and wife with a family, I was smitten by that ideal. I could not get it out of my mind on the drive home.

The Boggs and Mitchells followed. They were more straightforward, not that there were no issues we needed to discuss, but we had been in much more constant conversation. Steven was getting good value out of his half-day enhanced education. And the Boggs were delighted that we had figured out something to do for him. Heather and Danny just needed to pay attention.

Tuesday was busy; I went into Rifle to meet with the Sisk families, the Opitzes, the Forshees, and the Hesses.

I had not had as much interaction with the Hesses. Russel Hess was a large rig trucker. He too, was working at the Exxon project. He was a large man, quiet and not prone to soft words. He was primarily concerned that his children should be respectful and diligent. If they fell short on those measurements, I should call him or his wife right away. They would not tolerate incorrect behavior. His children were not too old for a spanking.

While I was in their home, Judy Hess was sitting in a rocker, giving her baby a bottle. She was all smiles, warmth, and acceptance. I assured them that their three children: Ron, Chrissie, and Angie, were three of the most well-behaved students in the class. They did their work, and they did it well. They got along with all of the other students. If I had seventeen more like them, my job would be half as hard.

When I met up with the Holderbaums at the end of the week, Bonnie had returned from her trip. Unfortunately, the meeting was less pleasant. Shon was not performing as well as he ought. I often found him just staring out the windows, staring at the mountains, the clouds, or just watching Bessie. I tried various motivational ploys, but getting him to buckle down and do his work was beyond me. And it was not that the work was too hard for him. He had plenty of intelligence. He just did not want to do it, and he had a strong will. There were days, however, when he would come into the schoolhouse in a good mood. On those days, he would cruise through his work. My ally in the classroom was Mike. Shon admired Mike immensely. Sure, Mike caused some difficulties with his cool persona, but Mike also knew deep in his soul that he was born to achieve. And he understood that schooling was essential to all the things he imagined he might do one day. So, in the classroom, he would encourage Shon to buckle down. That worked. Sometimes.

And while the conference with the Holderbaums was more difficult, in the context of this conversation, I want to add that of all the families that year; I often felt I had the most in common with them. Sure, Bill could go off on economic discussions that baffled me. He knew his economic literature and felt that Nixon had erred in going off the gold standard. I had taken Economics 101 in college, but I could not follow his line of reasoning. I did not even try to debate him. His position seemed too far out of the mainstream for me. Still, we had similar personalities. We loved people. We were optimistic and outgoing. As for Bonnie, my interactions in person with her were always pleasant. She was friendly. She was quick-witted and enjoyed a joke. In her home, she was the charming host, and of course, she was attractive. I always thought that if I had known Bill and Bonnie in college, we would have been good friends.

We ended our parent-teacher conference with an agreement to communicate regularly on how Shon was doing. And as I left, it seemed to me that it had been helpful for Shon to see that the three adults who were the most important in his life that year were all in agreement. We all wanted him to succeed. That was the most important takeaway from the meeting: Shon sitting there on the couch watching Bill, Bonnie, and I all coming together, all in agreement, all wanting him to prosper and be happy.

I skipped over the conference with the Sisks. Let me return to it. Meeting in their home was a joy. First off, Sandy was always positive, affirming, and welcoming. But more importantly, it was enjoyable talking about Mike. He and I were developing a special relationship. I treated him differently than the other students. He was leaving elementary school in a year, and I treated him as such. He also respected that I could help with the math problems that stumped him. Yes, he constantly tested my authority and often became moody when he lost those authority battles. That got tiring. On the other hand, Mike valued that I tried to be consistent—I was not always, but I tried. Furthermore, Mike overflowed with humor. Overall, I enjoyed having him, which made it fun to talk with his parents. Could he have received a better education in Southern California, with a better teacher-to-student ratio, and teachers who could do more classroom lectures? Probably. Then again, how do you measure it? He was happy here, and that had to count for something.

Sandy brought up the Friday afternoon when the students all raised their hands to say they liked me. She thought that was precious.

I agreed and chuckled and then stopped. "Did Mike tell you about his role last Friday?"

"No," Sandy replied, and both Jerald and Sandy looked at Mike.

Mike had his head down and was shaking his head. "Really, Mr. Brauer? Are you going to do this, really?"

Jerald and Sandy both smiled in anticipation of a story.

"Yeah, yeah, yeah," I started. "This is a little embarrassing." I hesitated before proceeding, "Last Friday, I again left some time for the students to comment. Bobo was the first to raise his hand, and when I called him, he didn't say that he liked his teacher. Instead, he said 'I love my teacher.'" And before I could call on the other hands, there was a chorus of 'I love you, Mr. Brauer!'

"At this point, Mike had to question it all. He said to me, 'I just don't get it, Mr. Brauer. It's crazy, don't you think?' And then he looked at Chrissie, who was sitting just ahead of him. 'Chrissie, what are you doing? Do you really love Mr. Brauer?'

"Chrissie responded, 'Ron likes him too.' She was implicating the seventh grade into the mass illusion.

"'Kelli, Danny, Carolyn, Cory, Heather, Chad? You guys as well?' Mike asked them"

I paused the story for a moment to look at Mike. He was glaring at me. "You can stop this anytime, Mr. Brauer."

His father spoke up. "Mike, this is a parent-teacher conference where Mr. Brauer is relating something important to the parents. So go ahead, Mr. Brauer." And Jerald had a definite gleam in his eye.

"Yes, please, Mr. Brauer, please continue," Sandy added and gave Mike a big smile.

Mike dropped his head in his hands.

"Well," I paused and grinned at Mike as I resumed the story. "I called to Mike. 'Okay, Mike, come on up here.' I was standing at the front of the classroom, and I waved him forward. He got up slowly and walked up warily.

"'What are you up to, Mr. Brauer? I want you to know I don't trust you.'" But he came up and stood there with his thumbs in his front pockets. Then I turned to address the class.

"'Guys, I think Mike here is envious.'" The class laughed and agreed vigorously

"Doug shouted a warning. 'Mike, it's a trap! Get out of there!'"

"'So, I am curious, Mr. Brauer,' Mike asked. 'What am I envious about?'

"At that, I stepped over and put my arms out wide. "Give me a hug, Mike. Give me a hug." And at that, the whole classroom erupted in laughter.

Jerald and Sandy were now also laughing. I have to say on Mike's behalf; he does love a good joke, even if the joke was on him. He was now looking at me, grinning and at the same time threatening he was going to kill me.

I continued, "So, Mike is standing up front, and all the school is hooting and hollering, and he is looking at me as if I was crazy."

At that, I looked over at Mike, "Yes, exactly that look!"

Mike was trying to suppress laughter. His parents were having a really good time.

"So, I wrapped him in a big bear hug in front of the classroom."

"When I let him go, he said with considerable sarcasm, 'Okay, that was wonderful. Are you happy now, Mr. Brauer?'

"And then I looked back at the classroom who loved it.

"'Who else needs a hug?' I asked.

"'Doug! Steven! Shon! Ron!' There were shouts from around the classroom for the older boys.

"'Get up here, Doug!' Mike called to his cousin. 'Hug it out!'

"And most of them came up." At that point, I stopped my narration.

Jerald and Sandy were laughing hard.

"You're so funny, Mr. Brauer, so funny." Mike had found his eighth-grade cool again.

Before I left, Sandy brought me a couple of food dishes that I could put in my refrigerator. She walked me out to the car and said she had talked to a couple of her neighbors. She had told them that I was coming to their home to visit. They said they had never heard of anything like that. What teacher comes to the house? Sandy was feeling very superior. "Well, our teacher does." Her two kindergarten daughters, Heidi and Ingrid, were hanging on her leg. She looked down at them. "I hope you stay for at least one more year. I want you to be the teacher for them in their first year."

The Schlisner's conference was not quite as easy. Carolyn, in particular, was underperforming, and Carolyn's performance was influencing Chad. Bob and Sheila Schlisner were in business with the Boggs and their carpeting business. Bob was a big guy, big chest, big biceps. It was obvious he worked hard each day. He was a good-looking guy but quite content to leave the talking to his wife. Sheila moved like a panther, all supple and full of confidence. She oozed femininity. I had somewhat dreaded this conversation. I was unsure how they would react to my less-than-perfect report. But I was pleased that Sheila was fully engaged. We were on the same team. We wanted good things for her children. Sheila shared with me that Carolyn had been in counseling for anxiety issues. That made sense to me, though I was amazed that a child of Carolyn's age could already need counseling. That was so far out of my world. I had a lot to learn. My unremarkable childhood was a handicap in understanding other people.

I was one of four boys. My father, a pastor in the conference, was highly esteemed by the conference office. He worked hard. He visited. He was a decent preacher who put time into his sermons. He read regularly and did not cause disturbances. He had one of the most desirable churches in the conference, and his parishioners loved him. At home, he helped with the cooking and the cleaning. He usually made the supper as the commute for my mother brought her home late, and my father liked to have his meals on a very regular basis. He was a good cook. My mother was better, and she usually made the weekend meals. He played sports with his sons. But, of course, now that we were older, it was mainly tennis. By this time, I learned how to get along with him — especially since my late teen rebellion against the church had resolved with a passionate, almost zealous belief. And so, I had little conflict left with my father.

My mother and father had occasional verbal spats when my father had not been as sensitive as she thought he should have been, and the truth was my father was not a demonstrative person. My mother was much more attuned to my feelings. She knew my daily routines. My mother was the one that I talked to on the phone about my girlfriend problems, mainly my lack of a girlfriend problems. She was a good listener.

Of course, they had issues, and I could spend a couple of chapters outlining them, but in the scope of parents, they were so much better than many that I had met. In his opening paragraph of *Anna Karenina*, Tolstoy wrote, "Happy families are all alike; every unhappy family is unhappy in its own way." So, I guess my family was part of the uninteresting uniformity.

The parent-teacher conferences ended at the McElvains with my beloved Thursday night dinner. Kim was excelling famously, so that went quickly, but then Ron added,

"So, we heard today that Mr. Hess has lost his job at the plant. They will probably be pulling their children out of the school."

And when I heard that, my first thought was not that reducing three students and one less grade would be so helpful. No, quite the opposite. My heart just revolted. They were three of the most well-behaved students. Ron was so interesting. Angie was cheerful and always coming by for quick hugs, such a delightful girl. And Chrissie, oh Chrissie, I would be so sad to lose Chrissie, quiet Chrissie, always looking for ways to help me. "Mr. Brauer, can I clean the chalkboards? Mr. Brauer, do you want me to help Katie with her math? Mr. Brauer, can I ring the bell to call in the children?" Chrissie would start off eating her lunch with the other children. Then, invariably, she would come in when she was eating her fruit to see what I was eating, try to figure out something else she could do for me, or stand at my desk reading a book—not talking, just standing there. The upshot was that I drove home thinking it would be an infinitely sadder place if the Hesses did indeed pull out. And I just had this dread of hearing the news confirmed.

CHAPTER THIRTY-THREE

WHAT DOES THE FAWN SAY

Monday morning, as I was preparing before the start of school, Katie came running in. She had been playing outside with her brothers. "Mr. Brauer, you have to see this!"

I got up, curious at what would cause quiet Katie to be so excited. I went to the door and saw Kelli and Shon riding their horses up the school driveway. Shon wore a western shirt with leather fringes, and Kelli was in jeans and a white blouse. They were both smiling. They swung out of their saddles and hitched their horses to the fence posts at the far end of the schoolyard. As the other kids ran up, Shon jumped in front of them.

"Keep back!" Shon yelled at Bobo.

At that moment everyone was distracted from the horses to their pet deer which had followed them down the road and was coming up the driveway.

Shon and Kelli tried to shoo her away.

As I briefly mentioned earlier, the Holderbaums had adopted an orphaned fawn at the end of summer. The Blehm's, who lived just below the Mitchell's, had found the motherless fawn when it was quite tiny. They had nursed it, but as it grew, they found it too much trouble and did not want to keep it. The Holderbaums had jumped at the chance of adopting her. When I say the Holderbaums, I mean the children. They persuaded their parents. After all, they already had hay for the horses. How hard could it be? At first, the deer had slept with their two dogs, but as it grew — it was a mule deer — the dogs did not want it so close. By the time it appeared in the schoolyard, it had grown a great deal, and its spots were beginning to fade.

Kelli related to me that they had been having a great deal of difficulty keeping the deer from following them to school. Lately, they had been feeding it potato chips to distract it while they ran on ahead, but today with riding the horses, they had not noticed the deer.

The deer's name was Bambi. Of course, what else would you name a baby deer? After tying up their horses, they chased the deer away.

So, as we had the opening activities that morning, after we did our pledge of allegiance and had our prayers, I had to give instructions to the students. I took all the children into the next room to look out at the horses tied at the far fence. No one was to go near the horses, period. Kelli and Shon could check on the horses, but no one else should go near them, not even with Kelli and Shon. I had worked with horses, and I did not want anyone to get kicked. I said maybe I could go out with Kelli and Shon at lunch, and we could let everyone pet the horses one or two at a time if they wanted.

Inwardly, however, I thought this was so fantastic. Two of my students had ridden their horses to school. I knew I would have to talk to the school board about this, and I was sure we would have to adopt a policy against horses in the schoolyard, but for today it was delightful. We had a brown milk cow with a bell and big brown eyes lying on the ground chewing its cud in the pasture behind the schoolyard. We had two horses in the front yard. And we had a pet deer that had to be chased away. Had I somehow been transported into the middle of a Disney movie?

Just the week before, when I had opened the schoolhouse in the morning, I had found a chocolate lab puppy that had

163

somehow been locked in the school all night. Barney, who lived three houses down the road and always showed up to play with the children at recess—what could be better for a puppy than a classroom of children wanting to play with him—had somehow been locked in all night long. How was that possible? He probably had fallen asleep in the other room. He was ecstatic and frantic when I opened the door and had quickly run home.

And the animated fantasy Disney movie was not over. The next day when the afternoon sun had started to make the room too hot, we opened the windows. (Obviously, since we heated the school with a coal furnace, we did not have any air-conditioning.) And when we then also opened the back door, Bambi walked into the classroom.

O, what squeals of joy! The deer strolled right through the desk rows slowly as if checking on the children's work; her little tail waggling back and forth; her big black nose stopping to gather in the smells; her dark brown, enormous eyes looking at them all. And she stopped to accept soft pets on her silky coat; she was delighted with the attention.

I was sure I had been time-warped. It was too fantastic to consider.

Later in the week, when I came home for my supper, my landlord was in the orchard working. He was such a curious character: intelligent, quirky, with his big black beard and black glasses. I saw him and walked over to him. He had been picking up some fallen branches. He stood up. We exchanged greetings. My cat came down from a nearby tree and scurried over between us. Chester leaned over and picked up the kitten. He was a snuggly cat and quickly took to purring.

"You gotta be careful with him," he said as he turned and walked up to the end of the orchard. I followed him. Evening was gathering, and it was late October. The leaves were all golden, and many had fallen. The sun was declining down the valley and shedding its last rays of last warmth for the day. Evenings quickly grew cool at this altitude.

I followed him as he went up to the irrigation canal and closed the chute. The water quit flowing into his orchard. He talked about how a neighbor about a mile away had misused the irrigation water and was found out by his neighbors. Misusing irrigation water was a serious offense in the dry west. I was holding Mittens by this time. Finally, he stood up, looked at the cat, and motioned me to follow him. We went into the middle of the orchard, where he pointed out a large pile of black scat.

"Black bear," he said, pointing to the round heap of stool in the grass in the midst of his orchard. "Bears will eat anything," he added, giving Mittens a suggestive pet.

Chester headed back to the house up the road, where he often stayed with a friend. I put Mittens down and went inside for a few minutes. When I came back outside, I saw Mittens investigating something else in the orchard. It was a squirrel trap. That night as Mittens curled on my pillow with me, I had a premonition my cat might have a short life.

CHAPTER THIRTY-FOUR

A POSITION OF INFLUENCE

A teacher has a unique position in society. They are not the parents. They can never be, but they are an extension. When it works best, the mother, father, and teacher are a continuum, a flow, like a river. The student knows and feels to his core that while the teacher is not the parent, the teacher is always there for him or her. Education succeeds, and may I say it, excels when the child knows that home and school are safe. The best teachers in my education were teachers who could create that environment, teachers who I knew understood and cared for me.

I went into elementary education switched from history and prelaw because I found such joy in being around children. I have known people that were able to relate incredibly well to horses. They knew what the horse thought when it refused to take the bit or when it paused in the middle of a trail — due to a stick looking like a snake. They knew which horses were shy and which were just lazy. I was always impressed. I have known others who were mathematical whizzes; they could rapidly solve any algebra, trigonometry, or advanced calculus problem. The world of numbers set down so easily for them. For me, it was children. I understood them. Somehow, I instinctively could look at a child and perceive. Or maybe, more accurately, it was not so much that I comprehended them, as that I was able to convince them that I liked them quickly. I also found the way they approached life fascinating.

But as I had prepared for teaching, I had to process my philosophies. One of the things I had to decide on was physical contact. It was a topic discussed in my education courses. They concluded the safest approach, especially for a male teacher, was the no-touch policy. In the eighties, the Catholic pedophilia scandal was still a couple of decades away, and while we were beginning to hear stories of sexual abuse among conservative Protestant faiths, we as Adventists did not think those stories fit us. Yes, it occurred, but it was unusual, wasn't it? There did seem to be a trend, however, the more conservative the church, the more the abuse prevailed. Also in those years, the Church Fathers were quick to stamp out any discovery — to be honest, that still has not changed. I understood these concerns, though I will admit I was naïve, but the no-touch policy seemed inhuman to me. They were children, especially with the early grades physical contact, a hand on the shoulder, a pat on the back, or head, how could you not? I had brought up my ideas in the college lectures.

"Dr. Bandiola, yes, I understand a policy of no-touch is safer, but since touch is so essential to the human, and especially in the young child, will this not severely stymie the educational environment. Clearly, in preschool, it is essential that you touch and hug. And I will agree that in high school, it would be perilous, but don't you think there is a continuum here."

Dr. Bandiola agreed. I discussed it with multiple professors. I explained how I felt that it was essential to give a little pat on the head or a quick hug, not just for their education, but just as a human being helping another human being. All the professors agreed and confessed that it had been impossible to adopt a no-touch policy.

"But things are changing, Marvin."

"Yes, but watch children when they are happy; they are constantly touching, aren't they?"

167

"Yes, they are, Marvin. It's true. But be careful. Be very careful."

"Hmmm."

And I decided that I wanted the very best for my children. I did not want to teach in an environment of fear and repression. I wanted to create a place where my students felt safe and secure, where they had the best chance to let their minds grow exponentially—a place where they could rapidly grow, knowing that the base was solid. The base must have layer after layer of solid sediment like the Colorado Plateau, the Book Cliffs. And I decided that when a child ran up asking for a hug, I would maintain the continuum of the parent-family-friend-mentor. The human need for contact is undeniable. I decided the base must be deep and rich, founded on understanding, respect, and care.

CHAPTER THIRTY-FIVE

TOO MUCH PRIDE AND JOY

I ran a little to the right, escaping the rush of Cory. We were on the football field at the morning recess. The sky was ultramarine and cloudless. I saw Mike breaking to the left end zone, and as I set my feet, I decided this time I would put some zip into the pass. I never gave it everything. These were children. The ball would sting, or they might try to catch it with their hands in front of their face, and then it would crash into their tiny noses. So, I always held back, throwing soft lobs. But as Mike was breaking free, I wanted to fire the football. I did. I threw a hot, tight spiral to the left endzone. Mike caught it, spiked it with jubilation, then shook his stinging hands, turned, and gave me the biggest smile. Everyone else was astounded. They were amazed that I was able to throw it that hard. They were in awe that Mike was able to catch it. He was a big, big hero.

As we walked back to the schoolroom at the end of recess, he was still glowing. Everybody had been praising him for catching the ball. "Mr. Brauer really through that one hard." They were still amazed as children so easily are. "And you caught it!" Mike was already admired but catching a football that fast moved Mike up the ladder almost to a demigod. He caught up beside me.

"You know, Mr. Brauer, I think we could, you and I, take on the whole school."

"Just you and me against the whole school?" I said as I looked him over.

He looked back at the other boys. "Yeah, I think we could." Mike was cocky.

"You know if we tried and failed…." I cautioned him. We both understood they would razz us to no end.

"Yes, I know we would be the butt of endless jokes," Mike acknowledged.

I nodded and gave him another once over. "I'll tell you, Mike, I agree." I paused and looked back at the other children following behind us. "I think we could." I was just as cocky as Mike. "I'm willing to take the chance of being laughed at." I patted Mike on the back. "We will do it at noon recess."

"Yes!" Mike said as he punched his fist into the air and displayed a big smile. He had a lovely smile, like a young Michael Douglas.

Thus, at the noon recess, I went to the blackboard. "Okay, listen up, recess will be football." There were cheers from the boys and a few girls. "I'm going to write down the teams on the board. Team A will include Ron, Doug, Steven, Shon, Kelli, Danny, Roy, Chrissie, Heather, Cory, Chad, Wayne, Angie, Kim, Doyle, Justin, Misty, and Katie. Team B, team B will be Mr. Brauer and Mike."

"What!" There was a large outcry.

"You and Mike against everyone," Doug questioned and looked back at Mike. "O, you guys are so smug."

"The word is conceited," Kelli corrected Doug. "Mr. Brauer and Mike are conceited."

"Arrogant," Ron added. "And you guys don't have a chance against all of us."

"Excuse me, everyone," I put up my hand and went to the blackboard, picked up some chalk, and wrote as I spoke. "The word you are looking for is… winner. Mike and I are going to win." I underlined the word and then turned around. "Although,

I have to admit that smug, arrogant, and conceited are probably equally appropriate."

Everyone was now highly motivated. The rest wanted to defeat us. Mike and Mr. Brauer were going down. Mike and Mr. Brauer would get their duly deserved deserts, their comeuppance. Let them win? Never.

Shon quarterbacked the first series of downs at the field, and they isolated Doug alone on the opposite side. Doug caught it and scored. The classroom was joyous — seven to zero.

To start the next series, I huddled up with Mike. His back was to the rest of the class. I looked at where they were positioned and then lowered my head. "Okay, Mike up ten yards then cut out; the ball will be there just after you turn." He ran a great pattern and got some space. I put the ball on his hands.

Back in the huddle, I looked at the students trying to figure out their defense. Finally, I dropped my head and said softly, "Okay, touchdown this time. Stop and go. Up five yards, give a quick stop, then take off."

I took the ball evaded the rush. He gave a convincing stop, then turned on the speed and outran the class as I floated it to him in the end zone.

All tied — seven to seven.

For the most part, through the year, I tried to tone down the obvious advantages I had as a twenty-three-year-old man versus children. But that day on the field, I played smart and fast. I watched the quarterback's eyes on defense and knocked down the passes, or better yet, intercepted.

Mike was in eighth grade and was an exceptional athlete. He ran great patterns and caught my bullets. And if he did get touched — we played two-hand-touch — close to the end zone, we would switch roles, he would quarterback and throw lobs too high for anyone else but me to catch. Touch down.

At the end of the game we were vilified; we were the goats, the victorious goats: twenty-eight to seven.

That was the only time Mike and I took on the school. Of course, it was unfair, and we repeatedly apologized for running up the score, but as we both kept laughing, the apology lacked the appearance of true repentance.

Oh man, it was fun.

CHAPTER THIRTY-SIX

BACK IN THE SADDLE

In the morning, the snow was lower. It was on the mesa just above my house. It was Sabbath. I could get up a little slower. I made some pancakes and read my Bible as my cat made figure-eight patterns between my legs. The sky was clear when I drove down the hill, over the bridge, and looked at the blue waters of the Colorado and the rapids just upriver. As I merged onto the quiet interstate, the Book Cliffs were grandiose, rising to my left. The sun was shining, and a light cover of snow draped the shoulders of the mountain. The sandstone of the cliffs tinted the snow with coral hues.

At church, I listened to the Sabbath School lesson then went out to the foyer for a drink of water. I shook a couple of hands and then returned to the sanctuary. I found an empty pew. I always sat on the right side. I'm not sure why; maybe there were fewer claimed pews on the right. I sat down, and a moment later, the little fourth-grader, Chrissie, in a cream-colored dress, sat down beside me. It was not surprising to have a student sit beside me. More times than not, one or two were there, but Chrissie had always been timid, more bashful. It was unusual for her to be the first to come and sit beside me. The Damocles sword of the Hesses leaving was still unresolved. Maybe that was it. But as she was sitting beside me, I thought what I wanted was to have a family and to have a daughter like Chrissie. Very much like Chrissie. Indeed, I would have loved to have Chrissie for a daughter, and I hoped that Russel and Judy could find a way to stay in Rifle.

That evening they had a Halloween party at the church. I drove back over. All of my children had on costumes: little pirate outfits, fairies, cowboys, or Indians (Sensitivity to calling Indians, Native Americans had little penetration in Western Colorado in those years.) They all looked so cute, and it was darling to see the girls wearing make-up for their costumes. They never wore any make-up at school.

The following day as I was going over my bills and looking at my finances, I was worried. I was as thrifty as I could be. I walked to the school rather than drove. For my groceries, I never bought pop or deserts. I had not purchased any new clothes since summer. My meals consisted of a lot of potatoes and or rice. In short, I bought nothing. As for the house, it was not extravagant. My family had made that clear. And I kept it on the colder side. It did not have a thermostat, so I wasn't sure of the exact temperature, but I kept it cool enough that I needed to wear a sweater. I did not entertain visitors. Other than my family, I had no visitors. No one wanted to visit me in this shack.

Nevertheless, despite these economies, my budget was marginal. On a good month, I had an extra five to fifteen dollars, which was not sustainable, and it worried me. It really worried me. How was I ever going to achieve my dream of being married and having children when I could not support them?

Mike and Doug were out of school all the following week. They were on an elk hunting trip with their dads near Craig in Northwest Colorado. The Sisk brothers, Jerald and Clifford, were very close. Tina said they were inseparable. When Jerald had gone to medical school at Loma Linda, Clifford moved there and did sheetrock. When Jerald moved to Rifle, Clifford followed and was building houses. And this being the first year Mike had lived in Rifle, the dads had taken the cousins camping.

The Hesses were gone that week as well. I heard that Russell had taken his family to Texas while he searched for a job.

Anyway, with five students gone and now down to six grades. I had more time that week. I spent more time on math with all the grade levels. It still was not enough, but I was appreciative of anything that made it better. However, more time with the students was not enough to keep Roy from becoming very upset on Thursday and threatening to leave the classroom and go home.

Not surprisingly, I woke up with a monstrous headache and nausea the following morning. I considered calling Tina Mitchell and taking a sick day, but I could not do that to her. I came in and struggled through it. Fortunately, Fridays were always much less structured. When it came to afternoon music, no one wanted to participate, and I did not have the energy to coerce them.

I was grateful when David Mitchell invited me to come up and go riding with him after church the following day. The Mitchells had five horses. It was cold and gray that day. Up at their house, there was a little snow on the ground, but I was not going to let a little snow prevent me from an opportunity to ride. We filled up buckets of grain, called in the horses, and tied them up in the paddock. Their white dog Sugar was at our feet. I followed David into the tack room, where he showed me the saddles and discussed the dispositions of their horses. He was going to ride Loni, a chestnut quarter horse. He suggested I ride Astro, Valerie's purebred Arabian--a deep bay with a black mane. That sounded good. I grabbed Astro's saddle and bridle.

We saddled them up. When I got on, Astro was frisky. He gave up a couple of half bucks. Nothing that significant, just a test by Astro to see if he had a novice on his back. Could he intimidate me and return to the fields? I was not a professional, but this didn't bother me. I could handle it, and it would not dissuade me from an afternoon on horseback. David nodded approvingly and told me Astro had cost fifteen hundred dollars. Not everyone was able to ride him. As we headed for the upper gate, he pointed out their other Arabian, Bushfire. He was a dappled gray gelding who was even feistier than Astro.

We headed south, uphill, toward the mountains, out the gate, and then through BLM land. Mostly we walked the horses. Occasionally we trotted through the sage. The mountain was before us. On the south side of the river, in contrast to the Book Cliffs on the north side, the incline was not vertical but a steady wedge. On this side, there was foliage: shrubs, scrub oak, and near the summit, a conifer forest. We reached the first plateau. Looking up the mountain, we could see that the snow would quickly get deeper. We turned east and onto a dirt road where the snow was minimal.

I was wearing my blue down jacket and a wool ski hat, but horses put off a lot of heat, and when my hands got cold, I laid them on the horse's hot neck. So, despite the snow and the cloudy day, I was comfortable.

We passed above the neighboring farms. Their horses galloped to the fence line, whinnying and snorting to greet us. The cattle in the fields, mostly Black Angus, did not pause from their grazing. Sugar though not a bird dog, did manage to flush out at least two coveys of quail, and the rush of their wings gave the horses a startle. I had to pull in the reins and settle Astro quickly. Across the field, a mule deer noticed us and bounced away and over the fence. We circled, down, and then returned onto a separate dirt road.

David tapped his boots to his horse a couple of times, took off in a canter, and then a slow gallop. I trailed behind. I was not synchronizing with my mount. But shortly thereafter, I found Astro's rhythm, and when I did, the gelding accelerated. That horse loved to run. We flew by David like a falcon in mid-dive. It was invigorating, energizing, exciting, exhilarating. It was pure joy, just speed, as I got low and felt my body moving together with his, such velocity — the cold wind blowing into my lungs. Everything was new and fresh. I was feeling it all.

I let Astro run for another few seconds and then reined him in. David caught up. "I told you that horse was hot-blooded, didn't I?" He said, and his respect for the Arabian had soared. Astro was pacing and prancing, wanting to explode again. "I don't think I have ever seen Astro completely unthrottled before," he said as we rode in circles with our dancing horses. "You ride well."

It had not been long, probably not even half a minute; still I was exultant. I felt like I had just brought Affirmed across the finish line at the Belmont, or rather an even greater hero, Secretariat.

We walked the horses the rest of the way. And we talked. He told me a story where he once had put a shotgun against a man's chest and pulled the trigger, but the gun did not go off. He knew how to weave a story. I was just never sure of his veracity. He also talked a lot about trying to get his life together. I encouraged him. He brought up women and admitted he was fond of Valerie's friend, Ruth.

CHAPTER THIRTY-SEVEN

HELP!

Mike and Doug, and the Hesses were all back the following week. It was good to have them back. Mike brought energy into the classroom, lots of energy. Doug balanced him. As for the Hesses, I had fretted over them. I had wondered if I might never see them again. Now they were back. Apparently, they had been able to resolve their issues. Their dad had found work, though I never heard further details.

On Tuesday night, we had a longer than usual board meeting. I tried to keep silent and bite my tongue. I reminded myself these lovely people were there to help me. If they were not as time conscious as me, not as aware of the lateness of the hour and how the minutes slid away into infinity, it was because many of them did not have a job they had to be at early the following morning. Still, they were here to aid me, and they were volunteers.

Watching how Dr. McElvain managed the meeting, my appreciation for him increased. I was beginning to understand his technique of patience, which was legendary. He let everybody have their say and then subtly worked it back. It was like fly fishing: give them a little line, pull it in, let it out, and then reach down with the net. Voila. Next topic. He had settled into the role.

They talked about finances, about the role of the aide, about any thoughts on a second teacher, about my living situation, about classroom discipline. Then they discussed an offer from the Hesses. As an offset to some tuition discounts, Mrs. Hess had proposed that she and the three older children help do some cleaning at the school a couple of times a week. Everyone was glad that the Hesses had been able to find a way to stay. The school needed cleaning. The proposal passed. As for me, I was delighted Ron, Chrissie, and Angie were back.

I hate confrontation and do what I can to avoid it, but in the classroom, my tension with Mrs. Mitchell had continued unabated; nothing egregious, just minor annoyances that accumulated and weighed on me. Finally, on Thursday, I mustered my nerve and asked her if she could talk to me. We sat down after school. When I told her I was feeling threatened and how I thought she undermined my authority in the classroom. She was taken aback, genuinely surprised. I told her that it sometimes made it difficult because she had such a long history with the children and was older. She assured me I was doing a good job, and she had not meant to undermine me. The meeting went better than I had imagined. We worked on defining our expectations. When I was in the room for discipline decisions, I wanted to handle it. If she disagreed with me, I would be glad to hear her advice later and in private. Although, as I said, it went well, I still felt terrible. It had surprised her. But it worked out.

After the meeting, I went outside. Cory was still waiting for his parents to pick him up. The other students had all left. He had the football in his hand and asked if I could show him how to throw the football. I particularly enjoyed these one-on-one times. Cory had no siblings to play with, and knowing his father, it was unlikely Cory was going to learn football at home. Knowing how to play football, throw the ball, and catch it had become a measure of status in the classroom. I had a fair amount of work left to do at my desk, but it was not a hard decision to teach a student how to throw a football versus grading papers. These moments were rare, and I could always stay a little later. I guided Cory's hand onto the proper grip. We were tossing the football around when I heard the school phone ring. I ran up the steps and answered it. Wes Petersen from the conference office was on the phone. He was calling to check in on me. How was it going?

"Well, to tell you the truth, I am overwhelmed. I really am. I'm just struggling to keep my head above water."

He encouraged me and added some platitudes about how all first-year teachers felt that way. That peeved me, and I asked if he remembered the details of my situation.

He tried to reassure me.

I was not having it. "Mr. Peterson, I'm not sure if you have heard, but I will be getting a new student in third grade next semester, Heather Savage. She will be starting in January, which will raise the number to twenty-one students and still all eight grades. Mr. Peterson, I am a first-year teacher. Yes, I am a rookie, barely out of school, hardly know anything. That's all true. Tell me what other teacher has twenty-one students in eight grades. Do you know of anybody? It doesn't have to be just the rookies; how about some of your more experienced teachers. How are they handling all eight grades and twenty-one students? They're doing okay, are they?"

He was smooth. He understood my frustration. He did not take offense and went on to tell me stories he had accumulated over the years of first-year teachers whom he had helped in their decompensation.

"My students are constantly asking me to help them with their work, and I have to tell them I have to start the next class, Mr. Petersen. I don't have the time to teach. Do you know how frustrating that is?" That stopped Mr. Petersen for a moment.

I continued, "Dr. Holderbaum suggested I threaten to resign. He told me I should tell you that I quit if I don't get a second teacher in two weeks. That's what he told me." I knew Mr. Peterson knew Dr. Holderbaum. Dr. Holderbaum had been school board chairman.

I heard him sigh. I had gotten his attention. "Neither the church nor the school board has the money for a second teacher, Marvin. We are in a tough position."

I was silent for a long time before answering, "I'm not quitting. I'm not resigning. I will not leave like this, but the conference manual says that the most allowed is fifteen students and six grades and that with an aide. This isn't right. Not for me. Not for the students."

"You're right, Marvin. You're right. Let me talk to Mr. Rice. I'll come out and see you next week. Let me see what we can do."

I had not meant to become so confrontational, but his attempt to distract me with stories from his past vaults had irritated me. However, when confronted, no one had ever known me to lie down or acquiesce, and I did not see that aspect of my personality making any sudden changes. (For the record, no, it never changed.)

I hung up. Cory was standing there looking at me. I think he respected me the way I had not backed down.

I stayed late that night. I was upset. And it was true there was a talk of another girl starting the second semester in third grade. Twenty-one students. Why not just send all of Western Colorado here! Maybe I should get a megaphone and teach to large crowds, you know, have a Billy Graham crusade, or better yet, I should go up to the top of the mountain and preach like Jesus. It was obvious they intended to crucify me. But do not brush me off with talk of new teacher burnout. Yes, I may be burning out, but there were reasons.

So, I stayed late and walked home and was pleased to see Orion in the west. I had been watching for it, and now it was visible. And as I was walking down the road, I looked over to the Book Cliffs. There was always a light high up on the cliff. I had seen it several times. Who lived on the face of the cliff? Tonight, I saw car lights coming down from that god-forsaken, remote spot. And I thought I would much rather have my job than be stuck in that isolated spot.

CHAPTER THIRTY-EIGHT

TEACH YOUR CHILDREN

It did not help that a couple of days later, after I dismissed the lower grades that the remaining students descended into a gripe session. They started complaining about perceived injustices, how I spent too much time with the first graders, or that I could never help them with their problems. They brought up previous teachers who gave longer and better lectures and had more creative projects. Ron, to his credit, tried to defend me, but no one accepted it.

And then I made an error. "You know what, guys. You can quit your complaining. I'm not going to be here next year anyway."

I should have never said that, and I regretted it at once. I knew I would hear about it from a panoply of sources. I tried to downplay it. Yes, I was considering not returning, but I had made no decisions. The students made an about-face. They were instantly better behaved and remonstrated with me not to leave. But the downtrend had begun, and the next day it was worse.

The following day was cold. The coal stove took a long time to heat the school. Everyone was in a foul mood: Carolyn spouted off at me; Heather complained that I hated her; Shon threw his lunch on the floor; Mike refused to go out when I said enough was enough, and we would be doing calisthenics for recess. At lunch, however, he wanted to sit outside.

"Well, if it was too cold for you at P.E., I'm sure it is still too cold," I said to him with little compassion.

"When did you make up that rule?" He replied with an insolent scowl.

"Just now."

But I could not function this way; hence on Friday, after the pledge of allegiance, I sent Danny and Steven out to raise the flag. Then I asked Mike, Ron, Doug, and Kelli to meet me in the next room.

They came in slowly, hesitantly, wondering what they had done. The rest of the class watched.

I let them go in first and then joined them. I shut the door behind me. The four were whispering among themselves. The lights were off, which cast the room into the early morning shadows.

I gave them each a look before beginning, "Guys, I thought yesterday was pretty miserable. What do you think?"

Ron chuckled. "That's an understatement."

"It was awful, Mr. Brauer," Kelli added.

Mike and Doug nodded their agreement, but Mike did not want to commit too much until he saw where this was going.

"You guys are the oldest ones in the classroom. With your support, we can have a better day. Or we can do yesterday all over again, déjà vu."

"Deja, what?" Kelli asked.

"Déjà vu," Doug responded. "It means the feeling of having seen this before."

"Bravo, Doug!" I responded and then looked at the group. "What do you say, guys? Shall we try? And that means me as well. It's not all you. It's me as well. What do you think?"

They looked around at each other.

"How about no calisthenics for recess?" Doug was always trying to negotiate.

Mike jumped on that and added, "And let us sit on the steps for lunch."

"Good attitude from the four of you this morning, and it's a deal."

They smiled. They valued having some added authority and being able to negotiate some improvements.

"Are we agreed?"

Everyone nodded. "Okay, then huddle up." And I put my hand in the middle of the circle. They added theirs. "Alright, 'Go Rulison' on three. One, two, three."

The chorus of "Go Rulison" was a little weak. And Mike's cynically laced "Rah, Rah, Rulison" lagged after the others. Nevertheless, as we all came back into the next room, they had smiles on their faces.

What had happened in the next room? The schoolroom was very curious. Had they been chewed out? Had they been given a lecture? Some of the students were sure that had happened because the older students deserved it. But in that case, why were they smiling? There was also envy. The fifth graders did not see why the sixth graders were called in and not them. And Roy and Heather, who had serious control issues for fourth graders, were put out.

When Danny asked Doug what had happened, Ron interjected, "We decided today was going to be awesome." The other students looked at the others for confirmation. The girls looked to Kelli, and the boys looked to Mike. Kelli agreed, "It's Friday. And we are going to have a good day." Mike patted Doyle's and Misty's heads as he walked by. "If you guys need any help today, come ask me. Okay." They looked up in amazement and hero worship. Mike turned to me, "Mr. Brauer, aren't the first graders just so darn cute?"

"Most certainly, Mike, they are so darn cute."

For a couple of hours in the morning, the day was great, and the rest was mostly better than average. Although when we did our monthly rearranging of the desks, Steven refused. I tried to counsel him telling him it was only for a month. He, however, would not budge. Then he tried to run out the door. I caught him by the shoulders. Heather warned me to be careful. "He is very strong, Mr. Brauer. He can hurt you." I thought that was amusing. Steven was wiry and strong, but he was eleven, and he was not a violent child. I brought him back to his desk, and he moved it.

CHAPTER THIRTY-NINE

THE ZOO

Watching children at a zoo, especially the first graders: Doyle, Justin, Katie, Misty, and Kim, was heavenly. Watching them get so excited seeing the bear, the lions and tigers, the monkeys, the elephants was beatific. They were such darling cherubs. It made the trip worthwhile, just to see their enthusiasm. And the older children, though with slightly less wonder, still found it engaging.

It was the week before Thanksgiving, and we had made the trip over the pass from Rifle to Denver. This was the big field trip of the year, the big excursion. The Sisks had loaned me their van, and I had driven it over the pass. Around Vail, it had started to snow. A little snow would not usually bother me. Living in Colorado, I had a lot of experience with snow, but I did not have a lot of experience with a large van, and I had ten boys in the back. Poor Tina sitting in the passenger seat had tried to keep them under control. Still, Shon and Steven had decided to make the trip a test of their ability to absorb pain and had spent much of the trip alternatively punching each other in the arm as hard as they could. I understood this; my brother, Ron, and I growing up had felt a day was incomplete without a quick round of fist fighting. I understood it; nevertheless, driving a big vehicle in the snow with Mrs. Mitchell trying to stop them from her front seat was nerve-wracking. Not surprisingly, I was pleased when we finally arrived at my parent's house.

Rather than rest, however, the first thing I did was to take the boys across the street to the big ballfield. We played a vigorous game of capture the flag. The boys would be sleeping downstairs in a massive slumber party, and I needed them to run out of their energy. Ten rambunctious boys would have been catastrophic.

The girls would be staying separately with a relative of the Holderbaums. Tina had gone on to fetch Valerie. Bonnie was in charge of the girls.

So, on Monday, we went to the Denver Zoo. It had been in existence since the 1890s. It had started with the donation of a baby bear to the city. And the zoo had become distinguished as the first zoo to use a more natural approach rather than cages and bars.

It was cold and grey on Monday, which dampened the enthusiasm and made interior exhibits more appealing.

With Tina still gone, Bonnie was my aide. As I have said before, Bonnie was slim and attractive. We got along fine, but she had limited skills in dealing with children. In addition, the stress of having responsibility for them in an unstructured environment like the zoo quickly tired her. Kelli, poor Kelli, spent much of the day helping her mother, trying to corral the children, trying to keep it under control so that Bonnie would not have to raise her voice in exasperation. Shon studiously ignored his mother and hung with the older boys. The farther away he was, the less she embarrassed him.

I missed Tina. I missed her disposition, nature, skills, and ability to grow with the children. We had worked together well.

After supper, I assigned my boys to help with clean up. My mother and I supervised. This type of feeding should have come naturally to her — she had raised four boys. But not so; my mother was never comfortable orchestrating large gatherings. She did it well, but it caused her great stress. After we had dismissed the

187

boys, the two of us finished up and began talking. This was a familiar time for me. I often helped my mother clean up in the kitchen, which was the best time to share with her. I told her about the day and how it had gone, and then she said she had heard Wes Peterson in the hall talking to his secretary. He said these first-year teachers think they can do just fine until they run into trouble, then they wail for help. His tone was disparaging. My mother was worried about me. She said Mr. Petersen said he thought he could quickly help. I thought otherwise.

On Tuesday we went to the capital. I felt every child in Colorado should visit the capital at some point in their elementary education. The tour guide engaged the children such that I hardly noticed Bonnie's lack of skill.

And then it was back into the van and drive across the pass. We picked up Tina. Valerie was with her. There were no extra seats, so Tina and Valerie shared the passenger seat.

Tina and I talked. She wanted to know how it all went. I spoke of the little children seeing the animals. She laughed and asked how Bonnie had done. I knew there was bad blood between them, so I tried not to say too much, but I could not help involuntarily shuddering.

"Let's just say I'm pleased to have you back."

She gave just the slightest smile and then offered to drive if I got tired. I told her I would at least drive over the pass, and then we would see how I felt. Around Eagle, after filling up with gas, I let her take the wheel. I was surprised that Valerie did not change seats with her brother. Instead, she stayed where she was and shared the passenger seat with me. She might be too young to date, but she was warm and attractive. Was it wrong of me to enjoy this? She started talking to me, and I was impressed at how comfortable she was. There was no silliness.

We had school on Wednesday, and then it was Thanksgiving vacation. I packed up my suitcase, threw in a sleeping bag, picked up my cat, and was back on the road to Denver. It was snowing harder this time. My Toyota Corolla was light with rear-wheel drive and no snow tires. The snow accumulated quickly, and although the snowplows in Colorado are the best in the world, they were not keeping up. The interstate was empty; traffic was sparse. As mentioned, I had experience driving in the snow, but this was taxing me. It was essential to keep a steady momentum. I held it steady at thirty-five miles an hour. If I slowed below that, all was lost.

I made it through Glenwood Canyon, which was not as bad as feared, but as the elevation climbed, it worsened. Driving past Eagle, I became more and more apprehensive, and I pulled off at the West Vail exit. Before attempting the pass, I topped off the tank as a precaution. If the car got stuck, I wanted enough gas to run the heat intermittently through the night. At the gas station, I asked the attendant about the road condition for the pass. He said chains were required. That was ominous on the face of it, plus I did not have chains.

I went outside into the storm. The lights from a Holiday Inn just across the parking lot were appealing. The lobby had a gas fireplace blazing and was warm. I asked the clerk at the counter if they had rooms and what the bed rate was.

"Yes, we have rooms. Forty dollars."

I thanked him and exited the lobby's toasty coziness. Forty dollars might as well have been four hundred. Poverty had me firmly in its grips; I could not afford it. I looked at the big snowflakes falling all around and felt overwhelmed, discouraged, full of self-pity. Back in my car, I picked up my cat and petted him. I was glad for the company and then looked into the hatchback. I had brought my sleeping bag as insurance. I pulled down the rear seat, made a small bed, and cuddled Mittens beneath the down covers. I would sleep in the car.

Early the next morning, I awoke. The sky had cleared. So very like Colorado to snow one day and be cloudless the next. I wiped the snow off the car and then turned the key in the ignition. The snowplows had done their work, and the interstate was passable. I made it through the Eisenhauer tunnel and then down, down, down to Denver.

189

My mom and dad were surprised to see me so early. Then again, they were not. I had done things like this before. Like the summer I had spent selling encyclopedias on a trip all the way to Joplin, Missouri. I had called them from a payphone on the outskirts of Denver. Could they come and get me? Where was I? Just north of Aurora, Colorado. My dad had answered. Well, of course, that's close, but wasn't I in Missouri? I told him I had hitchhiked across Kansas and Eastern Colorado starting two days ago. I had gotten fed up with the endless lies my sales managers wanted me to use, and it was one-two I'm through. I had slept in my sleeping bag that night as well, rolled it out in a rest stop along the interstate. But, of course, that had been summer. Of all my brothers, I was the most likely one in the family to appear suddenly.

Back at home, I needed to take care of a situation.

On my once-a-month trip home to Denver, I had taken out a girl. It had started at the end of summer. She was a full-bodied girl of German stock, and the dates had been fun. She thought I was funny and liked me. But I was not sure where it was going. Then, finally, my brother, Ron, clarified it for me.

It was Thanksgiving, and since none of my brothers would be there, they had called. I listened in on a line in my dad's study in the basement. Bob and Jim got into theological and pastoring conversations with my father. That bored me. Ron and Nancy had bought a Morgan horse which they were hoping to show and maybe later breed. Nancy loved horses. Ron liked to be busy. They had found a stable near them in San Bernardino where they could board it. Nancy said that Morgans could make money. Ron was supportive.

Ron asked about my girlfriend.

"Well, I don't know that she is a girlfriend," I replied.

"What!" Ron said in his most derogatory tone. "You have been going out with her since August, and you don't call her your girlfriend. That doesn't sound good."

Nancy chimed in and brought up her old roommate, "I was talking to Judy a couple of weeks ago. She asked about you."

190

I laughed, "And she is still on the east coast, right? A little bit far, Nancy."

Ron ignored Nancy's conversation and was back on lecturing me. He loved to lecture me. "Marv, you know this is stupid." He also loved a chance to call me stupid. "You gotta break up with her."

"Break up! She is not my girlfriend."

Ron guffawed, "Un-huh, sure. So, what does she think?"

I sighed, "Well, she might think she is."

"Exactly. Geez, Marvin. You get good grades in school, but you are really stupid as shit with girls."

"Ron!" My mom exclaimed.

"Sorry, Mom," Ron apologized.

I laughed. This was precisely how our humor went, and it might help you understand how when we were younger if the party of the first part did not find the humor of the second part funny, well then, a fist might be shortly coming your way. Since we were older, however, our sense of what was hilarious had broadened. And being abused, belittled, cursed at, well that was indeed great mirth, especially since it was true.

I knew he was right. Yes, I did have a good time on the dates. The girl was amiable and not unpleasant to look at. But the truth was when I left each time; I was glad that I would not be seeing her for another month. Once a moon was often enough. And that did not need deep soul searching to realize it was not a good omen. I had been in love with other girls before her as well as dumped before. However, my attachment to her felt nothing like what I had had previously.

So not to belabor it. We had our talk. And I realized as I talked to her, she was much more involved with me than I had been with her. I felt bad, but it made me more certain it was the right thing to do. I was not in love, and she needed to find someone else.

CHAPTER FORTY

LET IT SNOW

With chalk in my hand, I worked out some long division problems for the fourth graders on the blackboard. But as the small cylinder filled my fingers, I kept getting distracted; I kept stopping to look out the windows. Snow was coming down in big wet flakes. The coal heater was doing its job, and the room was toasty warm. But the wall of windows filled with drifting snow like white fleece was mesmerizing. And on top of it all, as we kept turning back to watch, we saw that the clouds were thinning, and blue skies were beginning to peek through. Soon it was a wonderland of winter white beneath the richest of celestial skies, Colorado cobalt blue. I was sure nothing could match it anywhere in the world.

I turned around and looked at my fourth graders. They no longer made any pretense of paying attention as they all looked out the window. It was ten-twenty in the morning, ten minutes before recess. A few students were making attempts at industry, but almost everyone was glued to the magic occurring outside. It was such a siren song.

"You know what? That is too gorgeous! Put your boots and coats on, everyone. It's recess."

"But we can't play football in that," Shon protested, as everyone started hustling to get their coats, gloves, and snow boots.

"Right. You are so right, Shon. So, we are going to play snow trail tag."

"Snow trail tag? What's that?" There was a chorus of questions.

"Follow me."

I led the children up to the field. Instead of the cleared part of the field at the top we went to the lower part of the field that still had some sagebrush scattered throughout. I started to make a path in the snow. It was at least a foot deep. I directed some of the older children to create a maze of trails.

"Snow trail tag is simple. It is freeze tag, except you have to stay on the trail. If you get caught, you are frozen until someone touches you and unfreezes you. Two people are it."

"Ha, ha, Dr. Brauer!" Carolyn laughed. "Freeze tag in the snow. Clever."

I laughed. I thought it had been a nice play on words.

And there under the blue skies with the sun now shining on the snow-covered grounds, behind us the Book Cliffs rose, the air clear and cold, so fresh, the children and I ran the trails in innocent joy. Kelli and Doug volunteered to be it first. They worked as a pack herding the prey. The first graders squealed when they were trapped and tagged. Danny and Shon tried to distract Doug while I made a run to free the little kids. I released a couple, but then Kelli caught me. And O was she delighted.

"I got you, Mr. Brauer!" She chortled and hovered close. Her eyes glittered, and she kept tapping my coat with her gloved hand as if she could not believe her fortune. She was a big game hunter, and I was the trophy.

Steven tried to rush in, but Kelli charged, and he backed away.

"You can't stand so close, Kelli," Ron objected. The boys were like hyenas circling, trying to get close, using feints to draw Kelli off her prize. But she would not be distracted, except occasionally to capture a hyena.

193

They had firmly trapped me. The way we had set up the trails freeing me was the most challenging. But I was fine with that. It allowed me to observe, and as I watched it all, I was transported again. They were having fun outside in the fresh air playing a simple game. And I kept thinking how much I cherished my students from first grade to eighth. I was satisfied at that moment, as they darted, and laughed, and fell in the snow, and got up laughing. I could not imagine my happiness ever exceeding this moment.

We stayed out a little longer that recess, and while the snow stayed on the ground that winter, which was a perfect year for snow, while the snow lasted, snow trail tag was the most popular recess choice.

The next afternoon after school, I sat at my desk in the classroom doing my never-ending work: preparing for the next day, going through the teacher's textbooks, reading the instructions and suggestions on how to teach tomorrow's lessons; at about four-thirty, Tina called the school. She invited me to come up and eat with them. She had fixed a Mexican Dorito dish.

"I'm pretty sure it will be better than what you have at home." She deadpanned.

I laughed. "You mean better than canned Campbell's tomato soup? Is that even possible?"

"You were going to have canned soup? O, my, poor Mr. Brauer."

I drove up to their ranch. Danny answered the door. He was delighted to see me even though he had just spent the day with me and even though I had had to prod him on several occasions. "Danny, quit looking around and do your work." He would smile and try to concentrate. But that had been school, and this was after school. The two were completely separate.

I walked through the living room and back to the kitchen bar, where I sat down on one of the stools. The aromas coming from the oven were intoxicating. Danny was put to work setting the table. David and Mr. Mitchell came in from outside. They shed their overalls at the door. They had been working on some fencing in the upper pasture. Mr. Mitchell walked into the kitchen to assess the coming meal.

"My wife is a great cook," he said like a man, one who was continually amazed at his good fortune. And then he gave me a hardy handshake. I always felt welcomed by him.

David went downstairs to change.

At the meal David was in his usual form, entertaining, telling stories, filling his plate with far more food than I ate in a week.

"I feel like you were here with us at Thanksgiving," David said as he lifted a glass of milk to his lips and held it there for a moment. Then, he gave me a lifted eyebrow over the glass rim. He had big thick eyebrows.

"Yeah, why is that.?" I played the straight guy. I had no idea where this was going. It could be a joke on me or who knows what. But a comedian needs a straight guy, and I enjoyed playing along.

"Well, all weekend, my sister was like, Marvin this, Marvin that. He is such a gentleman. He's so smart."

Danny burst into laughter and corroborated the story. "It's true," He exclaimed.

David was on a roll, "All weekend long, all she kept saying 'Marvin is so cute. Isn't Mr. Brauer cute? O, he's so cute!'"

Mr. Mitchell smiled and said nothing. Tina laughed then tried to stop David. "I'm not sure Valerie wanted Mr. Brauer to hear all this."

"Mom, you have to admit that is all she talked about."

Tina tried to change the subject and passed me the green beans. She gave Mitch a quick look, and Mr. Mitchell told David to move on to another topic.

"Okay," David reluctantly agreed. Comedians sometimes do not know when to stop, but he was trying. "Okay, let's move on, but I just want to say," And he turned to me. "Don't take this personally. It's probably just me, but I don't see it. To me I don't find you that cute."

I had just taken a drink, and I snorted it out. Tina handed me a napkin, and I cleaned my face before responding, "Glad to hear that, David, you don't know how that has relieved my mind."

David looked at me and nodded.

After supper, I was in no hurry to leave. I helped with the cleanup and then sat down on the couch. Mr. Mitchell was watching the news. Walter Cronkite had retired earlier in the year, and Dan Rather was now the anchorman at CBS. He was good, but Cronkite had been such a presence it was taking some adjustment. In sports, Alabama beat Birmingham in the Iron Bowl. Bear Bryant won his three hundred and fifteenth game.

I heard Tina at the kitchen deck calling Valerie. It was a modern phone. It had punch buttons rather than rotary but was still tethered. Tina tried to coax Valerie into coming home for Danny's baptism the following Sabbath. She turned her back so I could not hear her. They were having the usual long conversation that mothers and daughters had. That was out of my experience.

Mr. Mitchell got on the phone for a couple of minutes and then went upstairs. Tina was still talking to Valerie. Tina had solved the issue; Valerie was coming home for the weekend. Then Tina called me. "Mr. Brauer, come and persuade Valerie to come."

I got up. It seemed a little contrived, not how I would have wanted to have a conversation with Valerie, but I complied.

"Hi, Valerie."

She laughed. "My mother is so crazy. You don't need to convince me to come, Marvin. I've already said I was coming."

I chuckled. "But you know it is hard to say no to your mother after she fed me such a wonderful meal."

"That is true."

"Okay, so I have persuaded you then, right? I mean, it was me, right? It was because I got on the phone that you are coming home?"

She laughed on the other end. "Absolutely. That was the deal closer."

"Okay, well, see you soon."

I handed the phone back to Tina.

I drove back down to my house and got ready for bed. So, Valerie liked me; that was obvious. I thought her novel and fresh and felt rosy warming with the contemplation. But if that was so, had we just landed in that rare place where predilection was known but profundities were not yet shared? Was I, too, a little infatuated? A high school student? Her parents seemed indifferent to the age gap. If anything, their comments were encouraging, even approving. But a high school student? It was nuts. In college, I had always dated college girls. Then again, in college, I had been surrounded by women my age. But, one thing was sure the apparition of the Mitchell's daughter was becoming more persistent.

CHAPTER FORTY-ONE

THE KIDS RALLY

I was in the adjacent room listening to Bobo read when Mr. Peterson's car drove into the school driveway. I saw it pull in but did not get up. Bobo was doing so well with his reading and other classes that sometimes he was overlooked. I wanted to stay in my seat and listen to him. I watched Mr. Peterson get out of his car and heard Tina greet him in the next room. A few moments later, she opened the door. He was standing behind her. I got up and shook hands. Tina took over for me and sat down to listen to Bobo.

"Good to see you, Marvin," Mr. Peterson said as I walked with him back into the main classroom. "We're hearing good things about you."

I took in a breath to launch into a protest, but he put up his hand to halt me before I got started. "I am confident that we can find some tricks to improve efficiency. So, you just go about your day, and I'll stay in the background." He had a comforting smile, and his mannerisms were reassuring.

We proceeded forward. As we came to math and I did some more division problems on the board for the fourth graders, Mr. Petersen walked around the room. He saw Ron, my seventh grader working with the third graders: Chad and Angie, and my eighth grader, Mike, helping out Danny and Shon. Mr. Peterson talked to Ron and Mike briefly.

"Un-huh," I thought to myself. "He is going to tell me to use the older students to help teach the younger students. Check. I've done that."

The morning went on. Heather finished her math assignment and came to the front. There was a desk in the front where students could review and grade their work. She sat down and checked her problems against the key. She took a red pen, marked her paper appropriately, and then put it in the basket. Mr. Petersen saw the whole thing. He also saw Kelli reading over some of Kim's handwriting. My students were all on their very best behavior. All the things I had been working with them to do, which they did haphazardly on bad days, today they were on point. They were performing. And on several occasions, I caught them giving me knowing little glances. They were sending messages, "We've got your back, Mr. Brauer. We've got you covered."

When we did social sciences, Mr. Peterson commented that he was pleased to see that I had grouped the grades to reduce the number of separate lectures.

"That's good, Marvin. Very nice."

Even though my children were quite proper, their comportment was exemplary, far exceeding the average day; still, there were always several students at my desk wanting help. There were always multiple hands going up in the room. Tina and I tried our best to get around; nevertheless, even on this day, the students' frustration was mounting. I did my best to multitask.

At recess, I went out with the children to play snow tag. Mr. Peterson stayed inside and talked to Tina.

At lunch, he took me into the next room. I grabbed my brown sack. He had a big, black lunch box, and we sat down with our sandwiches. He was in no hurry. He sat chewing his lunch in silence. He took out his mug and had a long drink of cold milk. He commented how much he liked cold milk with his sandwich and then took some carrot sticks and began eating them. He talked about how much snow was on the mountains as he came over the pass. Finally, after finishing his sandwich and throwing away the plastic bag, putting the cap back on his thermos, and sticking it back in his lunch box, finally after that, he took a big breath and began.

"You know Marvin. I've been doing this, what, maybe thirty years. I have a lot of tricks of the trade on how to run a classroom efficiently. I have seen a lot of new teachers and helped them. I have seen them struggling." He chuckled and then took a sideline. "It is an interesting profession this teaching is, isn't it? Where else can you have such an opportunity to affect children? Where else can you get to know these little kids? And where else can you go from hero to goat so quickly?" He smiled at me and then got up and walked across the room to the window. He leaned against the wall and gazed outside.

"These children really like you, don't they?" He paused and added, "I saw them giving you those little winks. The moment I walk in the door, it is never a typical day."

I chuckled. I was feeling fond of my students at the moment. They had stepped up.

"I thought I could help you." He continued, and he came back and sat down at the table. "I really thought I could help you, I did, but all the ideas I was going to suggest, you know, combining grade levels where you can, getting the older students to help the younger children, maximizing the use of your aide, even having the children grade some of their work, you're doing it all. I'm not here to flatter you. You don't need that. But frankly, you handle yourself like someone with years of experience. And what you're trying to do here is impossible. It's just not possible. Nobody can handle all eight grades with twenty students."

At this, he let out a long sigh. "Yes, yes, I am aware the school board is struggling financially." He was reciting the difficulties that would be proffered. "They all are. I will talk to Bob Rice, and I am certain we will insist that you have a second teacher."

And when he said that, my heart flooded with relief. The sense of unburdening was overwhelming, just the acknowledgment that help would come. I tried to speak, but my throat tightened up, and I could not. And I realized how much I had buried, how much my stress had inundated me. I had not even allowed myself to understand the severity of how this had affected me. I had been suppressing my feelings, sensing that if I opened up, it would be more than I could bear. What I did know was that I wanted to be here with my students.

He looked at me and smiled. He let me have the moment I needed.

"This is beautiful country. I love driving over here. I often stop on the bridge after I get off the interstate. The Colorado River is so beautiful." He picked up his lunch box. "Well, I'll let myself out. If I leave now, I can get back and talk to Bob before he leaves for the afternoon."

I walked him to the door.

That night as I walked home under a quarter moon. I was at rest—I had a warm home, plenty of food, adequate clothing. I had my health, and I did live in a beautiful part of the country. The air was fresh. I loved my students, and, on most days, they liked me. It was good.

Wes Peterson was as good as his word. Ron McElvain called an emergency school board for the following evening. He said he had a long and difficult conversation with Bob Rice, the education director for the conference. Mr. Rice had said it was imperative that the school board approved a new teacher. The number of students and grades taught here exceeded Colorado's laws. If discovered, the school and the conference could face a stiff fine. All they needed was for one disgruntled parent to complain. The school could even be shut down. The board members were upset. Of course, they did not want the school shut down, but really why had I not mentioned this before. If I was so overwhelmed, I should have brought it up. Both of the Ron's defended me: that is Ron McElvain and Ron Mitchell (Mitch).

"That is our responsibility, the school board's, not Mr. Brauer's. We hired him to teach ten students in five grades. Yes, it has grown, and we have all been astounded…and pleased." Dr. McElvain paused and looked at all the members around the table. They were all paying attention. "Still, Mr. Brauer told us he needed a second teacher. We all knew he did, and we tried to find him a second teacher. No one was willing."

Dr. McElvain paused, and Ron Mitchell jumped in. "I agree this is not on Marvin. I don't want to hear that. We are, however, at risk here. This school is at risk. If we get sanctioned by the state, it will kill the school. It will die, so it is up to us, the board, we can either dismiss students and bring us back into compliance, or we vote to get a second teacher."

Pastor Kungel grumbled beneath his breath.

Ron acknowledged him, "Pastor do you have something to say."

"No offense, Mr. Brauer, but I was never in favor of bringing someone with such inexperience, and now here we are, out of compliance?" He saw that Ron Mitchell was about to reprimand him, and so he added, "Of course, I don't mean to imply it was Mr. Brauer's fault." He stopped and gave his attempt at a smile.

Pastor Kungel was a corpulent gentleman, probably in his late fifties, early sixties at the time. He had a short thick neck and a gravelly, raspy voice. He and his wife lived a few houses above the school. Some pastors like to drop into the school on occasion to see the children. He never did, at least while I was the teacher. He was polite to me, though I sensed he did not like me. I assumed he thought I was too smart. For example, when I taught the adult Sabbath School lesson, I liked to quote from the commentaries and tried to integrate the effect and intellect.

On the other hand, his sermons were off the cuff and always a variant on the same theme. He would have heard something on the radio, the television, or have read in the newspaper, and he would talk about it and try to show how this proved the condition of our world. It was always the same. If he had given much thought to his sermons, it was not plain. Still, I did not dislike him—well, to be honest, I expected a lot more out of a pastor. I was not impressed.

Undoubtedly, I had come to Rifle with prejudices. I had been influenced by my mother, who worked for the conference president. She did not flat out say that Pastor Kungel was considered below average, but she did say the conference committee did not feel he was of the quality to be considered for any of the Denver area churches. It had occurred to me that some of the pastor's less than jovial encounters with me might be related to who my family was.

There was some further discussion, and when it looked like the board would pass the resolution Pastor Kungel spoke up again. "All right, you can pass this, but it will have to come to a church business meeting because…this means the church is going to have to subsidize the school even more. This will be a large drain on the church budget. So, this has to be decided by the church."

The upshot of the meeting was that the pastor would bring it to the church. I realized a part of the church that, while they liked the idea of a school, felt that we were becoming an annoyance. The children were lovely when they stood up front and sang, and it was nice to see the little ones sitting quietly beside their parents. But—and that BUT stood for a lot.

CHAPTER FORTY-TWO

JUST A LITTLE BIT OF MAGIC

An evangelistic campaign had been going on at the church for the last six weeks. Gunner Nelson, one of the two full-time evangelists for the conference, had been preaching four nights a week. I had rarely attended due to my workload but had felt guilty, nevertheless. Friday night was the penultimate meeting.

Evangelistic campaigns, crusades, the terminology was rife with military jargon; we were after all just soldiers like Pilgrim in Paul Bunyan's *Pilgrim's Progress*. We were in a battle on the side of Christ against the Prince of Darkness. We, as Adventists, had been given a rare, insightful glimpse into the very heart of the controversy between God and Lucifer. And we were in the last days, and truthfully, we were all amazed that Jesus had not come. I mean, it was nineteen eighty-one, for Pete's sake. No one had expected to be here in the nineteen-eighties. I certainly had not. I had never thought I would grow up and have a job. Jesus was coming soon—and yet here we were in these very end-of-days.

As Adventists, it was incumbent on us to tell as many people as possible the vital truths that had been hidden through the long dark ages, hidden by the antichrist. Truths like the understanding that man was not an immortal soul, and that at death he rested in the grave until the resurrection. This understanding was vital because it kept people away from spiritualism, which was the word we used to discuss the ever-growing practice of people having seances, trying to talk to the dead. We knew this was impossible. You could not speak to the dead. Instead, they were speaking to Satan's angels. O, the horror! When I write that, it sounds trivial but let me assure you we believed and were horrified that people were communicating with demons. And since the vast majority of Christianity, both Catholic and Protestant, believed in the immortality of the soul, we assuredly believed that all of Christianity was set up for the final deception of the devil when he would lead them astray. Only the remnant would make it through that time. Who the remnant was, we were certain.

The state of the dead and the Sabbath were both so important. The Sabbath was so clearly spelled out in the ten commandments. How could anyone not see it? The Sabbath was the mark of God's people. Sabbath-keeping would also be the mark that would allow the antichrist to find and persecute the faithful. Yes, it was all so deadly serious. It truly would be war. The horrors of the inquisition, the holocaust, and *Foxes Book of Martyrs*, however, would be minuscule compared to how we the remnant would be tortured at the end of time. It was a large factor in why we Adventists preferred to live in the country. If we lived in the country, it would be so much easier to flee to the mountains in those end times. And Western Colorado was ideal for this. Seriously, this was a frequent bit in any conversation on Sabbath. It was so ingrained that you did not even need to explain it. Every Adventist knew we would have to flee to the mountains. We had these truths so integrated into our very beings that we needed to tell our neighbors and warn them. How could we do otherwise?

In 1981 Billy Graham was still in full swing. We all loved Billy, even if he was not an Adventist. That man could preach. And his love for Christ was evident. Because, of course, the fundamental doctrine of Christianity was Christ. On that, we all agreed.

We, as Adventists, knew, however, that in the end days, the true believers of Christ would come out of all the false churches, which we believed—not to put too fine of a point on it—was anyone other than a Seventh-Day Adventist.

This belief was why we had our own evangelists. My Uncle Dick, Richard Barron, had been an evangelist, and was fondly remembered by many of the older members in Rifle. They still grieved his untimely death in a small plane, and that after he had miraculously beaten cancer.

This belief was also why my father regularly scheduled evangelistic meetings at his churches. And my father had an excellent reputation in the conference. He knew how run a campaign. He knew that if you were going to have any success, measured in baptisms, it was imperative that you got out and visited. And he did he got out and visited. He was not lazy like some pastors. I'm not going to mention any names, but my mother heard all the gossip.

Thus, on Friday night, I was at the meeting, and I was delighted that five of my students would be baptized the following day.

After the meeting, Tina invited me to come up to their ranch, which of course, I could not turn down. Valerie had come home from school, and she had long blonde hair, dark black, pearl eyes, and a rolling walk.

David and Danny rode with me as we drove up the Rifle-Rulison Road, turned left at their dirt road, drove over the small bridge covering their year-round mountain stream, and parked in the gravel driveway. David told me on the drive that Valerie found all the boys at school boring and did not want to go with any of them to the Junior-Senior banquet. (Adventists highly disapproved of dance. They had banquets instead of proms.)

As I got out, Valerie was lingering outside. She was looking down on the valley and marveling at how beautiful it was tonight. She was happy to be home, just bubbling with joy and trying to persuade her family to take a walk with her in the fields. Tina was being practical. It was nine p.m. It was December and the fields were covered in snow.

"Besides which Mr. Brauer is in his dress shoes."

Valerie looked at me and sighed. "Okay, but tomorrow night then." And looking directly at me, commanded, "Bring your boots tomorrow, Marvin."

Inside, David was in form and regaled us for a couple of hours with engaging stories. I sat on the opposite couch with Danny. Valerie was between David and her mother. Mr. Mitchell listened for a little while and then excused himself. He was known for his early-to-bed habits. Understandable since, as a nurse anesthetist, he kept early hours. Valerie got up and kissed him and then returned to the arm of the couch. Tina would periodically add little tidbits to David's stories.

They kept us laughing, though my eyes kept straying towards beauty. I thought, repetitively, she was too young. She was in high school and was forbidden fruit. But every time I looked — and I could not keep my eyes from gravitating back to her — every time I looked; she was looking at me. I do not know if she was always looking, or if by some magnetism, it just happened that when one looked, the other was drawn as well. But whenever David said something amusing, awkward, embarrassing, or outrageous, we looked at each other. It was unsettling and dulcet.

The curtain, usually drawn across the baptismal tank, was open the following morning. The clear water showed through the thick glass panel. All could see the tank sitting elevated and behind the pulpit. And I am not ashamed to say; it was all I could do to keep from sobbing as Danny, Heather, Bobo, and Chad came down from their respective sides — boys on the right, girls on the left — one by one in their black baptismal robes. They stood there in the water as the minister raised his right arm to heaven and pronounced, "In the name of the Father, the Son, and the Holy Ghost." He then submerged them fully into the water as we all witnessed, acclaimed, and shouted amen and welcomed them into membership. It was incredibly moving that Chad and his father were both baptized. What could be better than a father and son baptized on the same day?

After church, as they stood in a line, I stood back and beamed as I watched them shake hands or get hugs from the church members. These were my children. Education was important, but this was the real reason we had a church school, to bring them to Christ. I joined the line, and when I reached them, I stuck out my hand rather than hug them. It was my way of acknowledging them as having grown up.

There can be a very special relationship between student and teacher. It was like no other. You were not the parent, although you are responsible. It was not one of friendship, although, for a valuable pupil-mentor bond, you were, of course, a friend. What I did not realize at the time was that that bond was permanent. The color of the seal may fade on the bond, but if it was well made, the seal would never break.

I drove home and was in quite a mood of reverie; as I looked out my car window, I noted how pure white snow covered everything and how beautiful the skies were with the wispy clouds as they slipped over the crest. At times, the sun's reflection off the snow was so brilliant I had to look away, which made me think how this was like the love of God when reflected off of purity. It was so intense.

In this mood, as I drove into my driveway and heard my little yellow cat pitifully meowing, I looked around and saw him in one of the large white poplar trees at the front. He was too scared to come down. So, I went inside, put on my tennis shoes, and climbed up to retrieve him.

I poured my love from the morning onto him as I put water on the stove and picked out a boxed rice dish.

That night, consumed by the seventeen-year-old daughter of the Mitchell's, I drove up to their house around sunset. Mitch led in sundown worship and had a prayer of thanksgiving for Danny again. And then, while Tina worked on supper, Valerie asked if I could help her with algebra. I was willing and sat down beside her. She opened the textbook, and we looked at the problem. It took me a couple of minutes to see what concept they were teaching. She was not shy, and we looked at the book tete-a-tete. I had a well-developed ability to concentrate, but this tested that skill. Her hands were moving my hands to turn the page, and it was not always strictly necessary, which is to say I thought some of the page-turning was for reasons other than algebra.

After supper, they cleared the table for a game of Stocks and Bonds, another 3M game I had often played as a child. Everyone was having a good time, though I wanted to protest that it was somewhat unfair. It was difficult to concentrate on my stock picking when every time I looked across the table, she was looking at me with her big, dark, absorbing eyes. There was a Police song that was popular that year that just kept playing on a loop in my mind all night long, *Everything Little Thing She Does is Magic*. And I mean everything.

As the evening progressed into night, Mr. Mitchell made his usual apologies and went off to bed. It looked for a little while like everybody else was going to follow suit. Valerie protested. They had promised her we would take a walk tonight. Tina was tired, but she did not want to disappoint her daughter. David begged off. Tina, Valerie, Danny, and I bundled up. As commanded, I had brought my boots.

We went through the upper gate and walked towards the upper field. The half-moon cast shadows from the pinon pines to the west, but the land covered in snow was quite adequate to light our trail. I made it a point to walk with Danny. Valerie and her mother walked in front arm in arm. Danny told me about how they sometimes had to go down to break up the ice on the stream. When it got really cold in the winter, the stream froze over, and the horses relied on it for their water. Thus, sometimes he and his dad would go down and bust up the ice on the creek. I listened but could not help but admire the feminine presence ahead of me. It caused an entirely different glow. And as he was talking, I unconsciously started humming *Every Little Thing*. Valerie, recognizing the song, looked over her shoulder at me and laughed. I had not meant to hum it out loud.

That night as I drove home, I opened the windows and sang the song. I particularly resonated with the end of the third verse, where he stammeringly attempts to propose and then hauntingly realizes he will always stay alone.

This was totally crazy. She was seventeen. Yes, clearly, she was attracted to me, that was obvious. Yes, clearly, I was attracted to her, like I had not been attracted to a girl in a long time, but how could this possibly have any good result. There was none that I could foresee. What I could imagine was the song's pathetic depressing conclusion. Would I always be alone?

CHAPTER FORTY-THREE

SHARING THE LAND

Teaching had never been my dream as a child, and it had not been my major in college, not until the second half of my junior year. As a child, I had thought a lot about being a doctor. That was a good Adventist career, and it seemed foreordained. I remember being in the doctor's office when I was in elementary school and seeing the doctor's name on the door. The suffix for a doctor was M.D. I mean, how perfect would that be. My middle name was Donald, so I could write my name as M. D. Brauer, M. D. Clearly, that was what the fates had planned for me.

Of course, I had also considered ministry as an avocation. My father was a minister, and I enjoyed public speaking. I was quick to volunteer for opportunities to be upfront and had won numerous public speaking contests in elementary school. Everyone said I had the gift, but by the time I got to college both Bob and Jim had already become ministers. That was enough for one family.

As I started college and for my first two years, I was a history major with a pre-law emphasis. The idea of law intrigued me. I visited law schools with the law club, attended political gatherings, got a chance to talk to David Stockman when he was campaigning for a congressional seat in Michigan and was the Union College campus coordinator for the John Anderson presidential campaign. My grades were excellent, and the law seemed like a temperamental fit.

The problem was that Adventists were not keen on the law as a profession. They would not outrightly say it was wrong, but they had a dim opinion of it. They doubted that a person could be a sincere Adventist and a good lawyer. I had heard those comments a lot.

The comments carried more sway with me, because I had gone through a spiritual rebellion my first couple of years in college. At one point I even called myself an atheist. I did, however, find my way back to Christ and rededicated my life. (That's quite another story!) And when I came back, I gave up my dreams of the law. Instead, I turned to history. I would be a high school history teacher. That is until I discovered how much I loved interacting with elementary children.

But apparently my love for the law had not been completely eradicated, because on that first Monday in December I took the LSAT, the law school entrance exam. I was naïve about how people approached the LSAT. I did not realize most students set apart two to three months to study and prepare. I took Sunday afternoon off the day before the test to run over the sample questions included with the entrance fee.

I had arranged to have a substitute teacher for my classroom, and I drove up to Aspen on Monday. They gave me a religious exemption to have the test on a Monday rather than Saturday. The exam took place in a small room next to the physics lecture. The proctor was young, probably a graduate student, and I was the only one taking the test that day. As I went through the different test sections, I remember telling the proctor that I dreaded the math section and maybe I would not have it. The materials had said that each test was different, and some sections might not be included. The proctor thought the chances of not getting a math section were minimal. There were four sections; it was a three-and-a-half-hour test. When I picked up the last section and opened it, it was not math. I smiled at the proctor, and he gave me a thumbs up.

Afterwards, I drove home and got back to Rulison in the middle of the afternoon. That was amazing to be home in the middle of the afternoon with time on my hands. I put on my running shoes and ran down to the river and back, about three miles. I stopped on the bridge and watched the river for several minutes.

I looked around. There were many excellent fields for cultivating nearby: flat, reddish, silty loess soil. And I thought this was what I wanted. I did not need a fancy car or a large bank account. Sure, travel was nice on occasion. But what I wanted was a house and land. Preferably the land would have been in the Rifle-Rulison area. I wanted soil that I could run through my fingers and in which I could plant fruit trees, maybe have a small apple orchard and animals; enough land to have a small ranch, probably goats, maybe sheep, possibly cattle; and a dog that would walk at my feet when I put on my boots and when I went out to check on the livestock. That's what I wanted and, of course, a woman, a companion.

It was becoming more and more evident that I could not reach those goals as a teacher. And that was troubling. I loved my children, being a part of their lives. I knew that no one had more influence, nor could be as close to a child at this formative age than a teacher. Parents could not spend the hour-after-hour with a child, like a teacher. Nobody could. I was coming to a decision tree. How would my life play out? What was the trajectory, the script?

I ran back home, took a washcloth, and wiped myself down. It would have been nice to jump in a shower, but I did not have a shower, only a tub, and a bath would take too long.

It was about three-thirty as I walked into the schoolyard. Mike espied me first and shouted out, "Mr. Brauer is back!" After that, everyone came running out of the school. Angie was the first to reach me, and she leapt into my arms. I laughed, hugged her, and then let her down as the others grabbed me.

213

"How was the test?" They called out.

I shook my head from side to side. "It was long."

"You nailed it," Ron said with confidence.

"Yeah, probably." And everyone laughed.

Then they had to tell me what a disaster the substitute teacher had been. I listened, but I sympathized with the substitute. I knew that being a substitute teacher for just one day was an impossible task.

I worked for a couple of hours at my desk getting things ready for tomorrow, and then drove over to the church. It was the church business meeting, and the number one discussion point would be whether the church would support hiring a second teacher. I fully intended to remain quiet, but I knew I had to be in the room. It would be much harder for them to vote down the proposal if I was present.

The meeting went as most church business meetings went: laborious, longwinded, and distracted. Ron McElvain presented the statement from the conference. Mr. Rice had laid it out. The conference insisted the church either hire a second teacher or decide which grades they would not be teaching in the second semester, which is to say which students they would be disenrolling. If they chose against adding a second teacher, the conference recommended a reduction to no more than twelve students. Dr. McElvain noted that this could be carried out by eliminating grades five through eight: Danny Mitchell, Steven Boggs, Shon Holderbaum, Carolyn Schlisner, Doug Sisk, Kelli Holderbaum, Ron Borden, and Mike Sisk. Or, if that did not suit, they could drop the first grades. That would disenroll Justin, Misty Forshee, Katie Leatherman, Doyle Opitz, Kimberley McElvain, Bobo Leatherman, Chad Schlisner, Angie Hess, Heather Savage, Roy Leatherman, Heather Boggs, Cory Grant, and Chrissie Hess.

I thought Dr. McElvain's systematic presentation outlining their options and personally naming the students that would be disenrolled, which he read so-matter-of-factly, so unemotionally, was inspired and duly horrified the audience.

214

"So, we have to decide, people," Ron was closing up his presentation. "We have to decide. If we are not going to hire a second teacher, we would also like some guidance on which grades and which students we should cut. Do we cut grades five through eight? Or do we knock off grades one through three?"

Bill Holderbaum was not the first to be called on by the pastor, but he just stood up anyway. "I don't understand why we're even debating this. There is nothing more important than our children. This should be a slam dunk. Pastor, I move to hire a second teacher."

"Go Bill," I thought. There was a reason I liked him.

Elder Kungel—in the Adventist culture, a pastor is often referred to as elder—nodded and pointed to the church finance chair. Mr. Swissman stood up.

"Thank you, Ron, for your presentation. It was succinct and to the point." Mr. Swissman was a long-time member. His family had lived in the area for three generations. They owned land east of Rifle. "Bill, no one here is going to disagree with you. Our church school is essential to us. It has been here for over half a century. Bill, my family, has been here all of that time. And we have always supported it. We will always support it. But before we vote, we need to be sure that we are looking at the whole picture. The church already subsidizes the school. A great deal in fact." And he looked back up at the pastor.

"Can we have them pass out the finance report at this time?"

The pastor motioned for a couple of the deacons to pass out the finance report. They brought up the stack and went down the outside rows, handing a batch at the outside of each row. There was a rattling of papers as everybody took one and passed the stack onto the inside.

I was curious and quickly scanned the columns.

"Okay, as you can see, the church is already subsidizing the school considerably. We voted last spring as a policy that we would not deny any child from this church even if the parents were unable to pay." He paused to let that sink in. "All I am saying is that if we add a second teacher, this does not add any new students. There are not more tuition monies added to the pot. Any added expense of a second teacher comes completely, solely from subsidies. The conference will increase their subsidy somewhat. But let's be clear, this will put a strain on the budget." He again stopped to look around. "As I said, my family has always supported the school. I graduated from that school but getting bigger is not always better. So, I want you to consider that maybe the best way to have the school another half-century is to keep the costs sustainable."

Pastor Kungel thanked him and then discussed all of the other issues confronting the church. First, he brought up the evangelical series just concluded. Next, he brought up the electrical bills noting how the church had very little in its current emergency reserve, a position the conference was worried about. Finally, he noted how the school census had rapidly expanded this year. It was the largest in the school's history, almost twice the student population of any other year.

Mrs. Forshee stood up. Pastor Kungel acknowledged her.

"Misty is having a good first year. I don't want her to have to go to another school. I want her to stay there. So, I second the motion."

"Well, of course, your daughter will be staying there." Pastor Kungel assured her.

"Will she? Will she?" Mrs. Forshee said and then sat down.

There was some murmuring at that.

Pastor Kungel was unsettled. He gave a quick look in my direction, and I could tell he was vexed with me. First, he was annoyed that I was present. He was also irked that my school was consuming so much of the church budget, and that I had complained to the conference office. Who was I to cause such affliction?

I had met his type before. They resented me because I seemed to swim so easily in the current. They disliked me because my family had connections in the church, but I was a preacher's kid, of course we had connections. Also, my naturally buoyant nature peeved them, and that I was not easily cowed. But I think the aspect that bothered them the most was that people naturally liked me. That really rankled them. But then again, I genuinely liked most everyone.

There are a lot of ways to judge someone: beauty, intelligence, money, power. But to me, the highest compliment you could give someone was whether or not they were a good man, or a good woman. Yes, that is subjective, but there are always people in your life who, when the chips were down, had your back. You knew in your gut they were decent folk. That had always been my core assessment. At Rifle, I was impressed at how many people were good folk. But, unfortunately, I knew if I ever got into trouble, the pastor would not be there defending me.

The discussion continued on a number of sideline issues. People wanted to have their say but did not know how to keep it on topic. They often repeated the point of another with just a small variation. We were not progressing. If you have ever sat in a church board meeting, you know what I mean. This was the debate by erosion method. Wear them down. If you say nothing long enough, they will finally adopt your point, if only to shut you up. Obviously, it works. Look at the Grand Canyon. It might take several million years, or at least it seems that long.

Dr. McElvain Sr., Ron's father, and the head elder, was a very patient, deliberate man, but as the meeting wore on, he finally stood up. "Pastor, there is a motion on the floor and a second. I think it is time we voted."

Pastor Kungel took in a deliberate breath. He looked around and knew he had lost. He wanted a church school; every pastor wanted a church school. It looked good to have a school. But he did not want one this big.

"Well, how are we going to pay for this, Dr. McElvain?" He gave a last-ditch shot.

"The finance committee will look at that. But, tonight, the issue is whether we decide on a second teacher or cut some students. That's our issue tonight, and I know this church has always come through for our children. So, let's vote."

217

"Okay," Pastor Kungel acquiesced. "All in favor of adding a second teacher to the school, raise your right hands." And again, he looked at me; it was unintentional, he had not meant to glare at me, but it was all my fault.

A large number of hands shot up immediately, all the parents, grandparents, and a large proportion of the rest of the members. Then, upon seeing so many hands going up, the rest of the congregation went ahead and raised theirs as well.

"Well, it looks unanimous. We know that the most important thing we can do is bring up our children in the Lord. I have made this a central point of my ministry." The pastor was quick to take credit.

CHAPTER FORTY-FOUR

HEATING UP

The atmosphere in the classroom was mixed as always. Roy was complaining that I spent too much time with the first graders. It was a valid point. However, I did spend a lot of time with them—the first graders needed to have a solid start to their education.

"I'm sorry, Roy," I said as the first graders were going into the next room. I stopped at the door and added, "You're right. You're completely right. I wish I could spend more time working with you. But hang in there. The board has voted to get me help. They are going to try to find a second teacher."

Roy huffed.

Carolyn had been in an irritable mood as well and sniped, "Well, I hope I get the new teacher."

"I'm sorry you feel that way, Carolyn," I said. "I like being your teacher."

And she huffed as well. But her comment stung.

I went into the next room and started the children with their reading. They were doing well, and Kim was doing exceedingly well. When it became her turn to read, she read it flawlessly. I did not have to prompt her or correct her even once. When she finished, she just looked up at me and smiled.

"Very good, Kim, very good."

At lunch, we went outside. I sat on the steps to eat. Angie, Katie, and Justin gathered around me. It was cold, but the sun's warmth shining on our faces was encouraging. I heard the call of a red tail hawk and looked up into the sky to find it. I saw it drifting in the skies across the road and pointed it out to the group. Wayne saw us looking up and came over. I pointed the hawk out to him, and he was delighted to be part of the group.

After lunch, I read them to them from *Johnny Tremaine*, and then it was time for the first two grades to leave. As Kim was leaving, I gave her an envelope. I told her to give it to her mother.

It was a preprinted motivational card that said, Today _____ had been as wise as Solomon because _____. So, I filled in the spaces and wrote a little message complimenting Kim, "Today Kim read her whole reading assignment without any corrections or prompts."

She was hesitant as she took the envelope. What could be in a sealed envelope she had to give her mother? Was she in trouble?

I patted her head and reassured her, "It's good, Kim. You did well."

And the smile on her face, how do you put a value on that?

Tina left each day at one-fifteen with the first and second graders. Then, almost always, she came back at three-thirty to pick up Danny. On most occasions, she would come in and check on me. In her mind I was family.

On Wednesday afternoon, when she came in, she had to prod Danny to get his stuff packed. He and Shon were playing paper football on the craft table in the next room. It was the latest fad. All the boys were playing it whenever they could. Tina stood in the door between the rooms trying to be patient and get him going. He kept delaying. "Just a minute, Mom." And he would flash his most disarming smile. Now that school was over, this was a fun time, and he was in no hurry. Danny was gifted at being able to enjoy each moment of life.

Tina sighed and sat down at her desk. She figured since she had a couple of minutes, she might as well do something.

I had been thinking a lot about their daughter, how pretty she was, how clear it was she liked me, how clear it was that I liked her, and how young she was.

"Sometime, when you have a few minutes, I'd like to talk to you," I said to Tina.

She looked up from her desk gave a quick glance at the next room. "It seems I have time now. What's up?"

I blew out a puff of air and came out with it. "Well, I don't know if you have noticed. Well, of course, you have noticed, who am I kidding, but, well, Valerie."

She was smiling at me.

I laughed, "Okay maybe it was not such a hard thing to pick up on, but I find I have feelings for her. I am fond of her."

She shook her head and chuckled.

I continued. I was really in a sweat about this. "Well, I was wondering, you know, considering Valerie's age and all; what would you think; and your husband, what would he think; what would you both think if we were to date."

She paused to reflect. "She is young." And she looked me in the eye, and it was a serious gaze, but not an intimidating one. "For myself, I would be okay with it, but...you will need to talk to Mitch. Valerie is the apple of his eye, but I do know he does like and respect you."

I probably had some ridiculously excessive smile on my face when I heard that.

"I do know," she continued, "and I would not be betraying her confidence to say that she 'super likes you.'"

At that, I'm sure my face just exploded, unable to smile broader. "She is just so kind and pretty," I exclaimed.

Tina nodded and added, "Well, for some reason, and I don't know why she does tend to like older guys. The last guy she dated was twenty-five."

That made me feel a little better. It also made me more confident that Mr. Mitchell would also give permission. In my earlier dating experience, I had never asked permission from the parents, but this was different. She was seventeen, and I was twenty-three. Yes, I knew the Beatles had a great 'just seventeen' song—love that song—but I wanted to be entirely above board. I was the sole teacher in a small one-room school. I did not want to start a rumor mill. Or rather when the rumor mill did start—of course, if I dated a seventeen-year-old, there would be talk—when it started, I wanted to have done everything with decorum, above board, with propriety. Asking permission from the parents was the right thing.

After all, it was not like I dated much younger girls at college. I contemplated dating Valerie because there were no other girls my age here. Which was true, but who was I kidding? I was quickly becoming highly infatuated with her mellifluous voice, her bewitching nose, her soft full lips, the way she moved, the fact that she liked to be outside, hike, and ride horses, and that in all of our encounters, we ended up talking about God. And it was intoxicating how she was always looking at me. Those dark eyes were pulling me into the void. Struggle as I might, I would never be able to escape. Their gravitational pull was overwhelming. Resistance was futile.

The following day was all abuzz. The scuttlebutt was that Tina Mitchell, and Bonnie Holderbaum had gotten into a row. The details were not clear. I heard that Bonnie had called Tina and had started to complain about how Tina mistreated Shon and Kelli, particularly Shon. It had gotten ugly with shouting and unchristian language, words, and epithets that I eschewed. Both women were strong, smart, and had terrier instincts. Once the fight began, neither woman backed down. Bonnie told Tina she was not to discipline her children in the classroom; she did not want Tina even to talk to Shon. Tina said that was impossible. Her job required her to help with all the students, including discipline. And quite frankly, Tina told Bonnie that Shon could be stubborn and had a bad attitude. Maybe if Bonnie quit leaving home and running off back to Chicago, quit fighting with her husband, her children would do better.

Yeah, that went over well.

Bonnie made some comments about Tina's weight and how she should take care of her figure. It was descending fast. Bonnie could play this card because she did have an attractive figure.

Tina talked to me a little about it before the start of school. Of course, it would be impossible for Tina to be forbidden to speak or discipline any students. That was obvious. I supported her on that. Overall, however, I tried to stay out of the fight. I had to get along with both sets of parents. Kelli and Shon as well as Danny were my students. I loved them all.

It was important to keep the classroom out of the discord. The only ones who knew about it on the first day were Kelli, Shon, and Danny. I tried to give them extra attention during the day. I could see they were upset. They were wondering how this fight between their parents would influence their friendship.

For Danny, who genuinely liked all of humanity, who thrived in a network of friends, and tried to be inclusive whenever he could, the issue was whether this fight would subtract two of his good friends. And that was seriously disturbing.

I also sensed that Kelli and Shon were watching me extra close. They were trying to discern whose side I was on. Tina was my aide. All the children liked Tina. Did their mother's attack on Tina make them, Kelli and Shon, outcasts in the school? They presumed I would side with Tina. Or would I? What would be the consequences of their mother cursing out the warm and endearing, motherly Tina? Shon, in these circumstances, was much more prone to retreat into his little shell, say little, not do his work, avoid talking, except maybe to the other boys. Bonnie's fight was particularly destructive to Shon. For Kelli, however, being a recluse was not in her arsenal. She was an extrovert, by nature a very open person. If the battle came to her, she would stand with her family, and it would be a spectacular battle, but did she have to fight? She watched me. I understood her. She was outgoing, optimistic, clever, loved to laugh, and innately liked people. In many ways, our temperaments were similar, of all the children in the school, probably the most closely aligned. I tried not to be too plain but to make sure to give each of them eye contact during the day, just letting them know I knew they were having a hard day.

By the time of the home and school meeting, the news had spread; all the parents had heard. They did not talk to me directly about it, but it was clear the majority were on Tina's side. Tina was involved with the church, with pathfinders, she made wonderful dishes for the potluck, and she had been the only one to volunteer as a full-time aide at the school. Tina had stepped up. On the other hand, Bonnie was attractive, and you cannot discount the value of looks. Plus, in personal interaction, Bonnie could be charming.

They were all there for the home and school meeting that night, and the fight was discussed in soft tones before and after the meeting. This meeting, however, was not about the fight. It was a slide show given by Dr. Sisk. He had a carousel full of pictures of his wondrous ascent of Mt. McKinley (Mt. Denali). His climb with a team of mountaineers up the snow-covered peak, twenty thousand three hundred and twenty-two feet. And I just sat there in awe as the projector flipped between the lantern slides.

First, the screen went black, and then the following photograph projected onto the screen: pictures of his frosted snow beard; the bright colored tents red, blue, yellow staked into the snow on the side of the mountain; the team of climbers stretched in a line, roped together, up the slope, ice pick in hand, crampons on the boots; the impossibly blue sky on one day looking down, so far down to the valley; and then on the next picture close clouds and snow; pictures of him eating his quick prepared meals at nineteen-thousand feet; and the exultant images of him at the top.

And all through the pictures, he was giving commentary. He was downplaying it while at the same time emphasizing how arduous it had been, how much harder it was than he had imagined. The slides kept dropping while he spoke. And I was awe-struck. This was beyond my scope of what I would have considered. I liked to climb mountains, during the day, in the summer. But a multi-day winter ascent of a twenty-thousand-foot mountain was beyond my comprehension.

I just sat there, halfway back in the church's fellowship hall, sitting on my padded chair, of course with a whole row of students sitting beside me, Misty, Bobo, Kim, Carolyn, on my right, and tonight Kelli on my left.

After the meeting, everyone was standing around talking. Dr. Sisk was basking in the adulation. He kept repeating how it was more challenging than he had expected and doubted he would ever do anything like it again. This was for younger people.

Ron McElvain pulled me aside. He wanted to discuss the quarrel. He tried to get my take on it. I said Tina needed to be able to discipline all the students, but other than that, I was trying to stay out of it. If push came to shove, I believed Tina, but I really, really needed to stay out of it. He agreed and was pleased. He said this was not new. There had been bad blood between the Holderbaums and the Mitchell's for some time, though never this bad.

I noticed Bill Holderbaum at the door talking to a couple of the members. Kelli was standing beside him; she looked at me and smiled. When Ron and I finished our conversation, I grabbed my coat and paused to look around before leaving. When I turned around, Kelli was in front of me.

She was very grave. "I'm glad you are my teacher, Mr. Brauer." She was unusually reserved and dropped her eyes, "I just want you to know that I love you."

"O Kelli, you are so sweet." I hugged her. "I love you too, Kelli."

How could I ever consider leaving these children?

CHAPTER FORTY-FIVE

O CHRISTMAS TREE

On Friday morning, Tina informed me that Pastor Kungel had had a heart attack overnight and was admitted to the Rifle hospital. So, after the math drills, we got out the craft materials, and the children made him get-well cards.

After lunch, I looked at the assignment book. Ron, Mike, Doug, and Cory were the only ones fully caught up with their work. I called out their names and told them to put on their boots, gloves, and jackets and meet me in my car. I left Tina with the rest of the classroom, and the four of us drove up to the Mitchell's ranch. Mr. Mitchell had said we could cut down a small pinon pine for the school's Christmas tree. I felt a little bad leaving Tina with the complaining children. It did feel a lot like playing hooky, and it was delightful.

Up at the ranch, we piled out. Mike grabbed the axe from the shed. And we trod through the snow-covered fields. The sky was a sheet of monotonous gray; our mood was not. We joked and palled around. Cory, in particular, was embracing the moment. He was, after all, the only fourth grader with the older boys. We climbed the small Indian Hill on the eastern part of their land, which had a lot of pines. These were not specimen trees like spruce or scotch pine that you might buy in the city, but this was natural, going to the land to find our trophy. We cut it down and dragged it back to my Corolla. We laid down the back seats, and the boys climbed in around it.

The longer I lived in Rifle-Rulison, the more bonded to the ground I became. These excursions outside were embracing. I was being infiltrated, every pore of my body, all of my DNA becoming integrated with nature, and my boys were in complete agreement. It took energy, but it returned to life. Finally, we returned to the school and placed it in the front of the classroom. Mrs. Mitchell had had the children make decorations, and we sang some Christmas carols.

As I was driving home the following day, which was Sabbath, driving beside the snow covered Book Cliffs on my right; here up close to their stitched shoulders butting out from the so impressively steep cliffs; and on my left the snow and ice encrusted banks of the river; the cottonwood trees now barren and gray in their late fall forms; as I was driving home having spent the morning at church; and then lunch and the afternoon at the home of Mr. and Mrs. Opitz with their two boys, Doyle and Dustin; and the McElvains also there: Ron, Connie, Kim, and Jon; as I was driving home I was thinking, so many thoughts were lingering in my mind; pausing to be savored and then set aside maybe to have a second helping in a minute or two; like the wonderful spread of food that Vivian and Connie had combined to make for the table: eggplant parmesan, asparagus covered by cooked pear, beet greens, Italian bread toasted with butter and garlic, a fancy jello dish, veggie fried chicken nuggets battered and fried, and to finish an extra moist three layered chocolate cake with a dollop of vanilla ice cream; yes that was one of the thoughts that took its space, took its time to be at least mentally regurgitated and savored afresh; that and the delightful story Ron and Connie had contributed at the dinner table of their wedding day, a veritable comedy of errors — my admiration for them just continued to grow all year long — they were really funny; and I laughed out loud again as I remembered it; and as I was driving

227

home it was with such happiness how I had been welcomed into their homes. Doyle was bouncing so much more gregarious than I ever saw him at school. He insisted that he sit on my right hand while Kim claimed my left. The Opitzes had been so warm, accepting, gracious. No wonder Doyle was so comfortable in his skin and universally liked by all the grade levels.

Another prime thought that kept circling back as I had my right hand on the wheel; a choice memory — like that remarkable cake — O wow — was my utter satisfaction at being an integral part of the church, an essential cog of this community. Vivian had taken the get-well cards to Pastor Kungel, and he had been visibly moved when she had kept bringing card after card out of her bag. She said he had laid there, propped up on a couple of pillows, handling the cards so carefully, not wanting to put them down. She had talked to him for a little while, and he just kept fingering the cards, reading the children's names. I took satisfaction at what my children had done. And when I got home, I put Bach's Brandenburg Concerto on my turntable, and sat down with my cat and a pen and my journal and wrote, and I wrote the key to happiness was to be at peace with God and to be in love. I loved my children, and maybe something else was beginning.

CHAPTER FORTY-SIX

STAND WITH ME

Continuing the accelerated pace of trying to get help, the school board reconvened on Sunday evening. As usual, I had worked all day at the school, went home for supper, and then returned alongside the lonesome road board meeting in the dark. Ron announced that the conference had a teacher they recommended, Virginia Ryber. She was graduating in December, that is this month, from La Sierra College in Southern California. Mr. Rice had interviewed her and was very impressed. He thought she would fit in well. Her academic transcript was impressive. Her grades were as good as mine. (Quite a feat if I may humbly say so.)

Ron reported this to the committee. At first, the members were relieved, and then excited, and then began developing trepidations. Did we want another brand-new teacher? Wouldn't it be better to have a more mature teacher who had some years at the craft? No offense, but Mr. Brauer was also very young. Wouldn't that be better? Again, no offense, Mr. Brauer, you have done wonderfully.

Ron reiterated we were lucky to have any options at all, remember we had tried at the beginning of the year to find help and had drawn blanks. However, he tried to keep equipoise, and I was amazed at how well he carried it off.

Mr. Mitchell stepped in. "Ron, if I could just say something here."

Ron acknowledged him. "Mitch, what's on your mind."

"I would like to pause for just a moment. Yes, we must decide on do we hire this new teacher. I understand that. But there have been some comments that I know were not meant as offensive to Marvin, but still, you know it sounded to me that they were just a bit of a dig at Marvin's work thus far. And I just want to say Tina and I have been discussing this a lot. We have seen a fair number of teachers come and go here at this school. But, for my money, Marvin is an A+ teacher. A+. Marvin has a rare ability to see each child as an individual with unique needs and problems, and talents." Mr. Mitchell looked around at the board members. "You don't have to be a parent to have seen it. We see it every week at church. I mean, these kids are with him all week, yet they rush to him at church as if they hadn't seen him in forever. When have you ever seen that?"

He stopped and looked at the committee. They were nodding. Then he looked at me.

"I'm sorry. I didn't mean to embarrass you."

"No, no, don't stop on my account. I like it." I quipped. Mr. Mitchell burst out laughing, as did the rest of the committee.

Mr. Mitchell then turned a hand to me as if I was exhibit A. "I rest my case."

"Thank you, Mitch," Ron acknowledged. "Many of you know I went to this school my last couple years of elementary school."

The older members nodded. They remembered little Ronny.

"Mr. Brauer has done a good job. I think we are all agreed on that."

And then, he summarized the situation. We had twenty students in eight grades. We would be getting another student at the beginning of the year, twenty-one students. The conference made it clear this was unacceptable, actually against the law. Mr. Brauer had been, to his credit, able to make this work very well, but we must rectify this. The board had voted to find a second teacher. The church at the business meeting had voted unanimously to support two teachers. Now, the conference had found a teacher who could start, not in January, which would have been nice, but February 1. Yes, she was also young, unmarried, just out of school, with no earlier experience, but she had excellent recommendations and an excellent transcript. And yes, ideally, it would be better to have someone with experience, but that was not one of our options. The only decision for tonight's meeting was do we accept the only choice we have.

There were questions then about her character and personality, would it be a fit for Mr. Brauer, who of course had done such an excellent job, but you know not every two people would be able to work well together.

Even Ron's enormous equanimity was beginning to fray.

"We have no idea on her personality other than the recommendation from Mr. Rice. Do we hire or not?"

And that finally got the committee to agree to offer the position to Miss Ryber.

I would be getting help. If I could make it to February 1, I would have help. That was the beginning of hope.

The day broke bright and blue. The sun was brighter, the snow whiter, and the clouds softer. The mountains did not slouch but lifted their shoulders even higher. And I walked with long, firm, positive steps to school that morning. I shoveled the black coal pellets into the furnace and found the orange glow so rewarding, the rays of heat as it permeated the room satisfying.

Bambi made another appearance that morning. She had been absent for a couple of weeks, but this morning as I rose from my desk to follow the first graders into the adjoining room, she walked in, short black tail switching, and accepted with barely any acknowledgement the small hands stroking her back. She did, however, find interest in the green apple Mike pulled out of his lunch, quartered with his pocketknife, and offered on the palm of his hand.

Before Bambi, the children had started in good moods but were much more distracted now. I had a difficult time keeping them on task. I gave assignments to Chad and Wayne before exiting the room. When I returned, they had diddled away their minutes and had done little on their task. It was hard to improve their study skills when I was often distracted, but I kept trying.

By noon whimpering and complaining had once again gained the ascendancy. I remember standing at the front of the class as a chorus of whining washed back and forth across the classroom. It seemed to involve almost everyone. And I remember amid this plague of grumble and squawk, fuss and grouse; I remember looking at Steven sitting at his desk unaffected; his mop of black hair almost down to his eyes. It was like a separate air source fed only him; it made him impervious to the miasma. His air was pure and undefiled. He was a pleasure to have in the classroom.

Notwithstanding the bickering, I was happy. Relief was on the way. As I sat at my desk at lunch, I was reevaluating everything. With help coming, I could make it, and maybe I would not have to leave. Perhaps I could stay at Rifle teaching for another three to four years. After that I could work on my master's in education in the summers. The conference would help with that. Then I could work up. I could become a principal, maybe eventually the principal at Campion Academy. This way, I would not have to leave my students so soon. But naturally, I would have to figure out how to keep the parents from murdering each other.

At the end of the day, while the Hesses cleaned the school, I went into the bathroom and donned my running gear. Then, I ran up the hill. As I got near the top, I decided to jog in and see the Holderbaums. I wanted to talk to Bonnie. I wanted to try and deescalate the fight as much as possible, or at least to make sure she knew I was trying to stay neutral; I was trying to hold the centerline.

Bonnie was home and was affected that I had stopped by to visit. She was aware the whole church community was gossiping about the fight, and she was thankful I had not written her off. She admitted, however, she was bitter that I was so friendly with the Mitchells. I spent too much time with them. The conversation, which I had expected to take five to ten minutes, stretched on. Bill came home from his practice. The topic of discussion had moved on from the fight and had wandered to the children. How were they doing? In particular, how could we keep Shon motivated? The conversation then migrated to me. How was I doing? Did I like teaching?

Kelli and Shon came and grabbed me. They took me out to the corral to look at their horses. Shon scrambled up to the loft in the barn and threw down a bale of hay. Kelli divided it and began stuffing it into the feeder. She left a couple of flakes on the ground. When she did, Bambi came bounding into the corral and began eating alongside the horses. Shon and Kelli were delighted, not so much that Bambi was eating the hay; she did that all the time, but that I was there to see it.

Bonnie came out and took in the scene. Then she persuaded me to stay for supper. I had not expected to stay this long, and I tried to decline. Well, I did not try very hard. The idea of sitting down with them being part of their family circle at supper was such a better prospect than eating alone. So as the darkness came on, we sat down. Bill bowed his head and put out his hands to either side of him. I took Shon's and Bonnie's, and we made a prayer circle around the table. It was such an agreeable, such a cordial evening. I had heard there were difficulties in the marriage. I did not see them. I just saw happiness and warmth.

Bonnie had said I was too chummy with the Mitchell's. It was true; I spent a lot of time with the Mitchells and the McElvains. But honestly, I would have spent more time with Bill and Bonnie as well. In many ways, I felt close to them. I would have gladly divided my time, hiked with them on Sabbath, sat in the evenings in their living room, played table games on a Saturday night. I had always had a great time with Bill and Bonnie. But the fact was the Mitchells and the McElvains invited me, and I went where I was invited. I was lonely.

CHAPTER FORTY-SEVEN

I WANT TO FALL

Predawn the following morning, as I looked out my bedroom window, big flakes filled the sky and slowly filtered down. My bath was hot. I shaved at the sink. I had grown mustaches and beards during college from time to time, but I was clean-shaven this year. I thought it was a better look. I could not see the mountains on my walk to school, and I was worried. In the afternoon, I was supposed to drive to Rifle. It was Thursday, and I ate with the McElvains on Thursday. Yes, of course, I could drive in the snow. I did it many times, but my car was light and had rear-wheel drive. Thus, it had little traction. I did not fancy driving that evening.

At morning recess, we improved our trails, and the snow was steadily becoming wetter. Snow tag was still the most popular activity. Everybody liked to run in the snow.

Mrs. Mitchell and I started talking shop during lunch. She was curious about the new teacher and had mixed feelings. Certainly, we would no longer need an aide with a second teacher. But, on the other hand, she would miss the time with the children.

"I have really enjoyed working with you, Mr. Brauer. I really have."

"Thank you; you have been amazing. You have made it possible. Truly."

She went on to list the difficulties working as an aide had caused. Mitch's work required long and irregular hours, so running the house and keeping it together fell on her. So, while she would miss the children, in truth, she was relieved.

As for the new teacher, I did not know much beyond what her husband would have already told her. True, Mr. Rice had talked to Ron McElvain and me over the phone, and she did have excellent grades, which made a very positive impression on me. Mr. Rice also had been impressed with her poise. He had called her a handsome woman. That prompted Tina to bring up her conversation from the night before.

"I talked to Valerie last night," she said and smiled at me. That got my attention. "She said for me to tell you 'Hi.'"

I smiled.

"She also said something that I can't tell you." Tina gave me a hinting smirk.

What was that? I had grown up with three brothers. I had no clue what girls talked about. I knew it was not inappropriate; that was certain, but what was it? And why would she mention it? Not that I was unappreciative, certainly not. I stored it for later ruminations.

"O, yes and one more thing, and she said I could tell you this." Tina paused for effect. "She said that you are not to fall in love with the new teacher."

Show stopper there. Do not fall in love with the new teacher? Was Valerie staking her claim? Could there be any other way of interpreting it? And why was Tina telling me this? Was this just banter? Was this just a teenage girl's flirtations? Yeah, probably. In any case, I stashed it away to dwell on later, maybe as I was falling asleep that night.

By midafternoon the snow had turned to sleet and then to rain. That was reassuring. I could drive in the rain.

Chad and Carolyn's mother, Sheila, stopped in the classroom at the end of the day. I had asked her to come by. I wanted to see what we could do to help her children get their work caught up before the semester closed. They were well-behaved children whom I liked immensely. They were smart, but their work habits left something to be desired.

As always, I was pleased to work with Sheila. She was not prone to histrionics nor to get distracted in off-topic discussions. She was naturally confident and rational. She understood her children and wanted what was best for them. She said she would work with them at home. She mentioned in passing again, as an explanation, that Carolyn was in counseling, which made it more difficult for Carolyn.

I had not pursued that at the parent-teacher conference. I thought that whatever it was should remain between Carolyn and her counselor. Frankly, at that time of my life, I had no idea why a child of Carolyn's age would need a counselor. I was pleased, however, that whatever it was, she was getting help. And I felt a deeper bond for my little blonde girl. When I was a child, my mother had arranged for me to see a speech therapist twice a week for a couple of years. So maybe it was something like that. I did not need to know what it was for Carolyn, but in my mind, it made her a more sympathetic figure.

And then I drove into town. My first stop was the City Market to buy some necessary groceries. The rain was now just a drizzle. As I was standing behind my grocery cart waiting to check out, I became quite aware of the young woman just in front of me in the line. It gratified me that she gave me several looks while the clerk rang up her items. She was quite attractive in her blue jeans and a winter jacket. I figured she was in her early twenties. And then, after I went through the line, as I carried my bags into the parking lot, I saw her getting into her car. I passed it on the way to mine. And our eyes met again. When I sat down in my seat and shut the door, I looked back at her car. She was still looking at me.

And I mention this five-minute attraction by way of an introduction. Why did I drive off? Why did I not get out and talk to her? Ask her name? Why was the idea of this dismissed out of hand? Which it was. I absolutely rejected it. I was an Adventist and a good Adventist married within the church. *Do not be unequally yoked.* This idea had been engrained in me since childhood. Innumerable times, I heard my mother talking about how someone had married outside the church and drawn astray. Furthermore, as the teacher in a parochial school, I had to live an even more exemplary life. Many of my children's parents had married a non-believing partner. (And by non-believing, we really meant anyone who was not an Adventist) They had, in many cases, brought their partner into the church. That was wonderful. That was marvelous. That was not an option for me. It did not even occur to me. If I started dating a non-member, the uproar would be thunderous. It would have been as bad as the pastor being found smoking or having an affair. Maybe worse. The teacher, after all, had these impressionable minds to mold. They could move the pastor.

Besides which, how was I to approach this lovely — and she was lovely — stranger? Do you want to go out for a drink? I was a teetotaler. Do you want to grab a coffee sometime? I did not drink coffee or any caffeine, for that matter. Do you want to see a movie? Mr. Rice had explicitly warned me that they would fire any teacher who went to the theatre. Do you want to go dancing? Dancing was verboten. Wow, that would have been quite the juicy scandal! I might as well just have hopped in the backseat with her. It would have had the same impact. How about asking her out for dinner? Well, first, I had zip in the way of money. Second, I was a vegetarian, and the restaurants in meat-craved Rifle did not even know the word. The only thing I could have said is, "I think you are really, really very attractive, and I would love to get to know you, but I have no idea how we are ever going to get together, and once we do get to know each other, we will find that our lives are so vastly different that we will just split, so maybe, yes undoubtedly it is best that I just look at you in the parking lot and drive away."

Yes, that is who I was. And it was sad.

CHAPTER FORTY-EIGHT

MR. BRAUER HAS AN ANNOUNCEMENT

We had our Christmas party up at the Mitchell's. We started the day in the classroom, and then several parents came to help transport the children. To begin the party, we played a massive game of capture the flag on the Mitchell's he ten-acre front pasture. The tactics were vastly different with this expanse. I could make long, deep loping runs into enemy territory. With acres of room to maneuver, I had little risk of being trapped. For the first graders, the vast no man's land allowed them to dally without fear. They were delighted to cross the line and then shout out they were across the line to the older students. That was so daring for them, quite the thrill. The tactics of capturing the flag and making it all the way back across the line were a little more complicated. As always, I tried not to throw the odds too much to my team. But as usual, at least once, I had to display my speed and agility, much to the glee of my team members.

Some of the children had not brought their snow boots, and their feet froze. When we came inside, they warmed their feet by the fire. Then we opened presents and ate a lot of sugary confectionaries, and the students were so comfortable in the Mitchell's house. Danny enjoyed being the gracious host. Tina played Kenny Roger's brand-new Christmas album, and the house with its large great room and the downstairs family room seemed to be made just for such gatherings. The mothers: Sheila, Phyllis, Sandy, and Connie, helped Tina keep things orderly. For the most part, I let them. I stood by the fire and watched my little angels having so much fun. If they were happy, then I was content.

Back at the school, we did a little straightening up.

"Okay, guys. Everybody at your seats. Quiet down. We are going to have prayer."

It took a little bit of time but slowly, they quieted down. I said a closing prayer. And then announced, "Before everyone goes, I have a couple of comments I want to make."

"Really, Mr. Brauer! This is our vacation. You are cutting into our vacation," Mike sniped.

"This is important, Mike. It really is important."

"Okay, quiet everybody! Mr. Brauer has a couple of important announcements." Mike shouted.

"First off, I want to wish you all a Merry Christmas. Have a good time."

"Really, that was your important message?"

I put up my hand and took the smile off my face. "No, no, no. This is important." I paused and looked at each student before resuming my announcement with gravitas. "I know…I know you are not going to be able to see me for a couple of weeks, but don't cry yourselves to sleep tonight, okay?"

There was a cacophony of laughter and protests. The younger ones said they would, of course, cry themselves to sleep. Doug and Shon were protesting how ridiculous that was. Mike was sitting in the back, shaking his head, and beaming. He thought that had been well-played.

"What are you guys still doing here? You're on vacation. Get outta here!" I said.

Phyllis Boggs had previously mentioned that they would be preparing and delivering food baskets that afternoon, and if I was free, now that school was out, she was looking for volunteers. I said yes, and after everyone had cleared out, I drove to the church. Phyllis, Mary Dix, Elaine Cloninger, and I were the adults. The children present were Steven, Heather, the two Cloninger boys, Jayme and Aaron, and because Heather and Kelli were such good friends, Heather had brought her.

We formed an assembly line. As the basket came down the table, I put in a couple of cans of vegetables and one of cranberry sauce. Then passed it down the line for a box of dried mashed potatoes, a bag of dried pinto beans, a bag of lentils, a bag of stuffing, a loaf of bread, a can of pumpkin, and a frozen pie shell. And at the end, Phyllis added in a frozen turkey. She gave us each four baskets. Steven, Jayme, Aaron would ride with me. I sat down on one of the chairs while the ladies were doing some final preparations.

Heather had been disappointed that she was not riding with me and came and sat on my knees. Kellie sat down beside me. Kelli asked me if I would be around for Christmas or was I going home. Heather turned to me and said, "I miss my Mr. Brauer." It had been less than three hours since school let out.

Mrs. Boggs looked over, shook her head laughed, and told Heather to quit bothering Mr. Brauer.

We got in the cars. Steven rode up front and directed me. He knew Rifle much better than I did. The Cloninger boys admired Steven and were delighted to be part of the boy's group. Jayme would have been in first-grade class if he had not been homeschooled. He was a skinny dark-haired lad. In my limited interactions with him during the year, I was quite impressed. He was cheerful, curious, properly respectful, eager to interact, well adjusted, and impressively bright. He was a nice boy. We delivered our baskets, and I went home.

It was Christmas vacation.

Book Two:
A Shade of Winter

CHAPTER FORTY-NINE

COME ON UP

I was standing in the church foyer the following day when Mr. Mitchell came over. He said Tina had instructed him to be sure he invited me up for lunch. She also warned him that he must be prompt about it and find me immediately after the sermon because I was prone to disappear like a rabbit in the bush. I laughed. It was true. I usually did not linger; nothing as awkward as standing alone in the foyer. I thanked him and assured him I would, of course, accept.

He extended his hand to shake mine, "Excellent, Marvin, excellent." He paused while still in the handshake, placing his left hand on top of mine. "You know Marvin, I know you'll be going back to Denver for part of the holidays, but...." And here, he patted my hand with his left hand to emphasize the point. "When you're here, drop by the ranch whenever you please; consider our home like yours."

While Mr. Mitchell may not have had the hospitality instinct of his wife, he had sincerity in spades.

At their house, initially, I sat down on the couch and picked up a copy of the Adventist Review. I read a short article. I liked to keep current on themes emerging within the church.

But when I finished it, I sensed all the energy in the house was emanating from the kitchen. I moved to a kitchen stool. Tina barely looked up from chopping onions and began quizzing me. What were my holiday plans? When was I going home? A couple of minutes later, she noted that Valerie had said she was pleased I was not running off for home during her telephone conversation. I smiled. Obviously, if Valerie already knew I was hanging around, then Tina already knew my plans. She said she would be driving over to pick up Valerie on Monday.

And then we talked about the new teacher. Miss Ryber was expected to arrive tomorrow. She was making a quick visit to survey the area to try and secure a living situation. The Mitchell's had invited her to stay with them while she was looking around. Of course, they did.

After lunch, when I saw everyone else seemed to be keen on 'lay activities' — a typical witticism among Adventists, meaning they planned on taking a Sabbath afternoon nap — I pulled on my snow boots and walked outside. I spent a couple of hours maundering over their one hundred and sixty acres. It was quiet and my first semester of teaching was done.

I crossed the pasture and climbed up the juniper hill, and then descended into the small dale on the far side. I liked this draw because from here I was sheltered. I could see no marks of civilization: no houses, no telephone wires, no fences, just sagebrush, pinon pines, bunchgrass, a clump of yucca, greasewood, small patches of scattered cactus, and junipers. Here, save for the occasional cry of the killdeer, or the caw of the crow, there was silence. Here the crust of the snow was, for the most part, unbroken and smooth. When I stopped to examine it, I saw the small indentions from squirrels and rabbits. Mule deer also frequented the Mitchell's ranch, and from this draw, when I visited it, it was unusual if I did not see one or two.

I sat down for a few minutes on a granite boulder and meditated — though I would not have used that term in those years. According to my understanding, meditation was just a euphemism for yoga and the Eastern heresies. Still, I did sit there for a few minutes, just letting the tranquility absorb and penetrate me.

When I came back over the hill, I saw that David and a friend were saddling Bushfire. As I have previously mentioned, Bushfire was their other Arabian and known to be a hard ride. I saw David's friend fly off the grey's back a moment later. I chuckled. I had been pulling for Bushfire to keep his reputation, especially as the young man did not appear to be hurt, except maybe his ego, and in my opinion, his ego needed deflation.

When I came back to the house, they talked about Bushfire.

"You like to ride, don't you, Marvin?" Mitch asked.

"I do."

"Well then, come on up tomorrow, why don't you. Astro needs to be ridden more often."

There was no need to ask me twice. The next day I found myself in the saddle on Astro's back. I was above their land in a field of bitterbrush, sage, and dried buckwheat.

I understood that I was deep amid my most incredible childhood daydream: on horseback in a western landscape. But even my fantasies had not considered such a fabulous mount. They had not imagined the frosty air and how the measure after measure of stillness was enhanced by the emergence of a rhythmic squawking, a skein of geese in V formation against the gray sky headed toward the river.

As I watched, one of the geese broke formation, turned around, and flew back in the direction whence it had come. One gander flew all alone as the others passed on. Why would he do that? Why would he leave the flight? The gaggle hoarsely honked at him. They continued on their path. The gander disappeared to the west.

I nudged Astro, and we explored further.

In the afternoon, I drove my car to the corner of the county road off the Rulison exit. Miss Ryber was arriving. She expected to be there around three-thirty or four. I told her to get off I-70 at the Rulison exit and come up the road. I would have my silver

Toyota parked at the intersection. I could show them the schoolhouse and then guide them up to the Mitchell's house. She thanked me. Thus, I sat there waiting. I had my windows down. It was chilly, but I liked the fresh air.

I had wondered for some time what she would be like. Clearly, she was young and smart, and on the phone, her conversation had been refined, her voice dulcet. Mr. Rice had called her handsome. What did that mean?

I heard the motor of a car before I saw it. A moment later, a blue Ford Granada sedan appeared in view. It slowed down at the intersection. I waved, and then I pulled out in front. It was but a few hundred yards from the intersection to the school driveway. I turned left and came to a stop. She and her father got out. She was a tall woman with clear skin and a pleasant smile. We shook hands, and I pointed to the school.

"Well, here it is." I fished in my pocket to get the key. "Let me show you around."

She sighed and asked if we could postpone the inspection of the school. The trip had been tiring, and she would just as soon go directly on up to the Mitchell's.

"One classroom is just like another, isn't it?"

"Sure. Absolutely." I shoved the key back into the pocket and headed back toward my car.

Wow, I thought to myself. She did not want to see the school. Interesting. It had been my first stop. I had been so curious, and I would have gone in even if I was tired, even if I did not want to see it. It would have been the polite thing to do. After all, I had gone out of my way to assist her. And it was not as if it was late. It was four p.m., not nine or ten. I would have gone in. I would have. On the other hand, I had a strong first impression that she would be fine. She would be a good teacher, and she would control her classroom. This was going to work.

As I got in my car and started driving up to the Mitchell's, my other impression was that I felt small. I was nearly six feet tall, but I was small-boned. I could easily wrap my thumb and long finger around my wrist. On a good day, fully dressed, I might weigh one hundred and fifty pounds. Virginia, however, was an ample and buxom woman.

At the Mitchell's, Danny was the first to the door. He was all grins at seeing Miss Ryber. Tina was hospitable as always. She welcomed Virginia and her father and then had Danny show them to their rooms. Tina came back to the kitchen. I had taken a seat at the dining room table. Tina watched Virginia descend the stairs and then looked back at me. She had a little smirk on her face. It was the smirk of a mother watching out for her daughter's interest. Tina and I knew each other well. I knew what her expression meant, and she was right.

"I think she'll do just fine," she said.

I nodded.

And then, because we knew what this conversation was about, Tina transitioned to remind me that she would be driving to the Eastern Slope to get her daughter tomorrow. I smiled. I already knew this; of course, she had told me on several occasions she would be getting Valerie on Monday. I also knew Tina would be reporting to her daughter about Virginia later this evening. Women could be, shall we say, brutally honest in their evaluations of other women? But, on the other hand, Tina was going to be able to like Miss Ryber much easier and without conflicted feelings.

I did not stay long. I still had work to do at the school. Virginia may not want to see the school, but that was where I lived. I turned on the lights and worked until nearly ten p.m., tallying up the ledgers and putting in final grades. I was disappointed that I had to give some D's, and it was always due to failure to turn in their work. Maybe next semester, I could enlighten them better with fewer students and fewer grades. The fault was mine.

There was a big snowstorm that lasted for the next couple of days. Up at the Mitchell's, it snowed a foot. He had a large tractor that he hooked up with a plow to keep his road clear of snow. He had to. He got called in for emergency surgeries at all hours. I went up to visit.

On account of the snow, Tina could not pick up Valerie on Monday. But it was also because Valerie had invited two Nicaraguans home for the holidays, and they could not leave until Wednesday.

Miss Ryber and I had the opportunity to discuss how we should split up the grades. Traditionally, it should have been grades one through four in one room and five through eight in the other. She was more comfortable with the lower grades. The difficulty was twofold. First, the fourth graders were much closer with the older grades. Also Roy was a big kid. Putting him in the with first graders would have been awkward. Secondly, there were four fourth graders. Thus, if we gave the fourth grade to the lower grades, Virginia would have twelve pupils, and I would have eight. That seemed unfair to a brand-new teacher. Yes, I had had twenty students in all eight grades, which had been manifestly unfair. I got that. Still, I wanted Virginia to have a better start than I had.

Virginia kept returning to that topic. She was astounded that I had put up with it. She would have never stayed. I listened, but I had never considered leaving, not once the school year had started.

Also, in deciding how we would split up the classes, I considered how much I would miss the children. I was already going to miss the first, second, and third graders. The thought of adding injury to my grief by giving up Roy, Cory, Heather, and Chrissie was more than I cared to bear. The upshot was a split. Virginia and I agreed that grades one to three would be in the adjacent classroom. I would stay in the main room with grades four through eight. We would also exchange classes for Bible. I would teach the lower grades Bible, and she would teach the upper grades. The plan satisfied both of us.

The more I had the opportunity to interact with Virginia, the better I felt. She was smart, grounded, and balanced. She was confident, not needy, nor whiny. I had no qualms with her, nor did I anticipate discipline problems emanating from her classroom. She was also crafty, and I was sure her bulletin boards would vastly surpass mine. Children needed crafts. I sorely lacked in that accomplishment. To my mind, she had the ideal temperament, skills, and qualifications for an elementary teacher. We would get along just fine.

While I did not see us becoming close friends, I thought we would work well as associates. Our personalities were different. She was of good humor, but jokes and joking were irrelevant to her. At best, she might smile at one of David's jokes. I could see someone thinking my jokes were dumb, but David was funny. Also, she found everything much more serious than I did. And her emotions were more muted. She was an Adagio for strings, and I needed some Beethoven fortissimo.

From the first glance, I knew Valerie had nothing to fear. I would not be falling in love with the new teacher. It was equally apparent that Virginia, even as she was getting out of her car when we first met, was judging me. And I was not her type. The feelings were mutual.

Mr. Rice from the conference had been planning to come out on Monday, but the snow stopped that. So, he called and rescheduled for Wednesday.

Virginia had come here for that meeting. She was also here, and really more importantly, here with her dad to find a place to live. They drove into Rifle on Tuesday and looked at the apartments in town. I had looked at apartments in Rifle the summer before. The available units were small and unattractive. Furthermore, they were twenty minutes away. She was discouraged with the options. I commiserated, but what could I do?

Tina, however, could do something. She talked to Mitch. They thought it was unfair for Miss Ryber to try and find a place for just five months. Maybe she should live with them. They had extra rooms. Virginia asked me what I thought about taking a proffered room. Should she accept? Would it cause problems? I told her the Mitchell's had offered me a room as well. I had declined it to keep some independence, but in her case, as this was the middle of the year, it would be reasonable for her to accept. She did. She accepted and was thankful.

I ate supper Tuesday night with the Mitchells and helped Tina clean up the kitchen afterward. She was in a talkative mood giving me her little cryptic messages about Valerie, how she had talked to Valerie and that Valerie had several messages for me, but Tina could not tell me, and then she would laugh. When the subject of Miss Ryber surfaced and of her staying with them, Tina said she had come to a major conclusion. I paused from drying the stainless-steel pot and gave her full attention.

"I have concluded that teachers are vastly underpaid," she said and sadly shook her head.

I nodded and asked where to put the pot. Tina took it from me.

"I've just found Western Colorado so beautiful," I said. "I love coming up here and walking in your fields." I continued. "My dream would be to be able to save enough money to buy a nice house and land here in Rulison. Live here," I said and then sighed. "But I just don't see that happening on a teacher's salary." I took another pot and started to dry it with the blue and white striped hand towel.

"Are you going to stay another year?" She asked with both understanding and concern.

"I'm leaning towards at least one more year."

We finished up the clean-up, and I drove home. I got out in the darkness, walked across the street, and stuck my hand in the mailbox. There were several letters, including a short letter from Valerie.

CHAPTER FIFTY

WORKING TOGETHER

The weatherman predicted a small break in the snow, and Bob Rice drove across the pass to meet with us. We met at the school on Wednesday morning. He shook Virginia's hand and motioned us to be seated. He sat at the head of the table between us. He was always positive, organized, and personable. He did not waste words. He had a wry sense of humor, which you had to pay attention to catch. I liked him.

He started by addressing me. "Marvin, you hung in there, and we're grateful." Then turning to Virginia, he added, "What Marvin has done here has been nothing short of heroic. I'm not going to belabor it because words would be inadequate. I hired him to teach; what was it fourteen students in five grades?"

"Actually, it was supposed to be between ten and twelve."

"Really? I had forgotten. Hmm, well." And then he turned back to Virginia.

"And then it swelled to twenty and all eight grades." He paused and shook his head in wonder. "Twenty students in all eight grades. I have never seen the like in all my years. And he did it. Held it together, and all we heard at the conference was praise, well; of course, there were a few complaints."

He gave me a knowing smile. "Marvin, good job.

"But now we have help for you, welcome Miss Ryber." He opened his briefcase pulled out a legal pad and a nice Parker pen.

"First off, Marvin, now that we have two teachers, you will be the principal, and there'll be a small bump to your salary." He made a flourish with his pen and wrote on his pad.

"Okay, let's go over your school and figure out how we are going to divide this." And then, looking at me, said, "When I interviewed Miss Ryber, she told me she would prefer the lower grades. So, at the time, I thought we could work that out. What do you think?"

I nodded and told him how we had had a good discussion just a couple of days ago and our thoughts about dividing the grades. Then, I explained our rationale for dividing grades one to three and four to eight rather than the usual split.

Mr. Rice was not a narcissist; he did not have to hold all the reins of power. He found good people and let them do their work. He seemed pleased as he wrote down our proposed distribution in his notebook.

"This is good. I like it. Virginia, this works for you?"

She went over how we had decided the plan from her perspective, and her rationale was a little different but close enough.

"Well, good." And he underlined the distribution a couple of times in his notebook.

He talked to Virginia about how her house search was coming along. She said she had not been able to find any apartments and that the Mitchell's had offered for her to stay at their house. Mr. Rice thought that this was a good solution, particularly as she was coming mid-year, though in principle it was better not to be too tied to any one family.

He turned to me and asked, "Who was the lady who was so upset with Mrs. Mitchell? Do they have any students in the lower grades?"

I shook my head. "That's the Holderbaums, Bonnie Holderbaum, and it is just her, not her husband, Bill. And their two children are fifth grade and sixth grade." I realized even at the conference they had heard of the Mitchell-Holderbaum fight.

Mr. Rice clicked his Parker pen and stuck it in his pocket. He picked up his briefcase and set it on the table. He pulled out some other papers. He turned to me.

"I need to have Virginia sign some papers, and I want to give her a little orientation. If you have other work to do, feel free."

"Always have work to do," I smiled as I got up and went into the next room.

He talked to Virginia for another hour and then opened the door and walked into the classroom. Virginia followed him and stopped in the doorframe.

"Well, that's all taken care of. This went well. I think the two of you will be a strong team. I appreciate how the two of you took the initiative and worked it all out beforehand. You'd be surprised how many fights I have to moderate on this very topic."

He looked at both of us again with a great deal of satisfaction. "Unless you have any further questions, I have a meeting with Judy Porterfield up in Glenwood Springs."

We shook our heads. We had no further questions.

"In that case, good luck to you, and Merry Christmas."

Virginia and her father got on the road back to California a couple of hours later. I worked at the school in the afternoon and watched the snow start to fall again. The ski slopes would be delighted. In Colorado, in the nineteen-eighties, ski slopes did not make snow. Making artificial snow was an east coast thing. Making snow in Colorado would be sacrilegious. Colorado was the mountain state; God supplied the snow because God loved Colorado best.

I got out some of the education journals I had subscribed to and read some articles. I had fallen behind.

In the evening Tina called me and invited me to come up. She had returned from the Eastern Slope a couple of hours ago. They had been in a minor accident, but no one had been hurt. Still, that had delayed their trip over the mountains.

She lowered her voice to a whisper. "There is someone up here who is hoping to see you."

"That sounds wonderful."

I drove up about seven-thirty night. However, as I was driving I decided I would play it a little detached. She was young, still in high school. And I was not sure this was such a good idea. Of course, I would spend time with the Mitchell's, and I would be friendly with Valerie. She was a nice girl. She really was, but I had second thoughts about dating someone in high school.

The family was watching M*A*S*H when I came in. I came in and sat down on the couch next to Danny. I was determined to be reserved, but I did make mental notes to myself, little observations such as her waist was indeed flexuous, and her lips were full and pink. I had intended to stay for an hour and then leave. But everybody was so welcoming, and I was quickly engaged in all their conversations. I could not bring myself to leave.

I had taken off my snow boots at the door. As Valerie passed by to get a glass of water from the kitchen, she reached down to see if my feet were ticklish. I am inordinately and embarrassingly ticklish. She burst into pure, joyous laughter but restrained herself to just a couple of tickles and then went on to get her water. When she returned, she gave me a glance of superiority. She had a weapon that gave her an upper hand, which meant I had to trust her or else. It was a very knowing look.

When the show was over and Mr. Mitchell went to bed, Valerie came over and sat beside me. We talked for a long time. She was reading and working on being healthier, exercising, drinking more water, and limiting her sugar content, hoping to lose a few pounds. I had heard this talk about weight from girls a lot. However, most girls who talked about it did not need to lose weight, at least not from my perspective.

And I found that my intention to remain impervious to her charms had multiple flaws in its design. I had thought my defenses were tight, inviolable, staunch. But when she laid her hand beside her on the couch, an eyelash away from where I had my hand, and she left her hand lying so very still, besides my hand lying so very still. And they didn't even touch, but I knew my castle walls, thick stone as they were, nevertheless, had been breached. It would not be me who would move the hand.

CHAPTER FIFTY-ONE

WHAT'S GOING ON?

At three a.m., I awoke to a loud knocking. And amidst my deep sleep, that made no sense to me. I rolled over. The knocking returned louder and accompanied with shouts. Ron and Nancy were at the front door.

I had expected them around noon, but here they were. I opened the door. It was cold. I gave Ron and Nancy my bed, put the sleeping bag on the couch and went back to sleep.

It should not have surprised me. Ron and I had often made overnight drives. Sleep was for the weak. Who needed it? Once on a trip from Colorado to Michigan when we were sophomores in college, Ron drove. The night was almost gone, and we had made excellent time. We had driven all night across the flattest, most monotonous lands in these United States: Nebraska, Iowa, Indiana, Illinois. It was now predawn. There were a couple of coeds asleep on the backseat. I had somehow awoken a few minutes before and was silently watching the road when we started to veer off into the ditch. I grabbed the wheel and pulled us back on the road. Ron woke up. I asked him if he needed me to drive. He said no, he was fine. He had just been closing his eyes and counting to ten before opening them. He said that time he had not started counting, and he laughed. I told him he was crazy. As we were close to the school, I stayed awake the rest of the trip.

My brother, Ron, was fifteen months older than me. We were close; that is when we were not fighting. When we were fighting, we were really close. But our fighting days were years in the past. And by close, I mean close in a manner common to brothers. Very different than sisters. We didn't talk, not much. Why would we? What was the point? Why muddy the air with needless words? But we instinctually knew each other, and if there was a problem, we had each other's back. On one occasion, Ron had driven three hours through a big snowstorm to pick me up from a train station. No one else was on the road, but that didn't stop him.

The following day I rode with them to Denver. My brother Jim, his wife Jan, and their two boys, Jonathan and Joel, had come from Nebraska. We were all staying with my parents for the holidays. It had most of the usual features of a Brauer vacation: table games in the evening, shopping during the day, ping pong, desultory conversations, and good food. Due to the cold, however, the obligatory Brauer tennis match was postponed. We had hoped to replace it with skiing. Coming from Nebraska, Jim was anxious to hit the mountains, but the weather was too difficult in the high country. That was a bitter pill for him to swallow.

We replaced it with a Nuggets game. The Denver Nuggets set a record that year that has yet to be broken. They scored one hundred points a game with Alex English, Kiki Vandeweghe, and Dan Issel. But that was not what set the record. The record was that they also allowed one hundred points a game. The combination of prolific offense and horrible defense has not been repeated. With Magic Johnson and Kareem Abdul-Jabbar, the Lakers went on to win the championship that year, beating the Julius Erving-led Seventy-sixers. We saw the Nuggets play the Larry Bird-led Boston Celtics. The Nuggets won. It was hard for teams to keep up in the mile-high altitude. It was fun.

On Friday night, we practiced our instruments and played for dad's church on Sabbath. Our Brauer band included: Jim on

257

trumpet, Ron on French horn, me on trombone, and Dad anchored it with the clarinet. My Dad loved to display his family's musical talents: Jim was a good trumpet player, Ron and I were adequate, but Dad was exceptional on the clarinet. If he had not been so inhibited, believing jazz immoral, he could have made a living at it. He had rhythm and an excellent tone.

I will also add we were the second-best family band in the church. The Dunkins: Bob, Dave, Sherry, and Dr. Dunkin easily surpassed us. Two of them went on to become band teachers. But they were very gracious. And we had not embarrassed ourselves.

Jim was beginning to develop a lifelong interest in personal communication, moral theory, counseling, and how that all related to the work of the church. He quizzed us on Kohlberg's levels of moral development. He noted that most people fell into level two, internalizing moral standards but not necessarily questioning them. I scored at level six, universal principles. I then argued that Kohlberg had not allowed for the even higher level where one acknowledged a universal principle but then sublimated them to higher obedience. We, of course, came to no conclusions.

I also spent a lot of time lying on my bed finishing *Of Human Bondage*, which I had started in the fall. The book profoundly affected me, and I related immensely to the protagonist. Phillip, the book's hero, wanders around from school to school, profession to profession, accounting to art, and eventually to medicine. He travels from England to Germany to France and then back to England. I, too, had wandered around from major to major in college, from pre-law to history to education. I went to four different colleges from Michigan to California, Colorado, and then Nebraska. Phillip had had difficulties with female relationships. I understood that. Of course, Phillip was an orphan with a club foot and no siblings, which should have caused me to drop him from too close an identification, but that was not how my mind worked. I found similarities fascinating and almost escalated them to the level of spiritual guidance. I discounted discrepancies.

This pattern of accentuating what I found fit and discounting what did not fit was not too far removed from my use of religious texts. I memorized many Bible passages while completely ignoring the surrounding passages that did not fit into my template. In the end, Phillip's story, despite some severe setbacks, had ended up with him starting a life as a physician in some Southern England town, and he seemed happy with his lot. How would my story end?

My family, of course, asked about my love life. I told them about Valerie. They thought a seventeen-year-old girl was too young. I did not disagree, but she was pretty. And I was reasonably sure she liked me. Furthermore, it was a small town, and there was no one else in the church my age. I was lonely. They let it be.

Nancy had to leave early. Ron and I drove her to the airport. I had always liked Nancy and was pleased that she and Ron seemed to be getting along better.

Two days before New Year's, I rode with Ron back to Rifle. It snowed a little as we came over the pass. We unpacked at my house, and then about eight p.m., Ron went with me up to the Mitchell's. They were still cleaning up from supper, so Ron and I went downstairs to the family room, where David and a friend played a computer game with the Atari game system. He had gotten it for Christmas. It was the first time either Ron or I had seen a computer game. It was a simple game of hitting a bar of light against a wall and trying to predict where it would rebound. Straightforward concept but fascinating at the time.

Valerie came downstairs to talk. She wanted to know what I had done over the holidays, and she was curious to meet my brother. She thought going to a basketball game sounded like fun. She filled me in on all the little details of what had been happening on the ranch. She was much better at recalling little stories. She asked Ron if we had gotten along when we were young. Ron said we got along great when we were not beating each other up. She looked at me to see if he was just pulling her leg. I assured her that Ron and I had fought regularly. Fight, then go outside and play football. Danny had been lingering close — Danny was always lingering close — and asked if that was how I got so good at football.

"Marvin good at football? Are you talking about my brother because he always sucked at football?" Ron deadpanned.

"What, are you still jealous I was the Senior captain and not you?" I protested.

"You weren't the Senior captain! Neither of us were."

"Yeah, but I should've been."

And we both looked at each other and laughed. We still had the same routines.

Danny and Valerie looked back and forth at us. They found my interactions with my brother, who was also blonde, and nearly the same height as me, fascinating.

Mr. Mitchell called down to say that the president was about to start his address on national television. We all went upstairs and sat on the couches to listen to Reagan. He had a very warm persona and always made America feel better after his television addresses.

The phone rang, and Tina answered it. She asked her husband to turn down the TV a little. When she hung up, she said everyone wanted to go skiing tomorrow and did we want to come along. I thought that sounded like fun. Ron was heading on to California in the morning.

Valerie was sitting by her dad, and we found ourselves often looking at each other.

After the address, David invited Ron to try the computer game. The whole concept immensely intrigued Ron. So, he went downstairs into the family room with David. Valerie sat down on the fireplace near my seat on the couch and talked to me. She was easy to talk to and quite adept at engaging in conversation. It was never awkward, and the periodic pauses when they happened were not rushed.

On the drive back down to my house, Ron commented that she was very pretty. It was nice to get my brother's approval. I would later hear from Mom that Ron had told her it was obvious

Valerie liked me. He said she practically throws herself on Marv. I found that comment offensive. It demeaned her, and it was not like that at all. Yes, she did like me. I knew that. And she did not falsely hide it, but it would have been evident to her that her little attentions were received with relish and accepted. Saying that she was throwing herself on me suggested unwanted attention or, even worse, her intent to elicit physical intimacy. It was not like that at all. This was the purest of relationships, and we would keep it that way.

CHAPTER FIFTY-TWO

NEW YEAR'S DAY

The sky was deep space blue, cold, pure, and undefiled the following day. "Big Mike" was back from college for winter break, and we had been skiing together most of the day. I was an intermediate skier at best. Though I had learned skiing in fifth grade my family was not wealthy and I had only skied once or at most twice a year. Also I had never owned my own skis. Two ways to guarantee you did not get expertise . Still, skiing made a merry life. And I was young, and Mike and I were having a high time. He was a skiing proficient. His balance, his form, the way his skis were bonded to him was straight out of a Warren Miller ski movie. On the other hand, Mike by nature, was humble and rarely showed off.

But watching him made me anticipate the school's upcoming weekly ski program even more. I was certain the practice would dramatically improve my skills. In the meantime, today the pistes were groomed with packed snow, and we were both thrilled to embrace the speed, point the tips downhill, cut, find a little hill, catch some air, land, and at the bottom feel the endorphin rush, take the lift, and go again. Skiing with Mike was a grand time.

On the lift rides up the mountain we talked about the school. He said his little brother was constantly referencing me. Mr. Brauer did this. Mr. Brauer said that. Apparently, I had really impressed his little brother. According to Little Mike, I was "very cool."

"Really? Very cool? Huh." I replied as we rode up the lift together. "Well...He's probably right, don't you think?"

Mike just shook his head. "Pretty sad, when you have to rely on an eighth grader for your confirmation, don't you think?"

"Good point, Mike, good point, but..." And I paused to push up the lift bar as we neared the top. "But the truth is, that's my life, pretty sad, huh."

Mike looked at me and then punched me in the arm. "That bad huh?"

We skied off the ramp and pulled our masks down.

On other lift rides we talked about his classes and the grades he was getting. I talked about getting a second teacher, and that I had taken my LSAT's and had applied to a couple of law schools. I wasn't sure what I would do the following year, but it was hard to make ends meet on a teacher's salary. He said he needed to be able to make enough to keep up with his outdoor hobbies, but if had his druthers he really would like to be able to live in the Rifle area for the rest of his life. He just loved it here. It was good to talk to someone my age with ambition.

On occasion we would go down to the lower slopes and ski a couple runs with Valerie. She had invited a classmate from Nicaragua home for the holidays, and she was trying to help him learn how to ski. She looked so enviously at the two of us. Mike offered to work with the young man for a little bit. She should go up with me and do a couple of the more difficult runs. Mike did not know we liked each other. Then again maybe he did.

Valerie jumped at the idea. We rode up the lift. She was just bouncing with energy, so delighted to get up the mountain. Her skiing form was better than mine. Again, she had her own skis, and had pretty much grown up on them. I was more adventurous, and liked speed, so I usually led.

At one point as she caught up to me where I was waiting for her, she complimented me on my skiing ability. I thanked her, but thought she was just being nice. Then she said, "I love looking at you as I am following you. You are so delightfully thin." That one caught me off guard. I could have said the same, or that she was so delightfully curved, maybe I should have, instead I just thanked her.

Thomas, the Nicaraguan boy, twisted his knee and they had to put an ACE wrap on it. At the end of the day, I offered for him to ride in the front seat of my car. I could move the seat back and he could stretch his leg out straight. Thomas had hoped to ride back in the same vehicle with Valerie. He liked her. But I got him settled in my car. David walked up slowly beside the open driver door. I was standing there waiting for everyone to get into the other cars before I started the engine. He thought maybe we should put Thomas in the Mitchell's large Jeep Cherokee.

I motioned to the kid. "He is comfortable here. It'll be okay."

"I just think he'd be better in the Cherokee; don't ya think?"

"Whatever you want, but I'm okay with him here. I can bring him by your house."

David pulled me off to the side. "Valerie was disappointed she didn't get to ski with you more. She was hoping," and he paused to give me a conspiratorial wink, before adding, "She was hoping to ride home in your car."

I had never been in a relationship like this. A relationship where I was constantly being aided and encouraged by the family. All the family. They were watching out for her. They liked me and were actively abetting me at every opportunity. It was a romance accelerant. Valerie wanted to ride with me.

Well, if that was the lay of the land... well...well I pulled Thomas out of the car and dragged him kicking and screaming into the Jeep Cherokee.

No, of course not.

I would have never done that, but... David and I did forthwith help him to the Mitchell's car. He preferred that, at least he did until he saw Valerie slide in beside me.

This was New Year's Eve Day. New Year's Eve itself would go on for a lot longer. It had barely started.

First off, I stopped off at home to change and check on little Mittens. Then I drove up to the ranch. David and Ruthie were sitting by the fireplace chatting intimately. That relationship was clearly heating up. (Okay that is really corny—sitting by the fireplace, relationship heating up. Yes, I can see that…hmm… no, I'm going to keep it.) Ruthie seemed enamored by David, which was not too hard to understand. David was charismatic. He oozed personality. He was funny, inclusive, acerbic, and Ruthie hovered closer and closer. On the other hand, she was pretty with long straight, blond hair and an impossibly thin waste. David was infatuated with her.

I sat down on the couch. They had Dick Clark's New Year's Rockin' Eve countdown on the television. It was the number one show at the time. I was a little surprised that the Mitchell's had it on. Mitch and Tina were more country music fans than rock. But when I saw that Alabama was to be a featured group that made more sense. Alabama and Barry Manilow. It hardly seemed proper to call it a Rockin' Eve. To be fair, however, most songs on the radio could hardly be called rock'n roll.

Valerie came up behind me on the couch she laid her hand on my shoulder for a moment as way of greeting. Mitch came in from outside. He had been on his tractor shoveling the snow. He shook the snow off his yellow warm coverall and then pulled off his boots.

"You gotta stay ahead of it." He said to me. Then turning to Valerie added. "It's cold out there. You better go out and knock a hole in the ice over the stream. The horses are going to need water."

Valerie gave me an inquiring look as if to ask if I would help. Before I could answer Ruthie had already volunteered. Ruthie loved horses even more than Valerie, if that was possible. She was a trick rider, could do handstands on horses, and swing over touch the ground on one side, and then swing to the other side. I never saw her do it, but Valerie vouched for her. Taking care of the horses was something she loved to do. But Valerie was still giving me a supplicating look.

"Let me put on my boots."

Valerie, Ruthie, David, and I bundled up. It was cold and dark. Valerie and I took the lead. Our exhaled breath formed vapors before us. Valerie pointed out that they were merging to become one cloud. That charmed her and she turned her head to blow her breath over mine. We made our way carefully down the hill. The snow was deep here, and below the crest of the hill, the lights of the house did not penetrate. She gave me a couple of playful pushes.

"Really, you're in trouble now." I was tantalized by the flirtation and her intention to provoke touch. So, I grabbed her, slipped my leg behind her and let her down slowly to the snow. Let her down slowly until about a foot off the ground then dropped her.

She screamed with protest and delight. Got up and put a handful of snow in my face. I pretended to resist. Some guys might have had to continue to win, would have needed to show their physical dominance. That was not my style.

Touch, the enfolding of an embraceable girl who desired to be embraced, especially for the first time, in the cold and the darkness down behind her house, by a boy who yearned for the very same; these were the occurrences, the happenings, the indelible affairs of the human repertoire; these were the experiences that when they transpired inflamed the heart. They were often discoursed in literature, but it was never sufficient. For the impressions made on the mind could not be effaced. It was tattooed on the brain.

We were now at the stream. It was indeed frozen. David took the hammer and knocked a large hole in the stream. A couple of horses had followed us down and bent over to drink. Our task was done we could go back inside to the warmth of the house, but none of us were in any hurry. Instead, we meandered up to the fence where the other horses were standing. We petted their full and rich winter coats and just stood out there in the winter night couple by couple talking.

Valerie put both hands behind her neck and drew out her hair. She fashioned it into a little knot at the nape. "My hair is so unruly," she complained as she looked at me apologetically. "Sometimes it forms these gnarly elflocks, just a mess."

I was mesmerized by how deftly she manipulated her hair and could not agree with her. I thought her hair was glorious especially in the starlight.

Back inside games were starting. Other young people joined the party: Mike Duerhssen, Thomas, and John Boggs and his girlfriend. Tina brought out Funny Bones a Parker Brothers game where a couple picked a card and then had to do what it said. If it said ear bone you put the card between you and held it there: ear to ear, or knee to knee, or hip to hip. You did it until the cards dropped. Tina assigned Valerie as my partner. She was pleased to see her daughter laughing. On the second round Thomas wanted to be with Valerie. The game died about then. It had lost its appeal. Then it was Wink'em where the goal was to keep you partner in the chair ahead of you. If someone winked at her, you had to tap her before she could get out of the chair. I tried my best to keep Valerie in front of me. For the most part she played along, but on occasion she felt she had to try and escape. After that it was Murder. The lights were turned down, and still sitting in a circle, an unknown murderer winks at you and you slowly die. I entertained the group with theatrical death contortions and "Holy Grail" references,

"I'm not dead yet."

Danny burst out laughing.David got the Monty Python reference, and added with his best English accent, "Well, he's almost dead."

Midnight arrived and we wished each other a Happy New Year. I would have liked to have kissed Valerie, but she was seventeen, and I was in her parent's house.

Mitch had long since gone to bed. Tina was headed that way, but none of us young bloods were in the least bit tired.

267

Mike opened the door and looked outside.

"Hey guys! The moon is up, and the fields are bright. Let's go sledding." Mike said with verve.

"Man, I hate to be the downer, but the fields are full of rocks," David cautioned. "Who am I? I can't believe I am the party pooper."

"Well, then let's take them down to the road." Mike was not going to be discouraged.

"You can put them in my jeep," Ruthie offered.

And we did. We loaded two toboggans in the back of her jeep and went down to the country road. There were of course no cars, and it was snow packed and fast. On the first trip Mike set up for Valerie to ride with him.

"So, who am I riding with?" Valerie asked.

Mike waved at her.

Before the next run I took Mike aside and told him I really wanted to sled with Valerie. He gave me a nod of understanding. He had not put it together before then. I laid down first on the toboggan. She laid down on top of me. Ah, the magic of appetency, the tangency of her body laid over me, clinging to me. These were bonding memories.

Then Ruthie suggested we make a little train of toboggans, and she would pull us with her jeep. We roped them together. Valerie fit in behind me and wrapped her arms and legs around me. She was not timid about being close. It totally made up for me not kissing her.

We drove back up to the ranch. It was now after two a.m. Still, nobody was tired. We stood outside and talked some more and gradually realized we should part.

The next evening, I went back up. It was Friday after sunset, which for Adventists meant the Sabbath had begun, and our activities should reflect it. Mr. Mitchell got out his slide projector and set up a screen. He showed slides of family vacations camping in the National Parks: Yosemite, the Grand Canyon, and Yellowstone. Valerie laid on the floor. My attention was split between the slides and the winsome girl in jeans lying on her stomach on the rug. She turned around and saw me looking at her.

And the day after that, at church, I turned around and saw her sitting beside her mother. She was looking well put together in a new lavender dress. She did it justice. And when I did turn around, she was looking at me.

Following the service David came up and started talking. He told me he had rededicated his life to God. I gave him a pat on the shoulders.

"Good for you. I'm really pleased."

"Yeah, so am I, and you know Marvin, I don't think it would have happened without you. You've been a good friend to me these months. I really appreciate your listening and encouraging me."

I felt really good about that. Valerie walked by and smiled. She was wearing high heels and had attractive ankles. I gave a little sigh after she passed.

David looked at me, "You really like my sister, don't you?"

"Pretty obvious, huh? Yes, I do. The problem is I think I like her a lot more than she likes me."

David leaned in and said softly "Believe me, Valerie has a big, big crush on you!"

"Really?"

He softly tapped my chest with his fist. I was dumbfounded, still I was so pathetically infatuated I could not believe it to be real.

I spent the afternoon at their house. Near sunset we all returned to the church for vespers. As I walked into the sanctuary and sat down beside Valerie, I was aware that my proximity to the high school girl had been noted. I figured I would hear about it.

On the way out, David took me aside again. "The other thing I wanted to tell you—I didn't mention it this morning—but everyone in my family likes you. Valerie was talking about you this morning at breakfast, and my dad told her that you were as good a man as he had ever met. If it turned out that you and her started dating, and if it ever got serious, well, he doubted she could find a finer man."

David stepped back and gave me a very knowing look.

I swallowed hard. I had no idea what to think.

CHAPTER FIFTY-THREE

MISTS IN THE SNOW

The Mitchell's were going skiing the next day, and they invited me to join them. I really wanted to, but I had so much work to do. So as a conciliation, Tina suggested I join them in the evening. She said after skiing, they would stop off at the hot springs. I thanked her and said I would surely do that.

Early Sunday morning, I was back at the school. I was there before the sun came up. I shoveled in black coal and opened the damper, came upstairs, flipped on the lights, and took my familiar chair behind the pale oak desk.

On the morrow, it would all restart, winter semester. The students would be at their desks. I stacked up the teacher's edition texts on my right. It made an impressive and somewhat intimidating stack. Then, I began systematically reading through them, making notes in my large lesson plan book. Fortunately, I enjoyed the process of writing annotations as I read through the helps. And I would stop and mentally work through how I would teach the subject. I was very much looking forward to February when Miss Ryber would arrive and take the lower grades, how my life would change when that blessed event arrived.

Periodically, I would pause to watch the progression of colors as dawn played out across the sky, and then the first rays of sunshine touched the plateau of the Book Cliffs.

I lamented that the vacation had been brief, but I knew I could not dwell on that. I had to keep my mind fully in gear. I had to concentrate and be attentive to the work at hand. Work would give me balance. It was true; I was besotted with the girl; nevertheless, I needed to claw my way back up, get some air, get some perspective. This level of attachment was unsustainable.

I walked home for a little lunch and then drove back up. As the sun got low in the sky, I closed the school, shoveled more coal into the stove in the cellar, and banked it down. Then, I got in my car and drove east to Glenwood Springs. I drove along the river and noted the coal seam fire that burned deep in the Grand Hogback since 1910. It was especially obvious in the winter, where you could see the snowless patch on the slope and see the steam rising. How could a fire keep burning underground that long? What a mystery!

I pulled into the parking lot at the Glenwood Hot Springs.

The Ute tribe had used the Yampa hot springs for eons. In 1881 Jonas Lindgren had found the springs to be helpful for his arthritis. So, he built a wooden tub. He cooled it with river water and sold a bath for a dime. The miners from Aspen and Leadville flocked to it. In 1887, a much larger pool, Glenwood Hot Springs, was built when the railroad came through. It opened in 1888 with over one million gallons. They created the pool and bathhouse with a reddish sandstone called Peachblow. In 1893 the Hotel Colorado was opened, which offered the wealthy newly minted mining millionaires a chance to 'take the waters' in a European-style spa. The pool was a hit. Presidents Harrison and Taft had visited it. And Teddy Roosevelt had once spent three weeks here while he had hunted bear in the nearby lands.

I arrived just after sunset. Valerie was sitting in the lobby when I arrived. She nodded at me as I passed by. I could tell by the nod that her infatuation was quickly cooling, and I started feeling bad. Maybe I should not have come.

I changed into my swimsuit and exited the changing rooms. I went out to the pool. I loved the hot springs, but this was the first time I had been in them in winter, and the pools in winter were a magical experience. I walked outside into the cold air in my swimsuit and my towel wrapped around my shoulders. A few snowflakes were falling, into the sulfurous steam rising off the waters. I slipped into the water and let the warmth submerge me in its mineral heat. It was delectation of the highest order.

There were two pools. The smaller one to the east was hotter. On the near side, where you entered, it was one hundred and four degrees. Across the pool, where the hot springs waters entered, the temperature could be as hot as one hundred and ten. That was too hot for me. I preferred the second pool, which was much larger, nearly five hundred feet. It was cooler in the mid ninety degrees, still warm enough to enjoy even in winter. Tina and Mr. Mitchell were indulging in the hotter pool. Danny, David, and Ruth had moved to the big pool.

I dunked myself for courage and then went over and slid into the larger pool. I started walking the length of the pool, feeling the smooth cement on my soles, and looking out at the fading silhouette of the mountains to the west.

Valerie was taking a long time to come out. Oh well. It had been fun. David slipped away from Ruthie for a moment and came over to me.

He gave me the once over and then leaned in and said confidentially, "Valerie thinks you don't like her anymore."

"What! No, that's not true at all."

He gave me a little shrug of his shoulders as if he could not explain it.

She came out a little later and initially sat down beside her parents in the hot pool. I wondered if I should go over to her but thought better of it. Let them have their moment.

David suggested a game of chicken fights. Ruthie got on his shoulders, and Danny got on mine. Danny was no match for Ruthie. She was not a big girl, but she was wiry and strong.

Valerie came over and tried to encourage Danny to be a little tougher. Danny gave a good effort, but we kept losing.

"Let me try this time," she said to Danny and then turned to me, "Would that be okay?"

"Yes, of course."

"Prepare yourself, Ruthie; your domination is coming to an end," She joked.

Ruthie laughed. "We'll see, girlfriend."

I dropped to my knees, and Valerie climbed onto my shoulders. She was light and lissome, her legs soft and smooth. We moved toward the fight.

David was a sturdier base than me. Ruthie was somewhat more athletic, but Valerie was stronger and more to the point she was motivated. She was determined she was not coming off my shoulders. The two best friends had heroic wrestling matches perched on our shoulders. It did not always go Valerie's way, but in the end, we prevailed. After three or four bouts, the game ebbed to an end.

Valerie and I wandered off into the steam. She faced me and stood on my toes. She held my fingers and leaned back. When I raised my foot, she raised hers. And when I put mine down, she lowered her foot back on top of mine. We walked like that for a while. At that time of night on a Sunday evening, the crowds had dissipated, and the pool was largely empty. We moved farther and farther away. There were some lights around the outside of the pool, but the night was falling fast; it was darkening. The conversations of others had fallen away, and we only heard each other. Concealed in the mists, we were cloistered in columns of sacred vapors, alone.

It was a rare moment not to be rushed.

I kept looking at her and said, "I really, really like you."

She stopped walking. "Are you serious?" Her tone expressed complete surprise.

"I don't think I've met as nice a girl as you in a long time."

She swallowed and smiled. "Well, I don't know what to say, 'cept...I really like you too. I really do." She turned away for a moment and then added, "I wasn't sure. I thought maybe..."

I took in a deep breath and pulled her close to me. She wrapped her arms around my neck and buried her head on my shoulder. The steam enveloped us.

"I wish this moment would never pass," she whispered.

"So do I."

Afterward, we walked back slowly to where the others were and reengaged in the conversations of Ruthie, David, and Danny, except that while we were otherwise so fully involved in their concerns, beneath the dark waters, we held hands.

CHAPTER FIFTY-FOUR

BURNING COAL

We had kept the school's furnace burning through the vacation, Mr. Massey and I, but this morning I cranked it open. Christmas break was over, and the children were returning. The first half hour was frosty as I sat at my desk going through my preschool routines: reading the Bible, praying, then reviewing the day's agenda.

The children came back with energy. The Leathermans were the first, with Wayne bursting into the room ahead of Roy and Katie.

"Good morning, Mr. Brauer!"

"Good morning, Wayne." And then, as Roy and Katie entered the room. "Roy, Katie, Wayne, do you want to put up the flag?" I pulled it out of the lower left drawer of the desk. Wayne and Katie were excited about doing it but had to persuade Roy to go back out into the cold.

The other students came rushing like a dam break and a wave of cold air behind them.

"Shut the door. Don't let the hot air out."

The children from Rifle: Kim, Doyle, Chrissie, Ron, Angie, came in one car. Mike, Doug, Carolyn, and Chad came with Mrs. Sisk.

And then there was the new girl, the second Heather. She stood at the back of the classroom, surveying the energetic chaos of the classroom before the opening bell. Her mother was standing behind her. I quickly went back to welcome her. Heather had long brown hair that flowed over her shoulders. Being her first day in a new school, she was understandably bashful, but watching how quickly she assimilated the information coming at her was fun. She was in third grade, and I guided her to her desk right behind Angie's.

"Heather, this is Angie. She is also in third grade."

Angie was all smiles and welcoming. Heather's mom put down a small backpack filled with her school essentials. She started to organize it for her daughter. Heather dismissed her mother.

"I can do that, mom. I'll be fine."

Her mother and I gave each other a little smile, and she hugged her daughter and exited.

When I turned around, Kelli, Chrissie, and the other Heather were all surrounding 'little Heather.' She fit in quickly. She was a smart, curious, social child who wanted to belong.

And now I had twenty-one students.

"Take a big breath," I told myself. "Help is on the way."

We followed all the usual routines: we took roll; we pledged allegiance to the flag; we had prayer, and then it was back into the books. It was piercing cold that first day with a biting wind coming up the valley. The furnace struggled to keep up, and I had to frequently send the older boys down to stoke the fire and shovel in more coal. Even with that, everybody kept their jackets on for most of the day. Recess was short, and everyone wanted to do inside games at lunch. Nobody wanted to brave the frigid winter.

I reminded everyone that this semester on Fridays would be snow skiing. That brought a cheer. The first ski day was scheduled for January 22, but "Pay attention everyone, to go skiing you must have all your work up-to-date. So, do not be a laggard! Do not fall behind." And everybody voiced how determined they were. They were not going to miss skiing.

"Also, we have a new teacher coming! She will be here at the end of the month. She will be teaching grades one through three."

There were protests from the lower grades. They did not want to leave me. There were equally loud protests from the upper grades that they did want to leave. That quickly passed, and then they all started asking questions about what the new teacher was like, what did she look like, was she nice. I told them she was very smart, very affable, and would make an excellent teacher.

"What does affable mean?" Doug shouted out.

"Did I say affable? Really? That is an excellent word. Who wants to read the definition from the dictionary?"

Ron was closest to the dictionary and had it in a moment. "Affable: good-natured and sociable," he read aloud.

"Thank you, Ron. I daresay you are an affable young man." I affected a light British intonation.

"Why, thank you, Mr. Brauer, and I believe you too are also affable." His English accent might have been better than mine.

"That's nice," Doug interrupted, "But is she pretty?"

Kelli jumped in, "I heard she is young and single, and as Mr. Brauer says, she is affable. I think Mr. Brauer will fall in love with her."

There was a round of assents that followed. I stood at the front of the classroom with all eyes fastened on me. All my children wanted to know if I was attracted to the new teacher. Would we date? Would we become a couple? Would we fall in love? And then I made a mistake.

"The truth is I already like someone." That quieted the room. "And you all know who she is."

First, I want to note that Tina's mother-in-law was ill that morning, and Tina had called; she would be late.

Second, I must mention that Danny said nothing. He had seen the new teacher, Miss Ryber. He knew exactly what she looked like, and he also knew I liked his sister. He might not have known how much, but he had a good idea. And he could have, with insider trading information, made a killing on the Rulison Dollar Exchange. However, he did not because Danny had a superior value system.

When I was up at his house, we hung out. He was always beside me, chatting away. He was a family boy and did not betray the family secrets, and certainly not those of his beloved sister. He kept that information inside. The fact that I, his teacher, liked his sister, he could have gossiped. But he did not divulge it. That was just one of the many things I liked about him. Now, if he would only buckle down and do his schoolwork.

Danny said nothing, but Mike piped up. He shouted out from the back of the room. "It's Valerie."

The students gasped. They all knew Valerie. Kelli and Doug had been in first and second graders when Valerie was still in grade school. They had grown up with her. They liked her and universally agreed that she was pretty. Kelli, in particular, was surprised.

Ron remarked, "Poor Chrissie is heartbroken."

I looked over at the fay fourth grader. The rest of the class was abuzz. She was downcast.

A couple of seats behind her, Heather Savage was delighted. This classroom was so much fun. There was laughing and joking. Even the teacher was laughing. Was it always like this?

There were, of course, a lot of jokes the rest of the day about Mr. Brauer and Valerie. Some even tried to say Marvin and Valerie, but I told them I would remain Mr. Brauer in this classroom.

It was a mistake to have said anything, and I knew I would hear about it. Sometimes, you say too much when you are an open and forthright person. On the other hand, while I acknowledged it was a mistake, I was not sorry about it. It was not a secret. I had, after all, shown up to vespers with her and sat beside her. Furthermore, I liked her. I liked her a lot, and the community would have to deal with it. Besides, it was a long way from liking

279

someone to being serious or engaged. Nevertheless, it had been a mistake.

On Tuesday, I had to leave Mrs. Mitchell in the classroom for about a half-hour to drive down to the house and meet the propane man. My tank had run out overnight. Keeping track of all the little details on my first house was difficult. The propane man filled my tank and told me he would not charge me the emergency fee this time but keep a closer eye on the tank. It was much better to have it filled on a scheduled basis. I thanked him. As it was, the cost to fill the tank had been an expense I had not expected. I wrote out the check and handed it to him. It put a dent in my slim bank margin.

This heating bill came on top of a letter I had received a couple of days before. That letter had announced that the deferment on my college loans would run out in June, and I would need to start making payments. I pulled out my ledger and did some calculations. The numbers did not add up; my wages could not cover the expenses. So, out of curiosity, I calculated my wages on an hourly basis. It came to less than five dollars an hour, less than minimum wage. The system's only safety valve was for the teacher to find good work in the summer. But what job could I do? I was decidedly not handy. It was impossible.

I did not make my final decision to leave teaching at that time. I enjoyed teaching. I loved my children too much. But I was living a frugal life, and even now, I was sinking. Come June, and the college loans becoming due, the hole in the hull would become a gaping wound. My demise would be rapid. The decision to leave was becoming inevitable.

CHAPTER FIFTY-FIVE

PARTY PHONE

That week was particularly cold, and in fact, that winter was much colder than usual. In the Midwest, it set a slew of records. Time magazine had a cover article on how the earth had periodic ice ages and that we were headed for another one. The world was cooling. It was a frequent topic of conversation that winter. On Thursday, the pastor stopped by. The snow was coming down. He said the roads were becoming murder. I went outside with him and looked at the roads. They were quickly piling up. I told the children to call their parents and let them know we would let school out early.

Valerie had been home all week, but we had not been able to talk. First off, my work at the school severely limited my time, and the beginning of the semester was always more hectic with twenty-one students, all eight grades. Then her grandmother had taken sick and was hospitalized. Valerie had spent a lot of time in the hospital with her. When I tried to call her, my neighbors constantly occupied my party line. Damn neighbors! (Sorry, darn neighbors!) I tried. She tried. Neither of us could get through. Since I had publicly declared my affections, I was feeling vulnerable. My history of prolonged relationships was dismal, and in the early period of infatuation, I was insecure. I wanted to see her.

Tina was still working as my aide, so she kept me somewhat informed, but she was too busy taking care of her mother-in-law to give me much thought. However, I did hear from Connie McElvain that Tina had told her I liked Valerie. And I thought if she is telling Connie, then maybe I do not need to be paranoid.

On Thursday, I stopped by the Mitchell's house after eating with the McElvains. Mitch and Valerie were in town. They had planned to be back by now. But a surgery had come up, and Mr. Mitchell was attending as the nurse anesthetist. I sat down on the couch, intending to wait for them. Instead, Valerie called and talked to Tina. The surgery was running longer than expected. She would not be home until late and would call me tomorrow night. So, on Friday after work, I went home and waited by my phone. There was nothing worse than waiting by a phone that does not ring, especially when you want it to so badly. I pulled out my old journals, tried to read them, and kept looking at my watch. I really thought it best if she called me. I did not want to be pushy. But when she had not called by seven-thirty, I called. I asked if I could come up. She said, please do. But I wondered why she had not called. I drove up.

It was a pretty night, and when I arrived, she suggested we go for a walk in the fields. I quickly agreed. She went down to grab her boots.

Mr. Mitchell took me aside. "She has been calling you all night and kept getting busy signals. I told her it was your party line."

"And then you called," Danny added. "And I said someone's prayer has been answered." Mr. Mitchell chuckled and nodded at Danny's comment.

"Two prayers, actually," I said.

Mr. Mitchell gave me an encouraging pat on the back.

Valerie came back upstairs. She gave us a quizzical look, as in what could her dad, Danny, and Mr. Brauer all be laughing about.

It was biting cold, as it is when the clouds roll away. The moon was full. She checked on the horses and their feed. She told me she had already broken up the ice on the stream. I stood for a moment in the shadows while she checked the feed buckets. I just stood there and watched her silhouette in the night with a deep pervading peace and contentment. And since it was cold, I suggested we walk.

"You lead. I'll follow." She acquiesced.

"It's your land. I'll follow you."

But when we started walking, we were side by side, and we just naturally placed our arms around each other, and it was a kinesthetic delight, and all the ennui that had plagued me all week — does she really like me, does she really — all melted away. We came inside. Tina made some hot tea, and Valerie sat beside me in a green t-shirt and jeans.

She said, "It's really good to see you again." She looked at me and then repeated it for extra effect.

I smiled over my cup of tea. My beautiful doll was perfect in every way.

CHAPTER FIFTY-SIX

THE ALLURE OF LOVE

In seventh grade, I remember one Sabbath morning sitting beside my mother in the large Denver South church. I was reading a new youth magazine. The denomination was trying to replace the outdated *Youth Instructor*, which had been in print since 1852. It was, however, no longer read by the intended audience, and the church had started a new magazine, *Wayout*. It was a play on the vogue word, far out, as in "that is so cool, that is really far out." Anyway, the magazine was bright and garish with orange and green paper appropriating the colors of the Jesus Freaks. As I paged through it, they had an article on boys and girls and what they were looking for in romance and dating.

The author, a male, who was supposed to be one of the upcoming writing stars in the church, said that boys promised love to get to sex, while girls gave sex to get to love. And I remember very clearly as I sat in the church beside my mother when I read that comment; it blew me away. I was completely baffled. What in the world was the author talking about? This made no sense to me. Guys promised love to get to sex! Who thought this way? Certainly not me. The author must be nuts, crazy, out of touch. Well, okay, I knew some guys in my class were crass, but they were the abnormal ones, weren't they? I knew what I wanted—I mean, of course, in seventh grade, I was not dating—but I knew what I wanted from a girl: I wanted to be liked; I wanted to be cherished; I wanted a girl to love me; just me.

It has been said that the most romantic person in the world is a young man, or he could be, not always, but he could be. On the continuum between guys who wanted women for their physical needs versus those who deified the female gender, I was way over, maybe even far out, towards the romantic end of the spectrum. I often stayed up till midnight or beyond to watch old black and white romance movies at my parent's house. I did not relish the more modern adaptations where the love between a man and woman at once led to a frenzied stripping off of clothes. So, callous. What had happened to the concept of romance?

The other big motivator in my dealings with women was that I had this amplified anxiety that I would do something to a woman she did not want. Once when I was in college, a friend from high school had visited. Five of us had been in the car. She was sitting in the back between a couple of us guys. She was pretty, and I thought I would be cool by putting my arm around her. I remember her turning around and looking at me, and it was like, what are you doing? Who are you? Can I still trust you? I took my hand off her back. It had been unwanted. I had placed it there solely for my physical desires and her look at me; I hated that. Just the idea that I might take advantage of a woman caused me deep disquiet. It had always been there. It was the central guide, like the rail at a Disneyland ride where you were allowed to drive the cars any way you wanted because there was a central rail that you could never get off of. That was my rail.

The poet Rumi once wrote, "Someone who does not run/ to the allure of love/ walks a road where nothing lives." I was a marathon runner. What's up this road? Let's find out.

I had three brothers and no sisters. Girls were mythical. In my early years, I had lived on a missionary compound in Beirut with several other families. There were thirteen boys on the compound. No girls. None. Girls, girls, girls, who were they?

How could they be so amazingly thin, soft, graceful? How did they walk like that? No doubt they were mythical: fairies, elves, mermaids. They were princesses, angels, nymphs, pixies.

Guys? I understood. I fit in very well with them. We could hang out. We could play ball. I was good at all ball games. I could be as funny as the next guy if it came to jokes. I was comfortable in a group of guys. That was like hitting fastballs grooved down the middle. Yep, with the boys, I was good, no confusion.

The thing was however, it happened so often, no matter where I went, I would be just hanging out when the sirens' sweet, enchanting melody would arise, and if I was not firmly tied to the mast like Ulysses, then I was a goner. Their voices bewitched me.

The next day I entered the church with the Mitchell's. I followed Valerie. She was in a light blue, flowy chiffon dress, which came down to mid-calf. Her hair was blown out and stunning. I sat down beside her. I instinctively looked around the church to check on my children, and I smiled. They had all seen me and were all giving me little thumbs-up, little knowing smiles. They were nudging their siblings and nodding towards me. So, if I had not said something the week before, it would have been obvious today. Maybe it was not such a big mistake. You might as well head off what was going to become general knowledge. At least I thought so.

I taught the Sabbath School lesson for one of the adult classes that week. I am not sure how I had the time to study or why I agreed to do it, but I enjoyed teaching the lesson, and many people thought I was one of the better Sabbath School teachers. They liked my approach how I brought the affect and the intellect together. The people who did not like my style went to the other class.

When I came back and sat down beside Valerie, I saw that she had filled a pad with notes from my teaching. I am not going to lie; that was flattering.

After church, Valerie got in the front seat of my car. As we drove out of the church, I noticed a piece of paper flapping under the windshield wiper, and I pulled over where the shoulder widened at the top of the first hill. I got out. From here, we had a good view of the river valley and the shoulders of the mountain as they came down from the mesa, how they were staggered and provided the margins for the town's expansion. I looked back to my car and grabbed the paper. It was a note. I read it and handed it to Valerie. She laughed. The note's author had drawn a big heart, and inside the heart they had written, "Marvin loves Valerie." I had several ideas about who the author might have been, though one name was at the top of the list, and she was in sixth grade. In any case, it was funny, and I loved my kids.

As I was helping set the table at the Mitchell's house, Tina told me about her conversation with Elaine Cloninger. Apparently, Bonnie had confided to Elaine that she had called the conference office to complain about me. Bonnie complained that I was telling the students all about my sex life.

First off, I was thankful that Elaine had passed along the information. Forewarned was forearmed. And though I did not know Elaine very well; I always had the feeling she was on my side. She had been a teacher, and she could appreciate the difficulty of what I was trying to do. On the other hand, Bonnie, I was flabbergasted. I was telling the children about my sex life? What?

To the credit of the conference office, I never heard a word from them about this. I guess it was part of their job to field the disgruntled phone calls from parents, and whenever possible, they just dumped their notes into a trash can. Comments like that belonged in a trash can.

After Tina relayed the conversation, she added that she thought Bonnie was just jealous of my time with them. And the fact that I liked Valerie would aggravate her hatred.

"Maybe it will get better when Miss Ryber gets here," she said. "She won't be able to pick just on you. But, on the other hand," she paused and gave me a most wicked smile. "What do you think she will say when she finds out Miss Ryber is staying with us?"

"Yes, that will be interesting."

Still, I was disappointed. I had worked hard to keep a relationship with Bonnie. I had spent more time trying to repair fences with her than all the other parents combined. What was her problem? Was she deranged? Did she like to stir up trouble? Did that make her happy? I was not sure what else I could do.

I spent the day at the Mitchell's where Valerie and I took our usual walk in the fields. The clouds were all gone, just sunshine on snow. I took some pictures of her in her blue ski jacket and jeans so that I would have a picture to place on my table, and then we hiked over their fields. She was headed back to school the next day, and with the fates succeeding in denying us during the week we were determined to be together today.

After sunset, we took Danny, Steven, and Shon roller skating in Grand Junction. I drove on the completed interstate section and the two-lane section along the river near Debeque, where it was not. At the rink, we enjoyed the music and skating hand-in-hand. We could not get enough of it. At the Girls Only Skate, she felt obligated to go out alone for a little while. She was a better skater than me, graceful, and moved nicely in her backward skating. But she did not stay out long. She protested that skating alone was not much fun.

Meanwhile, the boys were entirely indifferent towards us. They raced around the rink as fast as they could. But Valerie and I were storing time.

The boys fell asleep in the back seat under the luminous full moon on the ride back. There was not a cloud in the night sky, and the fields were blanketed with flows of unbroken sanctified snow. It made the night exceptionally bright. It was ineffable, a Nordic fairy tale. I had the radio on in the background, and she laid back and closed her eyes. She laid her hand on my leg, and I took it in mine. Mostly she dozed lightly as I drove, though occasionally, she would open her eyes, smile, and squeeze my hand.

Christopher Cross's song *Arthur's Theme* was popular at the time, and it came on the radio. She opened her eyes when she heard it and gave my hand an extra squeeze. The lyrics of the chorus highlight the parallelism of love and moonshine, and advocate swift action when encountered. Amazing, another song written solely with me in mind.

FIFTY-SEVEN

BABY

As always, the next day, Sunday, I was up at the school early. Parent-teacher conferences were scheduled for the afternoon, though I was uncertain how many would show up with all the snow on the roads.

Mid-morning, while I worked at my desk, I heard a car enter the driveway. A moment later, the door opened. I looked up, and Valerie was standing at the door to the classroom.

"My dad is driving me back to school." She pointed back to the open door, and I could hear the idle of the diesel outside. She was wearing her blue ski jacket, tight jeans, and a baseball hat.

"I thought I would just drop in to say goodbye." She said apologetically. "I know you are busy on Sundays."

"You are always a wonderful distraction."

I stood up and sat on the front edge of my desk. She entered a little further and looked around the classroom. Then she wandered over to the windows and looked out.

"Well, I see it looks the same." She ran her hands across one of the desks. "The same desks. It even smells the same...." She took a big breath and paused to look at me.

"It doesn't change; only the people do," I answered.

"I was hoping you'd be here, at the school, so that I could look around." She smiled. We talked a little bit while the diesel idled in the driveway. Finally, she turned halfway toward the door and then back at me. "You better write."

"I am a prolific writer. You'll get tired of my letters," I responded.

She shook her head and smiled.

"Well, okay, bye." She waved.

"Bye, Valerie."

There was a little pause, a little hesitation, and then she headed down the staircase. I came to the door. Mr. Mitchell waved at me, and I nodded.

Valerie rolled down her window and waved as they backed out.

When I dated the girl in Denver, I had always been glad to leave at the end of the weekend. I had been ready for a break from her. And I had known that was not right, which was why I had broken it off. But this girl. I sat back down at my desk and sighed. But this girl.

As expected, not many parents made it to the parent-teacher conferences with all the snow. Phyllis Boggs came down the hill. She remained pleased that we had found resources for Steven. She said his attitude toward school was so much better than in previous years. Heather was doing fine. Yes, she did get behind on occasion, but she could turn out the work when she put her mind to it.

"She is always saying how much she likes school. She really, really likes you, Mr. Brauer." Phyllis laughed a little.

"Yes, she does." I chuckled. "She's a sweet kid."

Bill Holderbaum came down, but not his wife. He thought I was doing a good job but hoped I could lean a little harder on Shon to get his work done. I told him with help coming, that would be much more doable. I also thought Shon would be motivated by the ski program. Bill hardily agreed with that.

After he left, I sat at the desk for a little bit, steeled my resolve, and then called Bonnie. We talked for nearly an hour. She started to dump on me about Valerie. I listened and tried to keep my mouth shut. After a short while, her tone changed. She recognized it was probably hard to be here in Rifle so far away from anyone else my age and that Valerie was quite mature for her age. And she was pretty. I told her that I was very aware of Valerie's age and tried to be as circumspect as possible, respectful, and aware of the age difference. And I did agree that she was pretty. She apologized for all the trouble she had caused me and was so thankful that I kept talking to her.

"I tend to spout off and say a lot of things I shouldn't. Thank you for continuing to talk to me." She paused. "Do you think you could help set up some type of meeting between the Mitchell's and us? You know, maybe we can resolve our differences with a third party. I hate this."

I told her I would see what I could do. Later in the week, I talked with Mr. Mitchell about the conversation. He admitted there had been some bad blood between the two families for a while. He was unsure exactly how it had started, but it had been festering.

"You know, Marvin," His mannerisms were always so thoughtful and considerate, so sincere. "Maybe God has brought you here to bring our families together."

I thought that was an amazing concept, that God was using me; still, I had no idea how to do it or how to coordinate it. I did not have the training nor a natural inclination for family counseling. It seemed that should have been a job for the pastor. But, having grown up a pastor's kid, i.e., PK, I also knew that working through inter-family feuds was never high on a pastor's to-do list.

The reconciliation intervention between the families did not occur. But at least, for now, Bonnie was mollified. And after listening to her dump on me for an hour, her mollification lasted until Tuesday.

Before school, she called. I answered the phone. She went off at once. She said I was responsible for Shon not getting his work done and that I had to take full responsibility. She revisited the previous demand that Tina has nothing to do with them.

"If you have to sit beside him all day long, I don't care, but it is your responsibility to make sure my boy gets his work done."

I kept my composure. "I have twenty other students. That is not possible."

"Well, you better do it!"

"I'm sorry that is impossible."

"Well then, do you mind if I come and sit in the classroom with him?"

Bonnie, in the classroom, that would have been disastrous. "Yes, I do mind."

"You know, Marvin, if you spent more time thinking about your students and less time thinking about Valerie, you would be a much better teacher."

I was proud of myself and a little surprised that I could hold it together.

When Tina arrived, I talked to her about it. She was very sympathetic. She assured me this really had nothing to do with me. "Bill and Bonnie must be having another marital spat."

She said. I thought that was insightful. My teachers taught me that a child's poor behavior at school was almost always a spillover from home, and it rang true. Shon was a good kid. Most of the time, he had a pleasant disposition. Everyone liked him in school. He was bright. He was funny, but something was eating at him, obviously home issues.

Tina then told me that another family was upset that I spent so much time at the McElvain's. This was intolerable. Families who were nice to me and helping me were being attacked. I really needed Miss Ryber to come.

"On another note," Tina wanted to cheer me up. "I talked to Valerie last night. They are having a school benefit this Saturday night. She wanted me to invite you to come. We are going over. You could ride with us."

293

That did cheer me up.

At the end of the day, when I walked home, picked up my cat, walked across the street to the mailbox, I had an envelope. It was my LSAT scores. I had done very well, maybe not Ivy league well, but I knew I had a strong probability for admission to the Colorado University law program. That was comforting. And as I sat at my supper table eating a boxed pasta dish and canned vegetables, I read the materials. The brochure talked about the misconception that there was an overabundance of lawyers. The data from the government showed that demand and supply were evenly matched. Reassuring. They described the work of the lawyer, reading, analyzing, negotiating, trying to find compromises. It sounded very much aligned with my skill set. I decided if I got accepted at CU, I was going into law.

When I went to the McElvains that week, I told Ron and Connie my plans. He was disappointed but not surprised. To their credit, while they had a daughter in first grade who liked me and had done very well, they were able to view this from my perspective. They saw that a career in teaching was next to impossible. The pay was abysmal. If you were a male who was hoping to have a family, and even more so if you still subscribed to the idea that the man should be able to support the wife as a mother at home, then the probability of doing this on a teacher's salary dropped below absolute zero, nil. It was impossible. The McElvains were good parents, and they believed in Adventist education. He was the school board chairman, but, and this was astounding, first of all, they viewed this as my friends. He hoped I would reconsider. He also hoped I would not.

On Friday, we were having our typical end of the week airing of feelings. Kelli raised her hand. I called on her.

"I just want to say," and her tone was very matter of fact like she was about to tell me something that, even if I did not want to hear, just had to be said. "I think you baby Danny and Carolyn. You are always going so easy on them."

There was a general clamor of consensus. On earlier surveys, I knew the classroom thought Carolyn was my favorite. Carolyn was a favorite.

"It's true; you have to admit it, Mr. Brauer. You do baby them," Doug added his input. The sixth graders were unanimous on this.

I had been leaning at one end of the chalkboard. I looked around the classroom. I saw a lot of head-nodding going on.

I pushed off the wall. Carolyn and Danny were not protesting, but they did feel uncomfortable.

"It's true. I do pamper Danny and Carolyn. I don't deny it. You are right."

Kelli pumped her fist in the air. She was right and very proud that she had spoken truth to power. Roy was also pleased. A grave injustice was going to be righted.

"I do want to say, however," And I gave a little pause. "The truth is I baby all of you. I baby you Kelli, and Roy, and you Doug. Of course, I baby the first graders. They are so cute." No one was upset that I babied the first graders. They were so darn cute. "There is only one student in this classroom I don't baby."

I had their attention. Everyone looked around the classroom. Who could it be? Probably Mike, huh.

"And that's Ron."

And it was true. I never babied Ron. He had emotional stability that exceeded his seventh-grade status. He did not take part in the gripe sessions. He did not get engaged in the little petty fights. Occasionally I did have to tell him I would not further discuss his fascinating new idea, as he followed me around the room telling me about something he had read and what did I think about that. Of course, he was curious about everything. But I never worried that my comments to him would cause him to pout, get angry, or be sullen.

The Hesses had taken the job of cleaning the classroom a couple of days a week at the end of the day. The board had offered that as a trade-off against their tuition bill. Judy, their mother, would come, and the three children swept up, cleaned the bathrooms, dusted. Ron would do the cleaning, and often he and I would have some conversation about some topic of the day. He enjoyed talking about politics, science, astronomy. Danny had taken him up to his house, and Ron thought their computer game was fabulous. He was amazed when I said I had worked in a large computer lab while in college, changing the large reel to reel tape drives that fed the information to the computers. Ron took every word I said as absolute truth.

His mother had to intervene occasionally to allow me to continue doing my after-school work. His younger sisters, Chrissie and Angie just kept working while he walked and talked. And I enjoyed having them there.

They were three of the least complicated children in the classroom. Chrissie always started off doing the jobs the closest to my desk. She washed off the chalkboards emptied my trash can. She wanted to be close to me but was a little bashful.

Angie was much more straightforward. Statistically, if someone was likely to come running and jump into my arms or sit on my lap at church, Angie was the odds-on favorite.

Chrissie was always more subtle, leaning up against my chair and resting against me, while I engaged with the other students. A moon in close orbit.

CHAPTER FIFTY-EIGHT

THE LAW AND ME

I woke up Sabbath morning in my bed at my parent's house in Westminster. I liked their condominium. It was the most modern style of architecture they had ever lived in. I had ridden over the mountain yesterday with the Mitchell's. They were staying with some family in Denver and would be driving up to Loveland in the afternoon. So, I stayed overnight with my parents.

It was comfortable going to church and hearing my father preach. He was consistent. He avoided extremes and tried to guide his congregation towards the middle. Adventism was very much trying to find the moderate ground in those years. Morris Venden was the big name on the camp meeting circuit. The Adventist Book Center highlighted his tapes and books. He preached faith and grace as Adventism tried to get out of the legalism mud. That was a hard sell because many of its doctrines were works-based, i.e., strict Sabbath-keeping was by definition works-based. But my dad was trying, albeit not as quickly as my pastor brothers, Bob and Jim, were moving, but he was advancing.

I enjoyed the chance to sit in the living room beside the fire and talk to my parents. I told them about my LSAT scores and that I was leaning towards the law. My mother said they had a member in the Louisville church in law school at the University of Colorado. My mother admitted she was attractive but insinuated her attachment to the church was a little suspect, which I knew was a veiled reference to suggest that her morals were also a little suspect. Mom also said, again, that it was difficult for an Adventist to be a lawyer because lawyers had to lie. That was an understood truth in the church; lawyers had to lie. I thought it was ridiculous, but I heard her.

In my early college days, I had abandoned Christianity for a couple of years. I slowly quit going to church and ventured into more modern philosophy. Due to being tired of the strait-jacket constraints of evangelical Christianity, I called myself an atheist. Although to be correct, I was more of an agnostic rather than an atheist. I leaned more toward an epicurean approach than the Adventist stoicism. In any case, a couple of years later, I rediscovered Christ. I had an encounter where I felt the realness of his presence. (That is a whole different book.) I came back to the church.

Consequently, I wanted to avoid placing my faith in a position of jeopardy. My mom had successfully planted the doubt seed. Maybe the law was not for me.

After lunch, the Mitchell's picked me up, and I rode with them to Campion. They picked up Valerie at the academy, and we all drove up to the mountains for a Sabbath afternoon ride. Valerie rode in the backseat beside me. The car was full, so she had to sit close, which was no grievance to me. I sat by the window and rested my arm around her shoulders. She leaned in.

Rocky Mountain National Park was just up the road from Campion Academy, and the snow-covered mountains were beautiful. We saw four bucks with large racks standing in a field while driving by. Valerie called for her dad to stop. She had received a new telephoto lens for Christmas, and she wanted to photograph the bucks. We both got out. I took a couple of pictures, and she took a roll of film. It was a memorable sight, the four stags, the mountains, the snow lying on the blue spruce limbs. And I was taken aback. She took a whole roll of film. Who had that type of money?

I felt a little awkward in the evening when David and I went to the girl's dorm lobby to pick up Valerie and Ruthie. I knew many of the students from my summers working at Glacier View Camp. They had been campers. The guys asked who I was there to see. I told them. And they nodded. They could understand why I would be here for her. And the girls, when they entered the lobby, would see me, and it was fascinating how quickly their faces could register so many emotions: excited recognition, delight, then puzzlement, and finally comprehension, realizing one of their comrades had attracted a man.

Valerie came out. She looked more beautiful than ever and put her arm in mine. We rode with the Mitchell's to the auditorium in Loveland. It was a nice auditorium with excellent acoustics. I sat on the end with Valerie between her parents and me, then Danny and David and Ruthie on the end. Tina and Mitch were delighted to have their family all together listening to such wonderful music.

The benefit featured Hale and Wilder. Robert Hale and Dean Wilder were two opera singers who teamed up for about twenty years. They had a successful career doing concerts, singing gospel and country songs. Their voices were so much better than what I was accustomed to, world-class. And their song selection touched the audience. When they sang Amazing Grace, Valerie wrapped both of her hands around mine. And when Hale, who was the bass, sang Deep River, it sent chills up my spine.

After the program, as we were walking out, I said something about how much she meant to me, and she just smiled and said something to the effect that she was shy and wished she could be more verbal. At the pizzeria, David and Ruthie were sitting opposite us. David and Ruthie had really hit it off. It was clear their relationship was advancing even faster than ours. Topics were being tossed into the ring as all young people do. Ruthie said she thought people in love should not wait years and years. Valerie started to respond that she would never get married early and then stopped in mid-sentence and took another drink of her root beer.

The following day I rode back with Mr. Mitchell. Tina, Danny, and David were coming back later. As we were driving down the mountains, I broached the topic of dating Valerie, though I am not sure why I still felt like I needed to ask him. After all, he had just driven me over the mountains for a date with his daughter. Nevertheless, I thought it was proper. This was the convention. I needed to have "the talk" with the father.

Mitch was, as always, very contemplative. He said that he liked me very much and that yes, I had his approval. The conversation did not seem misplaced in his mind. He, of course, discussed Valerie's age, and I assured him that I wanted what was best for his daughter. He confided to me that he had told Valerie that, in his opinion, she would never meet a better man, and if she got serious with me, she would not be making a mistake. That confidence in me was humbling.

He also said that her last boyfriend had been twenty-five, but the last boyfriend had wanted her to get too serious too fast. When he said that, I interpreted that as the man wanting to push Valerie into inappropriate intimacy boundaries. I was besotted and thought of her only in the purest celestial imagery.

CHAPTER FIFTY-NINE

ONCE IN A LIFETIME

The other thing I was thinking about on the trip home was my future. My parents' comments had made their mark. Plus, Valerie, said she liked me as a teacher rather than a lawyer. I got the feeling she was not willing to live that far on the edge of conventional Adventism. While I loved my children, I still felt I would have to quit teaching. I simply could not make the dollars last. It was basic mathematics, economics 101. Thus, on the ride back, I started to think about medicine. I asked Mr. Mitchell a lot of questions on that trip.

On Monday morning before class, I called Dr. McCluskey at Union College. He was the chair of the Science Department. I had taken a class from him, and he was a pleasant, intelligent, godly man. I got straight through to him.

He remembered me well. As Student Body President, I sat on the college's judicial committee with him. The faculty on that committee had tagged me as the 'angel of mercy.' When students had shown up for disciplinary issues—which since we were an Adventist college was almost always alcohol related—if they were repentant, and it was not recurrent, I advocated strongly for leniency and probation. Also, in full disclosure, I was a sucker for those cases if they were female and pretty. It happened so often; the other committee faculty members had come to expect it. I do believe they liked it, and I suspected if I had not been there—I prevailed on them so easily—they would have come to the same conclusion.

But anyway, Dr. McCluskey remembered me well. I told him I was considering making a career revision, thinking about trying to get into medical school, coming back to Union College to complete my premed prerequisites. I had a question for him: could I do that in one year? In those years, the requirements for medicine were calculus, physics, biology, and general and organic chemistry. He was encouraging, positive, and affirmative.

He recommended I take general chemistry over the summer. I told him the University of Colorado at Boulder was only twenty minutes from my parent's house. So, I could take it there. He thought that was excellent. Then in the fall, I could enroll in calculus, physics, biology, and organic chemistry.

"That would be a heavy load," I replied with some concern.

"Yes, it would, Marvin, but when you get into medical school, this will seem easy. I would not recommend this to most students, but I think you can do this."

"Okay," I paused and then asked, "If I did this, what do you think my chances are of getting into Loma Linda the following year?" I really did not want to waste two years.

He asked me what my GPA had been. I told him.

"Yes, I remembered you as a serious student. Well, Marvin, if you really dedicate yourself to your studies next year, you could take your MCAT in the spring," He was working through the problem with me on the phone. He paused to reflect about it a moment. "Marvin, I am not going to lie. You will have to work hard, it might be a little shaky getting into Loma Linda for the 1983 class, but it all depends on your effort."

"Thank you so much, Dr. McCluskey. You have been so helpful."

I want to put on record that Union College was a fantastic experience for me. The best college I attended. The teachers were outstanding, and they knew your name. I found that personal relationship with the professor to be highly motivating and encouraging. And Nebraska, once you got over the flatness of the land, was quite pretty. Overall, the phone call was encouraging.

As the school week began, however, it was quite the opposite. The first thing was Bambi. She had often come to the school all fall, and the children just loved her. How cool was it that a deer wandered into their classroom? But she was growing; her fawn spots were now nearly invisible.

In the schoolyard, she liked to tease the neighbors' dogs. They would bark at her, and she would nonchalantly look up from grazing. If they were free and able to get into the schoolyard, they would rush at her. She would let them charge and then take a couple of bounds and jump the fence at the last moment. They could not get over the fence and would bark frantically, especially if Bambi, as she frequently did, would start to graze just a few meters from them, impervious to their despair.

But on Monday, she came inside the classroom and started to make her usual slow inspection of the aisles, seeing if the children had any offerings for her. One of the children surprised her, and she threatened a kick. I saw it. She had not kicked, but she could have, and her hooves were sharp. I realized she could do damage.

I told the children that Bambi would not be allowed inside anymore. The younger children were distraught. Mike sided with me. He was the eighth-grader and a hunter. He had credibility. He told stories of deer maiming people with their sharp hooves. So, Bambi was banished, and another aspect of my 'Disney' experience was fading.

That did not help the mood and bickering overtook the room. It got worse when two of the older boys got into a fight, which I had to break up. Then at the end of the day, Mr. Grant came into the classroom to tell me he would be withdrawing Cory. He said the classroom was a mess, not a suitable environment for his boy.

303

I was stunned and upset. Cory had been doing so well and had a clever mind constantly dropping dry witticisms. Plus, he got his work done and stayed out of trouble. For the most part, he was well-liked. Although, on occasion, his witticisms could be caustic. For instance, he never could understand why the others did not do their homework as fast as he did. That caused resentment. But I would miss him.

Not long after Mr. Grant left, Pastor Kungel dropped by. He rarely came to the school. He wanted to know if I had heard that Cory was leaving. The Grants had talked to him first. I said yes, Mr. Grant had just been here. The pastor looked around the classroom and shook his big head. "Frankly, you could do better, don't you think? It is messy."

I thought of several retorts, but I held my tongue. It was unbelievable.

After he left, I called Ron McElvain. As board chairman, he needed to know about Cory. I told him the reason stated by Mr. Grant and then of the pastor's surprise visit. I no longer held my tongue. How could the pastor say that? Didn't he know how hard I had been working? Was he so clueless? Didn't he remember that the school board had begged his wife, who was also a teacher, to come and help me? They had entreated her at the beginning of the year, but the Kungels had decided against helping me. And then the gall to come down here and complain that the school was not spotless. Ron was perturbed, though he was of a more even disposition than me and supplied an excellent sounding board on which to vent. He said he would call the Grants.

He did call, and Mr. Grant's decision was final.

And to top it all off, Ron told me that Sheila Schlisner had also started complaining about me. That hurt. I thought we had a good relationship and were on the same side. My school was unraveling.

CHAPTER SIXTY

BLUE SKIES

On the plus side — and it was a large plus — that Friday was our first ski day. We started much earlier in the morning. The logistics of getting to the ski resort, getting the children outfitted with their skis, tickets, and bringing them to the lessons necessitated a much earlier start. Those who lived in Rulison met at the school by seven a.m. There was barely a hint of dawn, just a faint lightening on the eastern horizon above the mountains at that time in the morning.

And it was cold, but everyone was excited. We loaded up in two cars, the Mitchell's and Holderbaums. I rode with Tina.

We drove over to the church. As we drove into the parking lot, several cars were already there, engines still running, exhaust steaming into the morning. Children jumped in and out of the vehicles, grabbing their lunches and winter supplies. In the church, the foyer lights were on. Sandy Sisk was inside with a clipboard checking off the names. Connie McElvain kept trying to corral the kids outside — if they had to go to the bathroom, okay, but no running in the sanctuary.

Sandy went around to each of the drivers and coordinated the lists. She made sure they knew the directions. We would go as a caravan, but did they know the directions if we got separated? The drivers had all been there before. We piled in. There were last-minute details such as a forgotten lunch, or gloves, where was my sibling little despairs. We were about ten minutes behind schedule. Amid it all, Sandy was calm and directive.

For several children, this would be their first-time skiing. The younger ones were a little nervous. As a seventh-grader, Ron was older and had to project bravado. He would be skiing, maybe not the black today, but at least the blue slopes. He was sure of it. Mike told him not to worry too much if it took longer than expected.

The caravan pulled out of the church parking lot. As we headed east on I-70, it was nice to be in the passenger seat, able to watch the cerise sky expand, to be able to look at the shadows of the river and to be able to listen to the children without having to hush them. Next, we drove to Sunlight Ski resort. It was a smaller mountain on the road to Aspen. In the parking lot, the excitement blossomed even more.

Sandy went to the ski school office while we took the kids who needed to rent to get fitted for boots, skis, and poles. There was whimpering among the younger ones at how tight the boots were and how hard they were to walk in. When Ron got up to walk in his boots, he gave me a glance to suggest his optimism was declining.

The kids went to their lessons based on their ability.

I always liked football, basketball, tennis, baseball, soccer, running, frisbee, but I loved skiing. There was nothing like it, nothing. As you ascended to the mountain peaks time after time, you breathed in the freshest air in the world, and life was placed on hold; you had entered a time warp. Yet, that little jolt of excitement, that thrill as you turned your skis downhill and embraced the acceleration, that little jolt never grew old. On the mountains, surrounded by the most ethereal landscapes, you could look out over crest after crest of ridges spanning the horizon. The skies, on a clear day, were bluer than you could fathom. The fir trees, the spruce, that lined the groomed trails beckoned us to come to take a short exploration in their shadowed interior. Or go down the piste if you prefer, gathering speed, carving, which was another way to say let us dance on the snow, feel the rhythm and let the snow subsume you into its ethos, the ethos of letting go and becoming.

As I have said before, I knew how to ski, but not well. I had never had this type of opportunity. So, I joined the class of intermediate students. The teacher gave good instruction. "Lean into the hill. If you lean back, you will sit down. Put your weight on the downhill ski."

At times I would leave to check on the other groups to encourage the beginners. The students were impressed that I knew how to ski. Even the advanced skiers: Mike, Shon, Doug, Danny, Kelli, and Steven, were gracious. Mike and Shon were exceptionally gifted; they could fly. They had such control of their bodies and their skis. Their athleticism knew no constraints. On the mountain, they were princes, and as such, they were benevolent to me. They gave me instructions and little compliments. They were so vastly above me that they could show mercy to their lower subjects.

You may have noticed I did not mention snowboards. They had been invented and were beginning to attract attention in some parts of Southern California, but they were a decade away from common use. None of my most ardent ski enthusiast friends were snowboarding in those years.

When I came down to eat some lunch, Tina wanted to tell me that she had heard that Phyllis Boggs had really gotten into a heated argument with Mrs. Schlisner in support of me. That felt good to know people were fighting for me.

In the afternoon, Bill Holderbaum and I did several runs together. He was, of course, better than me. But he was more cautious than his son. Bill could not afford to get injured and miss days at his practice. Still, we were having a good time.

As we came to the lip of a steeper section of an intermediate trail, he exclaimed, "Nothing like skiing!" Then added, "I try to take off at least a half-day on these ski days. What's the point of working so hard that you cannot enjoy it?"

Then as he set his poles to push himself downslope, he repeated himself, "Nothing better than skiing, except...." Then as he started down the slope, he pushed off and added, "Except sex."

That stopped me for a moment. Why would he say that? I was so obviously single and celibate, even monkishly so. There was something better than skiing? So, I had heard. But why would he prompt those thoughts in me of that from which I had to abstain? I did not need the reminder that I was still unmarried and could not participate in adult activities.

The day ended, and no one got hurt, which when you are skiing was the desired outcome. I had personal knowledge about getting injured while skiing. The year before I had suffered a fibula fracture at Steamboat Springs.

In the parking lot, everyone gathered around the vehicles. The first graders were tired. Kim and Misty were trying to project optimism as the older boys asked them how they had done. Ron was eating a candy bar on the back of the Sisk's vans. When I approached, he just lifted his eyebrows and sighed. "I am so tired." And then he glanced at the other boys. "It's fun, but I am sore."

CHAPTER SIXTY-ONE

FLY LIKE AN EAGLE

The next day was Sabbath, and it was a full day. Virginia Ryber had arrived the night before, and Tina had arranged for a little welcome dinner at their house. Tina had also invited The McElvains and me. While we waited for the McElvains to arrive, I helped Tina, to her objection, by setting the table. She insisted I did not need to help her. "You had a tough week, Marvin. Sit on the couch and relax. Read a magazine." But I liked doing something. Besides if I worked with her she invariably broke up her questions about me with little stories about her daughter. I ate them up. And they almost always had a special surprise, like a prize in a cereal box, a little tease comment Valerie had said, which of course Tina could not tell me. They drove me nuts. Why tell me and then not tell me? I loved them.

Virginia's boyfriend had come with her. He was a well-dressed, immaculately coiffed young man. He was handsome and refined, wearing a grey pinstripe suit, pink shirt, maroon tie, and a scarf tucked into his overcoat. To call him pretty would not have been inaccurate. He was much better looking than me. We tried conversation at church. He said how close he and Virginia were, had been best friends for years, and he was not looking forward to her being so far away. After saying that, however, the conversation struggled. We had little in common. That was another reason why I was helping Tina in the kitchen. I set the plates, the glasses, the silverware, the napkins, while Virginia and Roger sat on the couch with subdued conversation.

After the meal, most everyone wanted to take a Sabbath afternoon nap. Connie and Tina were sitting on the couch talking. Ron and I migrated into a conversation about birds. Ever since I had mentioned the American kestrel, Ron and I had been intermittently revisiting the topic of birding. He mentioned that you could see bald eagles along the Colorado in the winter. In the eighties, the bald eagle was just beginning to recover from the DDT scare of the sixties. I had been birding since high school and the idea of seeing a bald eagle! I could not have been more excited than if he had said he would show me a grizzly bear.

Since most everyone was napping, Ron suggested we drive by the river. He passed the idea by his wife. Though she liked birds and did not mind taking up an occasional afternoon ride with her husband, she was not an aficionado. "Go ahead, dear." She said, and she seemed pleased that he had someone who shared his enthusiasm.

We drove up along the river on the south bank past Silt toward New Castle. Ron knew the best spots. The sky was cloudy, and it was cold. We kept our eyes trained on the trees along the bank where their leafless branches extended over the water.

"There!" He said quietly — as if the bird could hear us in the car. He pulled off the road onto the dirt shoulder. He motioned to a large silhouette in a large sycamore across the river. After training my binoculars to where he was pointing, I saw the white head and black body.

For those of you who are not birders, let me explain the thrill: chefs are transported when tasting a new spice; gardeners revel in a new hybrid of lily or a variant of a tulip in the spring; philatelists go ape over a new or rare stamp. But, for me, seeing that bald eagle in the bare limbs of a sycamore, along the cold and grey river on a wintry January day; seeing the white head for the first time, and being amazed at the size of the bird; it was all so unforgettable; my first bald eagle. Ron had seen a number of them before, and though he might not have been as excited to see it, he took immense enjoyment at being able to show it to me, especially as I kept gushing about it. My first bald eagle.

It probably took us a couple of hours all in all to drive up past Rifle along the road, find the eagle, stop, get out for a couple of minutes, stand there, and train our binoculars on it, as it sat there watching for a fish, and then we drove back up to the Mitchell's.

When we arrived, Connie and Tina were still talking. Connie gave a quick look our way. Did her husband have a discovery smile? He did. She was pleased.

"You saw one," she said.

Ron was beaming. So was I.

As I said, the day was very full. It concluded with a social in the fellowship hall. In the evening, after Sabbath and in honor of the beginning of the ski program, the social committee showed "Snowball Express." It was a Disney movie starring Dean Jones, who inherits a small ski slope in Western Colorado from an uncle. The story is full of twists and blunders. Nevertheless, it was a funny movie.

Before video or DVD existed, these community church movies with 16mm reel to reel were a real social occasion. At Rifle, these events were always well attended. The community spirit of the church was unbelievable. All the parents with children were there. The members who no longer had children turned out as well. The energy and the laughter infected them. The film was threaded through the projector and fastened on the empty reel on the backside. Everyone had their bag of popcorn, their veggie corn-dog, their soda, and their seat.

When I sat down, the children hustled to claim their seats like a game of musical chairs. They had been waiting to see where I would sit. Finally, the lights went out, and the audience appreciated the craziness on the screen; with schadenfreude, they watched the actor trying to learn how to ski. We ate our popcorn and nearly choked as he mistakenly found himself skiing

311

backward down the hill. The first graders were slapping their legs and squealing with delight. They knew how to ski, and they knew you did not ski backward! That was so silly. Everyone was elated when in the end, Dean Jones outwits the villain who had been trying to hoodwink him out of the land.

In the intermission, at the end of the first reel, while they were setting up the second reel, I caught snippets of a story spreading among the students. Apparently, Mike had kissed Heather the day before at the ski slope. I thought that was odd. Mike was in the eighth grade, and Heather was in the fourth. When I looked concerned, Danny took me aside. He told me the details.

It had started on the ski lift with Mike and Doug. Mike had been bragging that he could kiss any girl he wanted. Doug thought Mike was getting too full of himself. So, Mike said, "Okay, I'll kiss Heather."

"Yeah, right, Mike. You won't kiss her. You're ridiculous."

Mike was insulted. "You don't believe me? I could kiss Heather."

"It's ridiculous. This whole conversation is ridiculous." Doug wanted to shut Mike up.

"You give me five dollars. I'll kiss Heather."

"Deal. Five dollars. But you have to kiss her today, and I have to see it."

"I'll do it after lunch."

Then after lunch, Mike had walked up to Heather and kissed her. She protested and pushed him away.

Doug was dumbfounded. He had never thought Mike would do it. He paid up.

When Danny told me this, I was a little disturbed. Then Danny broke into a great big smile.

"What!" I said, giving him a quizzical look. "Are you pulling my leg?"

"No, no, no. Mike did kiss Heather. I saw it." He burst into laughter and could not continue.

Doug was a little way off, and he saw Danny doubled over with laughter. He knew Danny had to be talking about him. He came over. Doug asked if Danny had been telling me the Mike and Heather story.

I nodded. "But he cannot finish the story."

Doug looked chagrinned. "The part he cannot tell you was that it was all a scam. Mike had worked it out with Heather beforehand. They split the five dollars."

It was my turn to laugh, pat Doug on the back, say, "That's not right. Not right at all," and then laugh some more.

CHAPTER SIXTY-TWO

THE TIDE TURNS

W hile everyone was gathering their things at the end of the evening, Ron McElvain mentioned to me that he had just heard that Judy Porterfield had announced her resignation. Judy was the teacher of the one-room school in Glenwood Springs. It was the nearest school to mine. I think it had ten students. She was also young, probably in her late twenties. I felt confirmation when I heard that. Bonnie Holderbaum had brought her up as an example of someone I should strive to emulate on a couple of occasions. So, yeah. Okay. I'll emulate her.

Virginia Ryber had arrived. She would be starting in another week; I could make it. The children were excited at school the next week, although it hurt when Roy, Heather, Shon, and Kelli all said they wished they had been assigned to Miss Ryber rather than me. Yes, I knew they were just children and mouthing off; still, I had invested so much in them. And then Chrissie joined the mutiny. Not Chrissie. Et tu Brutus?

It remained bitterly cold, and my propane tank's gauge was in free fall. Money, so scarce, was burning up. I hated having to deal with this, the ennui of insufficient cash. Poverty was such a crusher.

It would be impossible to overvalue what the McElvains meant to me that winter. They were crucial to my mental stability. Eating at their house on Thursday nights was such a balm. They were a safe sounding board. I could always count on Ron and Connie taking my side. I talked to them about my plans. Ron gently reminded me that I had promised to stay for three years. I grimaced. Then he said, "Well, I think you have done three years in one." I shrugged. I did feel bad that I was leaving so quickly that my career as an educator was melting away. But, in truth, I was still ambivalent. I knew I had to go. Every rational cell in my brain was punching the cancel ticket. But the brain is not rational, my attachments to my students, the friendships the parents had offered me, and my love of the land demanded my attention. Those strong bonds wanted equal airtime in my brain.

As I was leaving their house at the end of the evening, Connie stepped outside with me. She laughed and said that her precious first grader had wanted to tell me that I was handsome but had been too embarrassed. We both laughed. But that was what made leaving so hard.

The following Saturday, Ron took me birding again. We drove up by Piceance Creek, and he pointed out a rough-legged hawk and a marsh hawk. He could identify them across a field even as he drove. He could identify them just by their flight patterns. I was impressed. Then we saw a golden eagle.

He said that if indeed I was leaving, he was thankful I had been here one year. "I was in this school one year in my eighth grade," he said. "And I'll tell you the educational experience my daughter has received compared to what I got is incalculable." He compared me to a pastor who had been in Rifle for only one year. "We had a pastor named Robert Peck. He was here just one year and was headed straight up. That's how I think about you."

That was incredibly nice and more than I deserved. Though in truth, I rated my performance as mediocre. There was so much more I had wanted to do for the children. But I had been overwhelmed.

It did not help my leaving process when that week Misty and Kim went through a phase of calling me, Daddy. It was so touching, Misty coming up to my desk, "Daddy, can you help me with my math." Her voice was still that of a little child. It was adorable. I hugged her and kissed the top of her head. She was so cute.

Had I provided a better education to these students? Even with my overwhelming load, had the teaching really been superior? Must I stay because I could do a better job than the next teacher? I wrestled with this. And I did like living in the country, I really did. Obviously, not everybody agreed with me. I say obviously, because there just weren't many people in Rulison, but I thought it was gorgeous. I kept coming back to the call of the mountains, and the river kept running.

Shon came in one morning grumpy. I took him into the next room, talked with him, and had a prayer with him. The rest of the day, he was in a much better mood. So, maybe, I really was necessary.

Judy Porterfield, the Glenwood Springs teacher that was resigning, stopped by my Rifle school at the end of the month. It was late on a Sunday evening. She needed to borrow my movie projector. I got it out for her and showed her how this model worked. I told her of its idiosyncrasies. She told me she had announced her resignation; I told her I had heard. I said I was maybe a week or at most a month away from making that decision myself. As she left, she said, "Don't work too hard."

I gave a sad laugh. "Is that even possible?"

"Exactly. That's why I'm leaving."

When some of the students struck up their grumbling again and wished they could be with Miss Ryber rather than me, Steven told them to shut up. "You guys are nuts. Mr. Brauer is the best teacher we've ever had, and I'd much rather be in his class."

I do believe I choked up a little.

CHAPTER SIXTY-THREE

KEEP ON RUNNING

To prepare for Miss Ryber's start, they scheduled a work bee for Sunday. She started on Monday. It was a necessary deep clean. Mr. Grant, Cory's father, showed up, which was a surprise. I heard later, however, that he had spent most of the day complaining about me and justifying his withdrawal of Cory. In particular, he had cornered Vivian Opitz. Vivian was a vibrant redhead. Mr. Grant had thought she would be sympathetic, but she sought me out when he left.

"He is feeling guilty, Mr. Brauer," she said. "He knows Cory will never get this quality of schooling again." She paused and nodded her head a couple of times. "You know what I think?" She stopped; she had a bottle of Windex in her hand. She saw a smudge on a window, and she gave it a spray and then wiped it with the paper towel. She looked back at me with the knowing smile of a woman's intuition. "He asked me if you and Dr. McElvain had visited Bud and me. Didn't the two of you go visit some of the parents who were behind on their tuition?"

Suddenly it made sense. Of course! Yes, Ron McElvain and I had visited several parents who were behind on their payments. I had not put two and two together because Mr. Grant had been pleasant and apologetic and had gotten out his checkbook and caught up on his delinquent bill. Money was not a problem, and he was sorry that we had had to come out to visit him. Afterward, Ron and I had commented how easy that visit had been if only the others were like that.

"That's not what he told me," Vivian shook her head vigorously. "He thought it was very nervy of the two of you to come to his house and ask for money." Vivian gave me a look of understanding. "Mark my word, the Grants will have moved before the month is out."

She was right.

I came back in the evening to do some work. The work bee had been wonderful and all that, but it had retarded the work I had to put in on Sundays. Still, something was different. As I walked up the road toward the school, the lights were on. Miss Ryber was in the next room. I was no longer alone; that was nice. We really had not had much time to talk during the day. I stuck my head in the room and told her it was nice to have someone else here. She smiled.

"All right, I'm going to get some work done. I just wanted to say this is nice."

But before I could disappear, she burst into laughter. I stopped and looked back at her. That was odd.

"You're really looking forward to tomorrow?"

She laughed again. "I haven't told anybody here yet."

"Yeah? What?"

"Roger called me tonight. He proposed."

"Really? That's amazing!" I exclaimed.

"Yes, Roger said that after he left last week, he was feeling so miserable and realized he couldn't live without me."

"Virginia, that's so amazing," I repeated myself. "We've not known each other long, but I feel like I need to give you a hug." I said as I approached.

She laughed, stood up, and accepted the hug.

"Wow! Wow! Just Wow! I'm speechless," I said as I stepped back.

"I hear that you and Valerie are a couple," she said. "Tina is a talker."

"Yes, I like Valerie." And I was pleased that Tina was telling Virginia. That meant things were going well.

And with a second teacher, Miss Ryber, the next day, it was as if all the windows in the schoolhouse had been opened, as if sage breezes filled the room and perfumed the carpeted floor; as if the sun, which shined a lot in Western Colorado, had climbed to new heights; as if the river had burst it's ice cover and had begun an abundant spring run; as if time had slowed down so that now we could sense the earth's revolutions and the mountains ascending. With a second teacher in the schoolhouse it was different and manageable. It was lovely. Chrissie and Heather hung out around my desk even more. Roy was back to carrying on conversations with me. Mike and Doug were cracking jokes, and at Bible class the first, second, and third graders were so excited to come over into the big room. I had eleven students and five grades, and I had time to pay attention. In short, it was heaven.

For P.E. that week, we began running. They put on their tennis shoes and ran down the road. I gave them pointers on how to breathe, pattern the inhalation and exhalation, and find their running rhythm. The road in front of the schoolhouse had a car every half hour at most. So, I put one of the older students at the front and brought up the rear. Sometimes I would take the lead. We talked about building up stamina. They were astounded that I could run ten miles without stopping.

"I am going to do that, Mr. Brauer," Wayne proclaimed with confidence.

With the population increasing in Rifle, the number of surgeries performed at the hospital was going up. So, Mr. Mitchell brought in an associate, Jerry Smith. He was of a more rounded figure, with a round head and rapidly vanishing hair. It would be hard to overestimate how much Jerry admired Mitch. They had worked together before. Mitch had been his mentor, and Jerry was pleased to be here. He, too, was staying with the Mitchells at least until summer. His wife, Nancy, was still working as an elementary school teacher in the Midwest. Jerry loved the pastoral countryside. He was gregarious and took a liking to me. He gave me a lot of good advice.

I was up at the Mitchell's on Friday night. Mitch said the church asked him to look at a school feasibility study. With the enrollment on a sharp upward slope, it was becoming evident that the current two-room schoolhouse may soon be unable to accommodate the students. After supper, we sat on their couch as the fire burned in the fireplace. It was Mitch, Jerry, and I. Virginia had gone to her room to call her fiancé. Mitch said he had been wondering about renovating the second building on the grounds. But, of course, that was not ideal. Maybe they should build a new school on the church's property in town. They had plenty of room there. In any case, would I be willing to sit on that committee?

I was intrigued. No doubt, if this year was any indicator, the projections for students in the next few years were optimistic, and I would be very interested, but…

"Well, Mr. Mitchell, the truth is I think it is unlikely that I am back next year."

"Marvin, we don't want to hear that type of talk," he said, but he said it with an underlying understanding.

I told them I was strongly considering going back to Union College to finish my premed requirements. Mr. Mitchell and Jerry gave me a little pitch for considering nursing with the intention of becoming a nurse anesthetist like themselves. The advantages were a much shorter training period. That sounded good, but I was afraid I would always regret not having pursued the higher degree.

And at the school board meeting the following Tuesday night, I announced that I would be sending my resignation to the conference the next week.

CHAPTER SIXTY-FOUR

RUNAWAY

Kelli ran away from school! On Wednesday, she got upset and ran off the school grounds. Kelli ran away. O my! Yes, her mother had run away as well. Bonnie had gone back to Chicago, and Kelli and Shon were both upset about the disruption at home. Bill had been trying to hold it together. He was a good man and was trying to be both mother and father. But Kelli, running away, this could not be tolerated.

She was sorry, very sorry. I called Ron McElvain; we talked. I called Bill Holderbaum; we talked. I spoke to Miss Ryber. What were we going to do? I would have to suspend Kelli, and she was distraught. She was so sorry. She didn't want to miss school; she had come back after all. She didn't stay away.

She was standing beside my desk at the end of the day. The other students had gone. Her dad was on the way to pick her up. "I'm so sorry, Mr. Brauer. I'll never do it again, but don't suspend me, please."

"Kelli, we simply cannot let students run off the campus without consequences."

"Well then..." She was crying. "Can you spank me instead?"

"Yes, we could spank you." I spouted off.

"Well, then I want a spanking."

"Kelli, I wasn't serious." I remonstrated.

"Please, I don't want to be suspended. But, if you must punish me, I want a spanking."

I studied her. "You're serious? You want a spanking rather than a suspension."

She bowed her head and did not look at me. She was holding back her tears.

I sighed. I got up and went to the door between the rooms. I called in Virginia. "Kelli has suggested a spanking rather than a suspension."

This suggestion took Virginia aback. "I don't know! A spanking," She sighed. "I don't know, Marvin."

"Yeah, I agree. I'm not comfortable with this."

"I don't want to be suspended, Mr. Brauer. My dad still gives Shon spankings."

Bill's truck drove in the driveway. He came into the classroom. Kelli did not raise her head as he put a firm hand on her shoulder. The handgrip said that she had seriously messed up, but it did not change that she was his beloved daughter. She was very embarrassed.

I filled in Bill with what Kelli was choosing. He sent Kelli to the truck.

"Marvin, I'm going to support you in whatever decision you make. It has been very hard on the children with Bonnie being gone. Kelli has been very upset about it."

I acknowledged his point. He was trying in his way to argue for leniency.

"The problem is we cannot allow students to run away off the school grounds. That is dangerous for the students, and if we do not address this right now, it will worsen. We must do something. It is a liability risk."

Bill understood.

"A suspension or a spanking would both send the message that we don't tolerate this."

Virginia looked at me askance. "Are you really considering a spanking?"

"Yes, I am." I was, and the reason I was considering it, the only reason I was considering it was that Kelli had pleaded for it rather than suspension. She had been moodier with her mother gone, and she had been more difficult, but she did not want us to suspend her. Kelli did not want to be away from school, especially with her mother gone. Kelli was an amazing person, so open; she let her soul shine. She could be moody and cranky. She could be mean at times with the younger children, but then she also had the rare talent of seeing herself, repenting and then changing. She could be snide and then meek. She was imminently teachable. I really saw a lot of myself in her and given a choice between a suspension and a spanking, she had pleaded for a spanking.

Bill was sad. He was okay with a suspension or a spanking. He was just sorry that Kelli was so affected by the home distress. "This is just so unlike Kelli."

I was also very upset. I said I would call Ron McElvain and the conference before we made a final decision.

I did call the conference office. I talked with Mr. Rice. He said that spankings were still allowed policy, but he had significant reservations about them. I went through the story and discussed that the student had asked for it.

"Well, make sure Virginia is with you when you spank her."

"Yes, yes, of course."

The following morning at the start of school, I announced to the students that running off the school property would never be tolerated, and that Kelli had chosen a spanking. The students were aghast that Mr. Brauer was going to spank Kelli. Kelli was weeping. We got up. Kelli, Miss Ryber, and I went down into the coal room. She was crying. I spanked her four times with my belt.

When I came back upstairs, my legs were weak. I stood upfront.

"Listen up. I'm never, ever going to spank another child again. If you run off the property, I will suspend you."

And then I sank into my chair. Kelli had her head on her desk, and Heather was mad at me. All the other students were looking at Kelli. What they really wanted to know was, did it hurt?

CHAPTER SIXTY-FIVE

DÉJÀ VU

Blue skies never grow old. It had been another beautiful Sabbath afternoon in Western Colorado. The sky had been pristine, indigo blue with not a cloud in the sky. After church I went with the McElvains. They had packed sandwiches, and we drove up above Rifle on the backside of the Book Cliffs to a state trail.

They had borrowed snowshoes from Ron's father, and the five of us had strapped them on and then taken a hike. I had snowshoed only once before and never on an extended hike. The ability to traverse through areas of deep snow and see the hinterland amid winter was bedazzling. I was enthralled to walk up over the hill from the road and then enter the silent pinon forest, going where man rarely ever went. You stepped on a drift that under ordinary circumstances would have plunged your waist deep in snow, but with the snowshoes, you walked on water, albeit freeze-dried water, still.

We measured our pace since we had the younger children, Kim and Jon, with us, which gave me ample time to stand and reverentially take in the landscape. Of course, it was fun to have the wonder of children along. In this case, however, the wonder belonged to the whole party. We saw a couple of golden eagles soaring above us. And Ron and I had some time to talk about the week.

Mostly I downloaded on him, and he was a good listener. We were both hoping things would even out. He had heard further information about Mrs. Holderbaum. He could not understand how a mother could just go off and leave. The children were reaping the consequences and through them the whole school. Ron expressed appreciation of how Bill was handling this.

The day before, our second ski day had gone well. Two weeks of skiing without injury was an accomplishment, and my skills were rapidly improving. However, I had taken a couple of dandy head-over-heels falls when I pushed myself beyond my comfort level. Fortunately, I had the gift of being young.

In the ski lodge, Tina Mitchell had talked to me at lunch. Now that Miss Ryber was here, Tina was no longer the aide, and she said she missed the children and had really enjoyed working with me. She caught me up on her latest conversations with her daughter. Tina relished giving me little tidbits when she could. The juicy note for today was that her daughter had cried on the phone because she so desperately wanted to come home and had blown a kiss to give to Danny and me. It was as if Tina had to make sure my tank was full, so unscrew the cap and fill it up with premium gasoline. She also told me that Mitch said he would not invite me to come back and walk on their land if I left. I laughed and told her to tell her husband my intention of leaving was so that I could come back and buy land of my own. Tina enjoyed my comeback.

In the second week of February, Valerie came home for a couple of days. The Mitchells were going over to Denver for the weekend, but Valerie had wanted to spend more time with me, so Tina had arranged that I would drive her over on Friday after school got out, which would give Valerie and me some extended time. I was looking forward to it.

I went up to their house on Wednesday evening. After supper, as usual, we took our nocturnal promenade. The plans had been changing. She was now going to ride over with her parents. As we walked down to the bottom of the road, I told her I loved her, and she squeezed me. I asked if she wanted me to come over on Friday, even though she was riding the day before with her parents. She said, of course, she would love to see me but that her friend Ruthie had set up a blind date for her. She tried to assure me that this did not essentially change things. While I was with her and when she kissed me, I wanted to believe her, but when I got home, it all felt like the famous Yankees catcher and manager Yogi Berra had said, "It's like déjà vu all over again." I just ached.

I learned that a friend of David's from college was coming home to go out with Valerie. The friend had known Valerie and had a deep crush on her.

I carried on with teaching and was glad for Friday when I could go skiing. I was more aggressive than before and skied so much better. But I was still not good. I was only skiing intermediate slopes, but I was improving. On one trip down I went to the backside and at the top just stopped and looked out over the valleys of unbroken snow. I could see ridge after ridge and the majestic Sopris mountain. That made me sad because I knew Valerie would have loved the view as well, and I was sad that I couldn't share it.

At church the following day, I sat down beside Jerry Smith. His wife was still somewhere in the Midwest, and he was baching it. He was a little uncomfortable that it was just Virginia and him in the Mitchell's house and talked to me about maybe renting my extra room. I invited him to stop by after church. I could show him the room. I would, of course, be delighted to have someone else sharing the rent. He did drop by. He was amazed at how small my house was, and the extra room was even tinier and not well heated. He said he would give it some consideration. And then he talked to me about Valerie.

"You know Marvin; she's seventeen. I don't care how mature she is for her age. She is seventeen. Yes, she's attractive, but what are you, twenty-two?"

"I'm twenty-three."

"Yeah, right. You should be dating women your age, women who are at the same stage in life as you."

I nodded, and after he left, I thought about it. I thought about it a lot. But of course, the flaw to his argument was that there were no women my age to date, still trying to date someone younger just led inevitably to this heartbreak that I was in the middle of, smackdown deep.

I worked hard on Sunday. Miss Ryber had me move her desk for her. I could tell that she was aware something was going wrong with Valerie and me, but I did not want to discuss it. I went to a birthday party for my eighth grader, Mike, in the evening. It was a skating party in Grand Junction. It was fun to see the kids out of the schoolroom.

Dan Fogelberg's *Old Lang Syne* came on the radio on the way back. It had been a big hit for him in eighty-one. It is the song where he met his lover in the grocery store, and they drink beers in her car, and at the end, he just remembers the pain. And then, the song segues into a beautiful melancholic saxophone solo. It was a gorgeous song, and I was remembering that pain.

And for a little bit in the darkness of Colorado where there were no houses along the road, no other cars, just the mountains, the river, and my headlights, I floored the pedal. My car was no sports car, but I got it to ninety on the highway. What the hell! What was the worst that could happen? Okay, hitting a deer would be horrible. And my naturally conservative nature regained control; I probably had it at ninety for less than twenty seconds. My adrenaline needs were small.

CHAPTER SIXTY-SIX

I KNOW WHEN I'M LOSING

At school, we practiced for an upcoming music festival that the conference held at Campion Academy. Mr. Luke was the choir director at Campion Academy. He had a reputation among Adventists all over the state as an excellent choir director. My mother, a discerning judge of musical talent and not one to give needless compliments, praised his talent. Well, hell, Mr. Luke was my choir director in grade school.

The expectation was that the students would know the words and have practiced the songs. Unfortunately, many smaller schools were not participating. The teachers were not music teachers and were too intimidated to teach music. But I thought it would be beneficial for my students. It would broaden their education. We had a piano in the classroom, and I played a little. Unfortunately, I was not a proficient (to borrow from Pride and Prejudice). In fact, I was so not good that Kelli told me if I could not play better, she would no longer sing. (Kelli could be so tactful.) I told her that I was playing my best.

At lunch, Kelli and Heather sidelined me. They asked my advice on how to get Mike to like them. Kelli had been trying to get his attention by teasing and being an annoyance. On that particular day, they had nearly gotten in several fights. Her tactics were not working. Since teasing was not working, I suggested why not try to be nice. She gave me a little knowing smile, a smile that once again indicated she could see her behavior, and she would try to change.

Then in the afternoon, during the study time, Kelli asked if I was going to marry Valerie. That took me aback. Marry Valerie?

I would like to once more credit Danny for keeping his mouth shut. He knew a lot more than anyone else in the school. He knew that there had been a plan for me to drive Valerie over the mountains. The Mitchells were going over on Thursday. The original plan was for Valerie to stay an extra day to spend time with me. That had been what she had wanted. Until her friend had set up the blind date, and it had all fallen through. He did not know how much I liked his sister, but he could not have been too far off. Danny could have traded this information at the school for a profit, but he was not a source.

"Marry Valerie? I don't think so. Truth is, I doubt it will last another month."

"Really!" The whole classroom was instantly paying attention.

"Why's that," Mike called out from the back.

"I don't know," I knew they had drawn me in again. I should have kept my mouth shut. "I just don't tend to have relationships that last that long." I tried to portray insouciance. I won no Oscar nominations for the role. I was, in fact, barely able to keep my voice from cracking.

In the evening, I called my mom and talked for a long time. She tried to be encouraging. She said that I was a lot like my Uncle Dick. He would quickly fall in love, and if the girl didn't respond as quickly, he would be heartbroken and break it off. My Uncle Dick eventually did marry my mother's sister, and everybody had adored him, so take heart, Marvin.

And I got a Valentine's card from Valerie. So maybe it was not over.

I laid out my sleeping pad and sleeping bag. I put my backpack beside it on the gym floor. My boys were laying out theirs: Mike, Ron, Danny, Doug, Shon, Steven, and Roy. We were in the gymnasium at Campion Academy for the music festival.

And I thought it was awkward. Liking Valerie in her home where she was comfortable and everybody was pulling for me was much easier. Here, where she was a high school student, and I was a college graduate was disconcerting. There were no ways to change the facts. Still, I was not going to avoid her. Then again, neither did I plan to make a spectacle of myself.

But I could not disappear; I knew too many kids at the academy. Having worked at the conference's summer camp the last three years, I knew a lot of them. Lisa, Cindy, and Rhonda ran across the parking lot to hug me when they first saw me. After that, they and a whole host of students constantly came up to greet me. Mike was impressed, especially as he had developed a crush on Lisa at the medical conference last fall. Lisa Berg was a freshman who attended my dad's church. Lisa and I were good friends.

Sherri Dunkin and Annette Williams, both of whom I had known from camp, came over to talk to me. Sherri and I had worked at camp together last summer; she was also a member of my dad's church. I knew Annette as Annie. She came from Southwestern Colorado, down near Farmington. I remembered her because one Sunday, just before leaving, she had come up to the camp store where I was standing on the porch. She wanted to say goodbye to me, and then just before leaving, she had leaned up and kissed me on the cheek. That touched me. It was so sweet and innocent.

They came over to talk to me and started off talking about camp. Annie had applied to work the following summer. They were disappointed when I said I did not see a way to return. They teased me about being "Mr. Brauer."

"Mr. Brauer, is it? Marvin is not good enough."

I shrugged.

"And where is Mrs. Brauer?" Sherri asked, looking around the campus.

They were sitting beside me on my mat. I was waiting to take my boys to the music building.

"Mrs. Brauer? Well, the only Mrs. Brauer is my mother, and she will be up here this weekend, and there will not be another one for some time."

"Really, not for a long time? Well, I know someone who would like to be Mrs. Brauer." Sherri joked, which sent Annie into peals of laughter. "Valerie is talking all the time about how wonderful Marvin is...You know Marvin is so neat! Marvin is so funny. Marvin is so kind, so smart, so handsome." Sherrie had Annie doubling over. "And I keep telling her, 'Valerie, we know Marvin too. Yes, he's very neat. I worked with Marvin.'"

Annie jumped in, "You remember a couple weeks ago, Valerie running down the hall when she had a phone call. She was so sure it was you, and she was so excited."

I took the ribbing.

I got the children to the auditorium. I am not sure they had a fabulous time. Many of the other students had come from schools where they had someone with some musical ability. Those students were much better prepared. But my kids could outski them.

When the children were in their choir practice, Valerie came and got me the following day. She had to put together slides for a vespers program. She used some of her slides and a number from the principal Dick Duerksen who had a reputation as a great nature photographer. I sat with her all afternoon as she steadily built her slide carousel.

In the evening after the main program, there was an afterglow where Valerie showed her slides set to a musical accompaniment. I figured I would hang at the back against the wall and watch. She saw me, however, and patted an empty seat beside her. I had no choice. I sat down beside her. Her program was well done, but I kept looking around, and I saw that everyone was looking at us, really at me. Who the heck was that guy sitting beside Valerie? I leaned over and whispered to her. I told her everybody was looking at me. They were trying to figure out who was sitting beside her.

She smiled and replied, "You're just conceited."

That was funny. I'll give her that.

The next day was Sabbath. I spent Sabbath School, church, lunch, the afternoon program, supper, and the evening program with her. We held hands in church, and both were moved by Duerksen's slide presentation of Christ. We both had to wipe our eyes.

My parents were there, and Valerie came over and met them. She was warm friendly, and I loved having her by my side. She was coming home the next weekend for her birthday. So, I thought at the time; maybe my worries had been overestimated. Perhaps I had exaggerated my fears. Maybe we were okay.

Unfortunately, my intuition, as usual, was spot on.

CHAPTER SIXTY-SEVEN

SOME TIMES I FEEL

It was March. Spring was arriving. The snow in the valleys had melted, and the little stream that crossed the schoolyard was flowing. All the kids loved playing in it at recess. Steven and Doug kept building more and more complicated dams. They would back up all the water, then bust it up, and let it flood. The younger boys, Justin, Doyle, Wayne, and Chad wanted to help. They were assigned downstream dam projects. I watched Steven all year long, and I was still impressed at his visuospatial abilities and how he could envision complicated structures and build them. Unfortunately, others had falsely labeled him in the past.

While Steven and Doug built their bridges, some of the other children had found an amusing little trick on the backside of the school. Bessie, the brown Jersey cow, lived in a little pasture behind the school. There was fencing around the field. At the top of the fencing, the Massey's had strung an electric line. The children had discovered that if you held hands, only the person at the end of the line got the shock. They found this exciting, almost electric. Miss Ryber caught them at it and gave them a lecture on the dangers of electricity. It worried both of us, and I added my admonitions to Virginia's. What if one of my children had been hurt?

At P.E., we continued to run. On one of the runs, Carolyn collapsed. It seemed a little bit histrionic, but I helped her back up. All the boys teased her, except Steven and Danny, who were kind. Roy had developed a crush on Kelli and tried to run beside her all the time. Kelli tried her best to be polite, but she wanted to be running with Mike. On another of the runs, four of the boys broke away. One of them had a BB gun and shot a dog. That upset me. I sat them down and lectured them on being kind, not mean to animals.

In the evenings, I still spent my time at school. Miss Ryber followed my example in February, but by March I had the schoolhouse nights to myself again. I did not know how she got everything done. I figured she was more efficient, or maybe she was an eight-to-four teacher. In any case, the lights were on long into the night.

Mrs. Mitchell called me in advance of Valerie coming home for her birthday. She talked about many things in her usual chatty way and then casually added that it would be okay for me to date Valerie casually. Casually date? What did that even mean? Did it mean to date and not care? How did one do that? I certainly had no clue, but I did realize Tina was sending me a message.

Danny and I spent most of the day together on that Friday's ski trip. My relationship with his sister was getting complicated, but Danny and I were cool. He was still my buddy. We both were skiing faster. We had both improved this year and had a good time.

On Sunday it was Valerie's birthday. She had come home. As usual I was up working at the school preparing for the next week, but I kept one ear out for the phone. I did not know the plan, but I knew at the very least they would have a birthday supper. When my work at school ended, I drove home. There had been no call. I could not believe it; I had never, ever been treated like this. Was that what Tina had hinted at with her 'casual dating' comment?

I have always had an extremely low tolerance for ambiguity. It had to be one way or the other but make a choice. I did not fancy indecision, dithering, nor any variant of those love games. I did not have to be with her all the time. I understood her wanting to be with her family, but if on her birthday she did not want to be with me — well, I did not need it to be any clearer.

I got in my car and drove up to their house. I rang the doorbell. Virginia answered. She said the Mitchell's and Jerry had gone swimming at Glenwood Springs and then out to eat to celebrate Valerie's birthday. Although Virginia and I were not close, she did not offer any excuses for the Mitchell's. We both knew this was not how it should be done. I had written a note and sealed it in an envelope. I held the card in my hand and fidgeted with it several times. Finally, I asked Virginia if she would give it to Valerie. Virginia took the note.

"I'm sorry, Marvin," she said.

My message to Valerie was brief.

> Valerie,
> It's over. I can't love someone who doesn't care.
> Goodbye,
> Marvin

In her defense, she was seventeen. I credited that to her account.

And, it had not caught me by surprise. I had had my inklings. Nevertheless, I could not understand it. What had happened? Had she just gotten bored of me and wanted to move on? Had another guy started to show interest in her? That was likely; she oozed femininity. She was always drawing looks from the guys. Guys were constantly checking her out. Yes, they were.

Still, it hurt. It hurt like hell, even if she was not the first girl to develop a crush on me, get over it and then leave. It was an all too familiar pattern. Quite predictable right around three months. That seemed to be the longest a girl wanted to be with me, and it had honed excellent instincts. I could feel it from afar off, like some loner wolf, who could scent that the bitch he had been courting had just run off with another male. So, I was growing survival strategies. If she was no longer in love, then just run.

Another one in the garbage bag like all the earlier girls I had fallen for. It never survived three months, and the girl would break up with me. Well, to be honest, I was usually the one who started the conversation, but only because I could not stand being miserable. So, I would bring up the conversation, and they would confirm the feelings were gone, and we would walk away.

Still, I suffered. Valerie cast me off. I who had been so enthralled. She had fit so close, had had so many qualities that I admired, compassionate, in tune with nature, funny, spiritual, and beautiful. And too young.

At least I had nothing to regret. I had been honorable and decent, yet again.

Some people said I was too proud. Maybe that was it. I needed to be humbler. I had heard that enough times and I did not disagree. But how do you change your natural core? I could fake it. I could try, of course. I could play-act, pretend. But they — the friends I had talked to in the past when I had had difficulties with women — said that I thought I was more intelligent than other people. Again, I could fake it. If my fatal flaw was that I felt I was smarter than others; if this was my Greek tragedy; if this was the shortcoming that would bring my ruin; if this was it, what was I to do? Was I proud? Yes, I was. I knew that to be accurate, but I termed it self-confidence. All the Brauer boys were confident. We had a lot of confidence. Except I was the only one with girl problems.

And I was sad and alone.

There was one more great song that was just being introduced to the States about that time. Soft Cell was a small British band. They had not had much commercial success, but they had added a 60's song to their club repertoire. They released it as a single in Great Britain in 1981. It started getting played in the U.S. in the spring of 1982 and would stay on the charts for a record 43 weeks. As I drove home, *Tainted Love,* became my theme song.

I wanted to run away.

CHAPTER SIXTY-EIGHT

A SWEET CHILD

The next day at recess, I watched the children playing by the stream. Kim and Misty were hanging close. They liked Miss Ryber, but they missed me and frequently were by my side at recess.

Kim said, "If Mr. Brauer is daddy, then Valerie must be mommy." That was difficult. I choked up and had to get away to the bathroom to compose myself.

Later, in the afternoon, I had another moment where it came rushing on me again, and I felt like I was about to break into tears. Angie looked at me; dear little Angie was near my desk. She stopped and said with compassion. "What's wrong, Mr. Brauer?" That got the attention of several other students, and they gave me quizzical looks.

And at the end of the day, as Virginia and I were standing in the driveway supervising the children leaving, she asked me how I was doing. I hesitated, and as I hesitated, I saw that Danny had heard the question. He was anxiously looking at me.

I managed to hold it together enough to say two syllables, "Okay." I could not have handled any more than that.

337

But I had things that needed completing. First, I needed to talk to Bill Holderbaum. We needed to talk about Shon getting his work done and some attitude problems, so in the evening, I called to see if I could come up to talk.

"Of course," Bill had responded.

I drove up. I sat down with Bill and started to go over the incidents I had written down where Shon had totally refused to do his assignments. Bill brought in both Shon and Kelli. I have said it before; Bill was a good father. He always tried to combine compassion with reason and intelligence. We had an open discussion of the concerns. Shon and Kelli both loved their father. By the end of the evening, we had done a lot. Both children were happy with the school and with me. We were all back on the same team. In particular, Shon's attitude had had a reset. Kelli's attitude was mercurial, not requiring the hard reset.

I think that evening, with the mediation of his father, Shon saw again that I really did like him; even when he was acting out, I still liked him. And that made a difference.

When we felt like we were in a good place, Bill looked around. His children were smiling and laughing.

"I think we need to celebrate this. Marvin, will you join us for a banana split?"

"Sounds good to me."

Bill got up to get the ice cream. Kelli grabbed the bananas and Shon the bowls. It was delightful to sit at the table with Bill, Kelli, and Shon. We poured chocolate syrup over the base of bananas and vanilla ice cream. And as we sat there eating, Shon and Kelli kept looking back and forth from their dad to me. Kelli scooted close and hugged her father. Bill put an arm around her and then the other around Shon. And the three of them then looked at me with broad smiles. I loved the Holderbaums.

As I left to go to my car, Bill walked me out. I told him to pray for me. I was feeling bad. Valerie and I had broken up. He did not laugh nor tell me she was too young. Instead, Bill put an arm on my shoulder and confessed how hard it was with Bonnie gone.

He had talked to me a little bit before about her but standing in the night air by my car, he opened up and gave me more details.

Compared to my trifles of the heart, his sounded painful. We promised to pray for each other.

"I appreciate you, Marvin. I appreciate that you came and talked to me."

I stopped as I opened the door. "Bill, you've been a good friend."

March brought more snow. A foot of snow. I suggested that we put on our snow boots and cross the road. There was a large field of untouched sagebrush there. We could play a bigger game of capture the flag. We could use the large bushes to hide and go deep into enemy lines without being seen. Everyone was all excited. The younger grades danced across the no man's line and danced back.

The snow was deep, and a snowball fight was inevitable, and then, of course, they wanted to team up to put me in the snow, and they were so delighted with seven or eight of them draped on me like wolves on a moose they brought me down. Ah, the thrill of the hunt! It was still worth it to them even after I put Mike, all twisting and writhing, face down into the snow.

"But we got you, Mr. Brauer!" He was unrepentant.

I clapped my arm around his shoulder, "Yes, you did, Mike. Yes, you did."

Shon's attitude and schoolwork were in a steep ascent, and Kelli's mood had reset. But Roy refused to organize his Bible papers, and I found Carolyn in the hallway crying. I sat down and tried to counsel her. I did not know if I did any good, but she got up and returned to her desk.

In history, we had started studying the medieval ages. I had an unfinished Arthurian/Tolkien novel I had been working on. I brought it to school, and after lunch in the period where I read aloud to them, I read from my book for several days. When I got to the end of the manuscript, they were upset.

"Don't stop," they cried.

"Sorry, that is as far as I have gotten in it."

After school, on one of the days that Ron and his sisters stayed after to clean the school, he questioned me extensively about my book. He had a fertile mind. Ron started talking about Dungeons and Dragons. He had read about it and thought it sounded like a fun game. He was delighted when I said I had played it in college. He wanted to play it with me. I said maybe I would invite him over to the house to play some evening, maybe before Pathfinders. He was definitely on board with that.

And I will say that I very much enjoyed having Ron, Chrissie, and Angie stay after school a couple of times a week. Their mother would supervise the cleaning. They were three of the least complicated children. Intelligent, helpful. Angie was consistently happy open with such a cheerful disposition. Chrissie had the gift of helps. She showed her sentiments to me as her teacher, which were unwavering, by constantly being near, and if she could do a chore, clean the chalkboard. Take the erasers outside, bang them together, put out new chalk, empty the trash cans, clean the water fountain, grade the first-grader papers. Chrissie was happiest when she was doing something for me.

God, I loved my children.

CHAPTER SIXTY-NINE

ONLY GOD KNOWS

On Thursday night, the school board met. The group gathered around the craft table in Miss Ryber's room. We had met there many times throughout the year. These were all friends now since we had worked through some difficult times. The primary agenda for the meeting was to look at next year's teachers. They discussed Miss Ryber. As principal, they wanted my opinion. I had only positive comments, nothing negative. She was smart, personable, conscientious, and liked by the children. The conference also had given her positive marks. The board voted to rehire her.

"We would love to rehire you, Marvin."

I just smiled and shook my head. They moved on to other topics on the agenda, though they returned to me on several occasions. Had I really decided? Yes, I had sent my letter to the conference. I intended to go back to school in the fall and study and take my pre-med requirements.

On Saturday afternoon after church, I went up to the Mitchell's. I knew Valerie was not there. I had felt bad about the abruptness and brevity of my break-up. I did not like the way I had gone about it. So, I had called Valerie at school. We had talked. We had concluded that maybe we might date occasionally, and we would be friends. That was a little disingenuous on my part. I could never see myself dating her casually, and I knew she was never going to apologize for how she had treated me. Still, it felt better to at least pretend. I guess I did play some dating games. This was the game of we will be friends. Although everyone knows after you have dated being friends was rare. It was more likely to spot a unicorn.

In any case, it did clear the air and allowed me to be friends with the Mitchell's again. They invited me up to ride their horses. They did not get ridden unless I rode them. I was very willing to accommodate them since I loved to ride. Thus, I went up and rode their sorrel, Loni. It was a gorgeous day. Spring was rushing in. The branches of the willows were greening, and shoots were sprouting out of the ground. Three small colts came scampering to the fence line as I rode up the mountain from their house. Everywhere there was an abundant new birth. In the midst of this new life, my aloneness became amplified. I was doomed to be the traveler, the observer, the one who recorded it.

In the evening, the Pathfinder club had a benefit at the church. They had several skits that the children had worked up, and Bill had asked me to emcee. I had experience as an emcee as I had done it many times in high school. The audience was generous and laughed at my jokes. My jokes had always been lame, and the audience usually laughed that anyone had the nerve to stand on the stage and deliver such dumb jokes. Groans were as familiar as outright laughter, which was okay and equally appreciated. Of course, my students laughed and laughed, or at least the lower grades did.

The following day after putting in a long work session, we had our final parent-teacher conferences. Virginia did the younger grades, and I had the older grades. After the grumbling that occurred at the turn of the year, it seemed the parents were all back squarely in my corner. After talking to Virginia, even the parents of the younger children would poke their heads in. Vivian Opitz wanted to see how I was doing. Sandy Forshee wanted to talk to me. She had heard that Misty and Kim were calling me 'Daddy.' She thought that was so adorable. She thanked me for giving Misty such a good start. I did not get home until nine-thirty.

On Tuesday, I had a typical day. First, I had to talk to Steven about staying in his seat. Heather said she thought I hated her because I constantly had to reprimand her. Shon was still turning in his work, but it was getting sloppy. Roy took sides with anyone against me. Kelli had a moment of anger. Then the little children came over from the next room. Angie came up to me at my desk and whispered, "I like you, Mr. Brauer." The others heard and echoed the sentiments. It had been a long time since the older children had said anything like that. Still, I felt good about the work at the end of the day. Yes, I had to constantly stay on some of them, but as I understood it that was what a teacher did. And as I walked home, I felt satisfied.

I stopped at the mailbox as always, even though I no longer got letters from Valerie. My cat came over the street to greet me; I picked him up and opened the box—a letter from my sister-in-law, Nancy, and a large manilla envelope was inside. The large envelope was from the University of Colorado. I came inside, put the cat down, and opened it. Yes, I had decided for medicine against studying law; still, had I even been accepted? They noted that they only took the top fifteen percent, and yes, they granted me a seat, which meant I had to reopen that career box again and examine my options.

Accepted to law at a prestigious school, I could complete my degree in three years. Medicine was not certain, far from certain, plus I had to take another year of pre-med classes, then if I made it—a lot of people did not—but if I made it, medical school was four years, and then residency beyond all that. Was I really committed to medicine? I gave it thought and then more thought.

I turned to the letter from Nancy. Her letter was short. She said she had heard about my girl troubles and was sorry. She said that she had recently seen her friend Judy again, and Judy had asked about me. Nancy was enclosing a couple of pictures of

343

Judy. I pulled out the pictures. The girl was pretty and had lovely long legs. That was nice of Nancy. Nancy said that Judy was now at Loma Linda working on her Masters of Public Health. Curious, I taped the pictures on my wall.

In the evening, I drove to the church. The church was sponsoring a spiritual gifts seminar. In the eighties, this was the next big thing. The church had discovered spiritual gifts. They gave a survey. I scored high on knowledge and teaching and scored decently on discernment and leadership. After we scored the test, Sandy Forshee, sitting down the row from me, scooted over. She had heard about my break-up with Valerie. Everyone was talking about how they had scored on the survey, and she said that while she had been doing the test, she kept wondering about me and whether I had the gift of celibacy. I laughed and told her it was not really a gift if you had no choice in the matter. Then, she patted me on the shoulder with a smile. "You'll find someone," I took some comfort. We are creatures of touch, and just the hand on my shoulder was affirmative, especially since, as I have mentioned, nature had been particularly kind to her.

On the other hand, I had heard these comments about finding someone a lot. Their only use was in that they were well-meant. On the other hand, Sandy's comment on celibacy was humorous. I got a couple of chuckles remembering it as I drove home.

I want to say parenthetically while I am on the subject of spiritual gifts, my family has now commented that I had a high martyrdom gift for decades. My family was always funny.

There was always something going on. Always. I could have turned down activities. But, come to think about it, Virginia often was not at the activities. After work, she went to her room at the Mitchell's. Tina noted that while Virginia was pleasant and not a difficult guest, I talked to her more, even though I didn't even live at their house. On the next Saturday night, Danny, Kelli, and Steven had implored me to take them skating. But that Saturday morning, I did have a couple of hours at home. And as I was relaxing in my little house, eating my mashed-up bananas in lemon juice, water, and sugar over toast and peanut butter, and drinking a nice cold glass of milk, I thought how now that I did not have a girlfriend, my needs were so much less.

I had plenty of clothes. I did not need anymore. I had food. I loved my banana toast. I had a job, which I was good at and fulfilling. I had shelter. Yes, people thought it was a shack, but I liked it. It was warm and in the country. I really did not need anything else. My need for companionship drove my drive to pursue a career. If I could just learn to be content without a woman, I would not need to go back to school and put myself through the difficult studies of law or medicine. If I could only be satisfied. And for an hour or two that morning, it was sufficient, and that was nice.

I had Doyle on my right at church and Chrissie and Heather Savage on my left. In the evening, I met Danny, Steven, and Kelli at the school. I drove them to go skating in Grand Junction. I don't remember why Shon did not come, nor why it was these three. There was no romance between any of them. They were just good friends and I do remember they had a good time. They kept up a constant conversation all the way there and all the way back. Outside of school hours any of the discipline that I had to administer, any of the encouraging, motivating — that would be Danny — possibly even nagging; confiscating — that would be Steven and his knives; any trying to calm them from flying off the handle — that would be Kelli — any of these mannerisms or words that I had to engage in while in the school, I just dropped. When we were out of the school environment, I was a friend.

And as I was skating with them, I reflected on the teachers I had known. It was still a little odd to put myself in that category. I had known some great teachers. Some had taught because they needed a paycheck, they were not memorable. The best ones cared. They had gifts of understanding and enjoying humanity; gifts of fairness that were crucial; gifts of intelligence were mandatory; gifts of curiosity, and the gift of a sense of humor. They did not necessarily have to be funny, but they needed joie de vivre, as well as just pure joy. Those were different. A great teacher had to have the gifts of compassion, pity, and empathy.

345

They would need those in abundance. A great teacher had to have the gifts of compassion, pity, and empathy. They would need those in abundance. A great teacher had to have the gift of breaking down a problem and explaining it in manageable steps. Just as importantly, they needed the gift of listening. That was critical. To be a great teacher, they needed to want to be a mentor, and to do that; they needed to abound in balance, judgment, personal discipline, propriety. They needed to have a detailed understanding of boundaries and basic decency. The best teachers were not striving to develop disciples or obedient followers but were looking to develop the powers to evaluate and make mature decisions. The best teachers looked beyond their classroom or their discipline to see the student in all their fullness. Was this an impossible array of gifts? Yes, it was. None of even the best of teachers met all of these criteria, but a number of them were close. Where did I fit? I was aware of my deficiencies, but I had tried. I really had tried.

CHAPTER SEVENTY

MITTENS RETURNS

I arranged to attend a tour of the law campus during my spring break. As I drove up to the campus, I could see the flatirons above the school. They seemed almost to reach down and touch the campus. Those large granite slabs were impressive, as was the architecture of the school, the sandstone walls, the red tile roofs, the limestone trim, and black wrought iron accents, all in an Italianate style. I had not spent much time thinking about architecture, but I instantly appreciated the campus. In addition, the law school building itself was magnificent. I loved it and was really tempted to change my mind to pursue law rather than medicine. I joined several prospective students, and a young woman guided the tour. She was attractive. I tried to be extra polite, but she was just there doing her job and took no special notice of me.

I thought the classrooms with their large windows provided just the right atmosphere for mental stimulation. The library, of course, with its stacks and stacks of nicely bound volumes, appealed to me. I loved libraries. I knew that if I came, I would spend a lot of time sitting in a study carrel, with an array of books stacked up in front of me and a nice pen and paper. But what really caught my attention was the moot court. The tour guide stepped into the room and then proceeded to say how the school had won several competitions in the last few years with their trial teams. That sounded fabulous to me and a little scary.

I knew so little about the law. All the words she was throwing out were nearly lost on me. Contract, advocacy, litigation, with these I had an inkling, but what was tort? Some of the other students seemed to be so much better prepared. I wished I had had a background that had been more assimilated, not so very separate. But I was not going into the law, and I found myself grieving it just a little. A world of words sounded so wonderful. A profession that tried to defend injustice and assure fairness was so up my line. But I was not going into law.

I drove back to my parent's home. It was just a few miles from the Boulder campus. It could have been nice, but I had decided to stay within the accepted norms of my culture. I was going to try for medicine, even though I had already been accepted into law school and could finish in three years. Whereas in medicine, I was looking at least at eight more years of school and training; even though anyone who knew me objectively would have advised me to pursue the law, all my advisors were steeped with the same prejudices. "It was too hard to be a Christian and a lawyer." That was accepted truth, so I was not going into law.

Besides, as Adventists, we were all so proud of Loma Linda University and its school of medicine. Graduating from Loma Linda as a doctor gave you high status in the church. You could walk into any Adventist church around the world, and if they knew you were a doctor from Loma Linda, you were at least minor nobility. Doctor Brauer meant the same as Lord Brauer, or at least Count.

On the other hand, if in discourse at the Sabbath afternoon potluck, someone asked what my profession was if I had chosen the law and I had said, "I am an attorney-at-law. I am Marvin Brauer, Esquire." Well, that would have been a conversation stopper. They would have plastered on a fake smile, and the head would have turned to the next person in line.

I spent the spring break writing my fantasy novel, and on Saturday evening, I loaded up my car. We could not find my cat. We looked all around the house. I finally had to leave without him. I was worried he had gotten outside and had run away. Mitten's namesake, my cat when I was a child, had gotten outside and had run away. I had looked and looked and looked for that cat and had never found her.

I drove back over to Rulison alone. When I arrived at my house, it was silent and lonely, with no little furry friend to cuddle.

Tina Mitchell called to check on me the next day. She asked me about my vacation. I told her about my visit to the law school and how I was giving that some reconsideration. She said that David and Valerie had skied on Friday. David had been home from college. David had hurt his shoulder, and Valerie had really bruised her face. She told me that Valerie's new boyfriend, who was my age, had not come to visit as had been planned. I sensed that Mrs. Mitchell wanted me to ask questions about Valerie. I refrained. Tina noted that. She said Valerie was back at school, but I was most welcome to come up and visit them. They missed me.

Later in the day, my parents called. They had found Mittens! They were getting in their car to bring him to me. Even though it was three hours each way, my mom and dad brought me my cat. I had such excellent parents.

After the break, the children were all bright and cheerful. They were glad to be back and wanted to tell me what they had done and wanted to know what I had done. Ron wanted to know all the details of my tour of the law school. He was impressed. He thought I would make an excellent attorney. He liked to amplify things. The trial of John Hinckley's attempted assassination of Reagan was then in the media. Ron was sure I would be a famous lawyer. The conversation carried on through the day as he tried out different scenarios. At first, I was the prosecutor, and then he thought it would be more interesting if I were Hinckley's defense attorney. The defense was going to be by reason of insanity. Ron thought that was very clever. And then he returned to the topic of Dungeons and Dragons, and I suggested he could stay over after school on Wednesday. I would feed him some supper. We could play for an hour or two, and then he could ride with me to Pathfinders. He was over the moon about that idea.

The other thing that put the children in better moods was that the Cloningers had offered to take one student with them on a ski outing to Beaver Creek. Beaver Creek ski slope had only opened two years before. It was a little west of Vail and had quickly made a name for itself as an excellent place to ski. The children, especially the boys, came up to my desk to figure out how to help me. Could they help the first graders? Could they sweep the floor, wash the chalkboards? Doug even offered to clean the commodes! He was motivated. Any day skiing was so much better than a day at school, especially since our Friday skiing lessons were over. But in Colorado, you could ski well into April, especially when it kept snowing like it had been this year.

On Tuesday, another storm came through, bringing snow, and more than snow, big winds that laminated the earth with rippled, crusted layers of white. I found out who the motivated students were when I asked for volunteers to brave the wind and go down below to shovel in some more coal into the furnace. You had to grab the door when you opened it to keep it from slamming, and the gush of cold air rushed in. Which was accompanied by a round of "Shut the door!" emanating even from the little children. Everybody had their coat on or at least on the back of their chairs. The windows had snow-crusted streaks where the gales strung it.

Being stuck inside the classroom affected the moods of the young scholars. Even mild-mannered Chrissie smarted off. Chrissie!

And then, when I was checking over the students' work, I noted some odd patterns on the math papers of Heather. One of the tricks of the trade for multi-grade schools that I had been taught was to allow the students to grade their papers. It was considered a good learning experience. It was also an efficient tool for a teacher with too many classes, and I had incorporated it. It was particularly useful for arithmetic. The student just needed to check his answer with the published answer. It worked well. But I noted that Heather's work had the right answers to the wrong question number.

I called her up to the desk. I pointed to her paper and then showed her the correct answer next to the wrong question. Heather could be mouthy at times. She often spoke when she should have been silent. She could get in griping and whining moods. But when I looked up at her, she was instantly deeply repentant. Tears were already forming. She did not say anything; she could not speak.

"You copied the answers?"

She nodded.

I saw that Danny, with his extrasensory capabilities, had picked up that something was happening at Mr. Brauer's desk. I motioned for Heather to sit down, and I turned around to talk to her. Roy came up to the desk. I told him to sit down, and I would come to see him in a moment. He did not want to do that. He wanted to know why I was talking with his classmate, but of course, he could not ask that.

"I wanted to get all my math right this week."

"For the ski trip?"

She nodded.

"You want to go with the Cloningers? They only have boys."

She sighed. "It's skiing, Mr. Brauer."

"I am very disappointed, Heather."

"Don't say that Mr. Brauer. Don't say that." And then the tears came, and I hugged her, which made it worse. I told her to sit at my desk for a while and got up to see what Roy needed.

Ron came over to my house after school. So, I pulled out my D&D books. I had set up a short little scenario. I made some vegetable soup and showed him how, when I had lived in Lebanon, we had learned to put yogurt in our soup. I made some toast and cut some cheddar cheese strips. He thought it was a grand meal. My table was chipped Formica with metal legs. My

351

chairs were old and covered with cheap plastic that was ripping. But Ron thought it was a great little bachelor pad. I did not have to put up with anybody telling me what to do here. How great was that?

And over the next couple of hours, he was transported, grinning all over himself as we ran the D&D fantasy scenario. He killed some goblins with great 20 die rolls. He found some treasure, enough to buy himself a plus three sword with a small but ancient reputation. His character was surely on the path towards renown. Indeed, he had a great time, even though we only had a couple of hours to play. Which in D&D time was hardly anytime at all.

On the drive over to Rifle, he chatted the whole way.

For Pathfinders, we were getting ready for the Western Slope Pathfinder Fair. It was going to be held at the Rifle church later in the spring. Everyone looked so sharp in their dress uniform for inspection. The children stood at attention as Bill walked down the line checking out their attire: their sashes, the crease on their shirts, their white gloves, were their shoes polished. Of course, he pointed out discrepancies, but he always did it in a kind manner. They would smile and fix it. And like so many other times, as I walked behind him and watched my children, I was so proud of them. I just adored them.

On Thursday, I had to announce the winner of the ski trip. The children had been earning Rulison Dollars. Those that wanted to go came forward with their cash in hand. Mike had fifty. He was not optimistic about his chances. Steven and Danny both tied at forty-five. Ron looked at his money and did not bother coming forward. Chad had fifty-five. He gave me a fist pump as I recorded it on the blackboard. Roy told him to sit down. He came forward and counted out his money and had seventy-five. His smile was so broad.

I was curious that none of the girls had come forward. Did they not want to go? I also had my eye on Doug. I did not know how much money he had, but I knew he knew, and he was not feeling a bit worried. Doug slowly got up from his desk when none of the other boys came forward. He sauntered up very slowly. Roy did not like Doug's confidence.

"How much do you have?" Roy hissed with displeasure.

Doug had put the money in a lunch sack and dumped it on my desk.

"Mr. Brauer, would you count this for me. I don't want anyone to think I cheated."

I appreciated Doug's theatrical performance. I did not need to count it to know he had significantly more than anyone else, but I followed Doug's lead and counted them out slowly. As I counted, I knew that the girls were all congregating in the back: Kelli, Carolyn, Heather, Chrissie, Angie, Heather S., Kim, Misty, and Katie. They appeared to be doing some calculations of their own.

I counted out Doug's money and placed it in stacks of tens. He had twenty-two stacks. There was a cheer. Doug had two hundred twenty Rulison Dollars.

"All right, Doug. I guess cleaning the commode earned you a ski trip."

Doug grinned.

The girls glanced to the front as they continued to congregate in the back. Then they all passed their money to Heather. I loved this. The girls were all working together, determined to have a girl win.

Heather came forward with a huge stack of dollars in her hand.

"Mr. Brauer, I have three hundred fifty Rulison Dollars."

She could not hold all the money in her hand. Kelli and Chrissie had to help her bring it forward.

Doug was upset. He started asking the other boys if they would give him their money, but the boys were not nearly as collegial as the girls had been. Heather was going on the ski trip.

In Colorado, it snowed one day, and the next day it would be clear and in the seventies. In the mountains, the snow might last, but in the valleys, the snow melted quickly. So much sun; it was hard to be depressed with that much solar encouragement.

On Sabbath afternoon Ron McElvain took me for a hike. We returned to the trail we had snowshoed earlier in the winter. The path now was nearly free of snow, with just patches in the pinon pines or where the hills cast shadows. I was hiking in a pair of work boots. Ron told me about his boots made with a new material called Gortex, nearly waterproof. His feet were warm and dry, but mine became soggy and cold. My feet, however, were of no account. The day was spectacular. As we crested the hill, we saw a herd of elk down below in the pasture. We saw red-tailed hawks floating in the sky and at least two hundred mule deer. Winter had given way. Rivulets were streaming down the path. At the end of our walk, we could look off to a box canyon that Ron told me could only be reached on foot. It was magical, like a beacon calling me, "Beyond here is Shangri-la."

We came back to town as the sun edged toward the horizon. I drove home, changed my shoes, and then drove right back to the church for the Home and School benefit. They were showing the Disney movie, *The Computer who Wore Tennis Shoes*. I filled up on snacks, took my seat, and the children came and sat beside me. Angie curled up on my lap.

Mrs. Opitz came by and laughed. "You don't need to get married, Mr. Brauer. You always have a kid hugging you."

I laughed and put my arm around the children on either side of me. I did not take it for granted. I, too, was amazed that they were with me all week long, and even though I did have to discipline them at times, when it came to the weekend and fun was beginning, they came running to be with me. And it was definitely mutual. I never tired of them hanging around.

CHAPTER SEVENTY-ONE

ONE OF THE GOOD ONES

In the world news, on April 2, Argentina invaded the Falklands. Britain and Argentina were at war. It took us all as a surprise, Argentina in a land grab. And a European country in a war for territory. That had not happened since World War II. Great Britain was our closest ally. We were mesmerized by it and paid attention as the fleet set sail from England. We were awestruck when an Exocet missile from an Argentine plane sank a British destroyer. That a missile fired from twenty miles could take down a ship kept us watching the news. And then we watched as the British fought to retake the small South Atlantic islands.

Also, the recession was worsening. Inflation was out of control at 13%. The Federal Reserve was instituting a monetary contraction policy, and interest rates were 16%. Housing construction collapsed, and many banks that had lately been deregulated went bankrupt. Unemployment was at 10%, the worst since the Great Depression. All of this explained why Rifle, with its shale exploration, was in a boom.

A lot of people thought that the Republicans were trying to put money into the pockets of the rich. It had some merit. The very rich were getting richer and richer. Reagan started reducing the margin taxes on the rich and instituted tax on social security. A pattern that continued, and he would not agree to cut defense spending. The deficit accelerated. Still, he would be able to turn around the economy by his 1984 campaign and could tout that it was "Morning in America." I would vote for him in 1984.

At school, I was feeling a bit of a failure. Students who had started the year with poor study habits were not much better. Students who were poor at math had not busted through. The multiplication tables were still not mastered as they should have been. I had hoped to become a master teacher. Unfortunately, the evidence did not support that aspiration.

At recess, soccer had taken the fancy. The fields quickly dried out after the storm, and we ran across the mostly flat fields. Everyone liked soccer. Everyone could run, and children like to run. Everyone also liked soccer because Mike, Doug, and Shon liked soccer.

Jerry Smith's wife came out to interview for the job I would be vacating. She spent a couple of hours observing in the classroom. We discussed her at the school board meeting. She had been teaching for fifteen years and had experience. Mary Dix commented that an experienced teacher would be a good tonic. I heard the implication, but I kept my mouth shut. Mitch heard it too.

"Well, of course, Nancy (Smith) does have experience, but you know I was talking to her and Jerry this evening, and she said," And here he gave me a quick glance before directing his gaze at Mrs. Dix. "She said that in her observations, although she was not here long, in just watching the interaction of the students, it was obvious that Mr. Brauer was one of the good ones."

That made me feel better. I could admit that I had made my mistakes and had not achieved my goals, but I had tried. No one could say that I had not put in the effort.

"Oh, of course," Mrs. Dix was quick to backtrack. "I never meant to imply he was not. I just thought that Mrs. Smith's experience was a positive."

356

And they voted to hire Mrs. Smith to be the principal for the following year. I did have to admit, I doubted Mrs. Smith would have tolerated the attitudes I was battling. I suspected she would have squelched it quickly.

The meeting went very long, and I did not walk back into my driveway until nearly eleven p.m. As I did, my little cat was sitting in the driveway waiting for me. I picked the cat up and held him under my chin and when I went to bed, he crawled under the covers.

On Sabbath, I was over-involved at church. I taught the adult Sabbath School lesson, gave the offerings appeal, played my trombone for special music, which included the slide falling off as I climbed the stage, and gave the benediction. That was too much.

I went for a walk with Tina and Virginia on their property in the afternoon. We climbed up their Indian Hill. Tina and Virginia were engaged in a meditative discussion about the Second Coming of Christ. It could not be long now. What with the war, the recession, the oil crisis, clearly, we had never lived in time such as these before. Besides, we were now in the nineteen-eighties. We were never supposed to have been here this long. Christ was to have come long before this.

Virginia was looking forward to it but admitted she was pleased that she would get married before he returned. She did not say it specifically, but of course, she was referring to sex. She would get to experience sex. We all knew there would be no sex in heaven. I was fatalistic. I did not see any hope in my future in that regard, but I kept my silence.

I spent my time as we walked, just looking around, noticing the small patches of barrel cactus that I had not noticed before, looking down to the valley, looking across to the layered Book Cliffs. We saw deer in the draw below the hill, and rabbits, and a squirrel.

That Sunday, I pushed myself harder. I tried to improve my organization. What could I do in these last couple of months to make a difference for my students? How could I encourage them? How could I inculcate a life of self-discipline, a life of striving? I just wanted to get behind some of them, like an extra engine brought up behind a train to help push it over the pass. Surely, if a teacher had a task, it was to take his time with the students and be a life coach. But I recognized I had so much to learn in this area. I had worked hard, I could not deny that, and I had loved them that was unmistakable, but skillfully coaching them to improve? In that area, I was deficient. And I was leaving the field before I had mastered it. That bothered me.

In the early afternoon, I changed and went for a run down to the river. The snow was melting and the river was cresting. The power of the river always impressed me, but the river up to the edges of its banks was a mighty thing. The beatific sounds of rest that I had felt and heard late last summer when I had first come, those sounds were now replaced with a puissant force, and I was awed. If I could just be like a river to my students, inciting, urging, motivating, rushing them on to greater and greater things.

There was a story in the Bible about how God came to talk to Elijah. It was said that there was a mighty wind, an earthquake, and a fire, but God had not spoken to him in these majestic ways but in a still small voice. So, I would have to leave it in God's hands.

As the week started, I tried to install the new techniques I had pondered on Sunday, but it was hard. How could you be a serious disciplinarian when all the little comments, all the little pranks, all their actions just tickled me so. They were so amusing, and I loved laughing with them. Yes, there were problems. On Monday, I kept Danny after school to catch up on his work. On Tuesday, Kelli launched into a turbulent rant at me at the end of the day. She was carrying on. I tried to calm her as she erupted, then I looked at the back door. Her father was standing in the doorway; he had heard the whole tirade. Kelli saw me looking at the door and turned around. Her shoulders sank. On Wednesday, Roy had gone out of his way to tell me how much more he liked Miss Ryber than me. I said I was pleased, and that she was a very nice person and a good teacher. He just huffed.

But for the most part, the children were happy, and the mood in the room was better. Chrissie jumped on my back at recess and would not quit pestering me until I pulled her into a big bear hug. She squealed with laughter.

After lunch, I started reading *The Lion, the Witch, and the Wardrobe* aloud to the class. They found it fascinating, but at the end of the week, Danny told me that Miss Ryber had counseled him it was wrong for me to be reading that book to the children. She said it was not a book good Adventists should be reading. I was dumbfounded. Actually, maybe not.

One of the required courses for an elementary education major in college was children's literature. So, when the chair of the department had convinced me to switch majors, my biggest concern was being able to graduate on schedule. She assured me I could do it, and the department had even arranged for me to take a special summer class.

The teacher for the course was Kathy Bollinger. She taught at the elementary school, and Virginia Simmons asked her to teach the class. She was acknowledged as an up-and-coming teacher. She was young and enthusiastic and loved children's literature. She was a teacher I would remember for the rest of my life.

One of the requirements for the class was that we had to read forty books in the month-long course. I decided if I had to read books, I wanted to read only the best. So, I picked all of my books from the Caldecott and Newbury award winners. I spent every afternoon lying on my dorm room bed speed reading through a couple of books a day. And I remember as I laid there reading those great books with my stereo playing music, I realized I was leading a wonderful life. The books were deserving of their awards, well written, and engaging *Johnny Tremaine, The Door in the Wall, Carry on Mr. Bowditch, The Witch of Blackbird Pond, A Wrinkle in Time, Bridge to Terabithia*. They taught great life lessons in an effective method. That was what literature was supposed to do.

Mrs. Bollinger understood and approved my choices, especially as many of my classmates were surprised that I was reading fiction. I had a reputation as a devout and respected young man. How could I disappoint them by reading novels? One of my classmates was Kristen Peterson, Mr. Wes Peterson's daughter. She was not as strident as some of my classmates; however, she was uncomfortable with fiction. Mrs. Bollinger gave a couple of lectures addressing the issues of literature and its place in a Christian's life. Particularly what was the place for literature in the Adventist church. Was fiction ever proper? Should we allow children to read books where animals speak? After all, animals did not talk in real life. Would not this type of literature destroy the moral fabric of young people? The debate in the classroom was vigorous, and my classmates dismissed my support of truly beautiful writing as sophistry of the devil. Satan was trying to destroy the children while they were young. They quoted Ellen White, who had written against novel reading. And fantasy was one of the worst offenders. I remained unconvinced. After all, Ellen White did approve of *Pilgrim's Progress.*

Personally, I also was an advocate for the great books. I had a list of the great novels that I was steadily trying to check off my list. The Russian authors: Tolstoy, Gogol, Chekhov, Pushkin, and especially Dostoevsky had been my favorites for some time. Victor Hugo's *Les Misérables* had been a religious experience for me. I also was a big fan of Austen, Dickens, George Eliot, and Tolkien. But my reading had extended to such rebels as Thomas Hardy, Flaubert, and O my I even liked that low-life, Hemingway. My dad had been shocked that they taught Hemingway in an Adventist school.

But C.S. Lewis, and *The Chronicles of Narnia*? How could anyone object? The book was an openly known parable of Christ! How could anyone object to it? So, in my classroom, I had to defend C.S. Lewis. And I was so tired of ultra-conservatism. All it had to do was to sit back and lob artillery. One of the elements of Adventism that drove me crazy was this suppression of the brain, this attempt of thought control, and this denial of the greatness of human intellect.

I read the book to my students, and the children were moved by Aslan voluntarily laying down his life for the ones that he loved. And that is what I wanted my children to see, the beauty of self-sacrifice, the beauty of Christ.

I so disliked Miss Ryber's holier-than-thou attitude.

CHAPTER SEVENTY-TWO

IT'S RAINING AGAIN

Spring went ahead with anthems of blossoms displayed from every apple tree.

At church that week, the children sang. We had practiced at school, and I had had my hesitations, but they delivered when they stood upfront. Of course, you must be heartless not to be moved by little children singing their hearts out. I am not sure if any of them had any tremendous musical talents. I could not judge because I had no great musical talents and thus was not fit to judge. But I was proud of them.

The following week started off so-so. On the one hand, Chrissie got three marks on the board within five minutes for getting out of her chair and talking during a quiet period. On receiving the third mark, she was so upset that she put her head on her desk to hide her tears. Then later that same day, she fell in a cactus and filled her hand with cactus spines. I sent her to Mabel Livingood. When she returned, she brought her books up to my desk and worked from there.

On the other hand, a couple of the students missed class on Monday. And missing students almost always meant a quieter and more compliant classroom. On Thursday, I brought in a couple of dozen donuts and allowed the children to buy them with their Rulison Dollars.

But the week took a serious dive when Doug became vexed with Mike's and Shon's teasing of him. He just got up and ran away from school, out the door, down the road. I had to chase him and bring him back. There was no choice. That was an immediate suspension. I called Cliff, Doug's dad, and he came and picked up Doug. Before he arrived, Doug argued with great passion that it was Mike and Shon's fault, and I should punish them equally. The thought of his father having to come and pick him up in the middle of the day upset him greatly. No student ever likes that. When Cliff Sisk did arrive, he was supportive. I was grateful. He just had Doug grab his stuff, and out they went.

The truth was, while I enjoyed my children and liked being with them, their rudeness, their sassiness, and complaining all sapped my energy. The attitudes, especially of some older students, were a drain, and it was filtering down. I tried to be positive. Maybe this was the typical pattern that ran in a school year. Did students get cranky and impatient as spring arrived? Was this a manifestation of Spring Fever? Since this was my first year teaching, I had nothing with which to compare it to. As the grumbling continued, it occurred to me that even the Israelites had plagued Moses with incessant grumbling. Maybe I should not be too hard on myself.

On Friday afternoons, since we had finished our choral performance for the church, we turned our attention to practicing a play that we had scheduled to put on for the last Home and School benefit of the year.

I liked acting. I had been a drama club officer in high school. I had written several plays for camp skits over the years. On the other hand, in college when I auditioned, I had never been chosen. Apparently, my talents were not that impressive. Still, Phyllis Boggs, the chairwoman, thought it would be nice for us to perform a play for the last Home and School. Virginia helped. Tina came and helped as well. It was hard to get the children to take rehearsals seriously. I despaired that they would not memorize their parts. I foresaw the performance would be a disorganized catastrophe. They would forget their lines; ignore their cues; there would be long awkward pauses; and they would turn to me like a deer in the headlights. Still, it seemed that a school play was a mandatory rite of passage. A school always had a play. So, we practiced.

The other thing that we were planning was a camping trip. Mr. Boggs had offered to come with us. We were going to camp at Rifle Falls State Park. As for every extracurricular activity, the requirement of participation was having their work done. I was constantly tying activities to completed work. Motivation. Motivation. Motivation. I was racking my brain for ways to keep them involved, especially as the days were warming up. There was a lot of serious window watching going on. I confess I was not immune. After a winter like we had had, it was contagious. That was why a camping trip sounded terrific. Whenever we discussed it, the enthusiasm was fantastic. Everybody was arranging their gear: tents, sleeping bags, food.

The week following Doug's prison break, Kelli and Shon both got upset when I insisted, they get their work done. First, Kelli jumped up from her seat and shouted that she hated me. Then, she ran to the foyer and called her dad.

After it had settled down and Kelli had come back to her desk. After she had called her father, who, of course, had said it was proper for Mr. Brauer to tell them to get their work done. When the room was getting back into the swing of things, Ron quipped, "Mr. Brauer, last week we nominated Doug for best self-control."

Doug chuckled and raised his hand. "I have a nomination for this week, Mr. Brauer."

"Really, Doug? Who could that be?" I feigned ignorance.

Kelli could not resist a joke and smiled. Then she asked to talk to me outside. I opened the door at the front of the school. We stepped outside on the lawn in the spring sunshine. In the beginning, she hung her head. Then she peeked up at me. "You know what, Mr. Brauer? I don't hate you. I really don't. And I wish I wouldn't get so upset."

364

The meadowlarks were sending up lovely little songs from the nearby fences, and the sun's warmth felt so good. I paused and looked at her for a few moments. She raised her head.

"You know what, Kelli? I wish you would learn to control your temper, but...." And I paused. She dropped her head again and nodded. "But..." I repeated. Her head was still down. "I like you, Kelli. I always have. I really do like you."

She kept her head down and took a deep breath. She nodded several times. "I know you do, and I'm sorry." She raised her head, looked around at the school grounds, and then glanced at me. She gave me a shy smile.

That Friday we were supposed to leave for camping, but on Friday it was raining. We thought it might clear up, so we loaded up the Sisk's van and drove over to Rifle Falls State Park after school. It continued to rain. We waited for a while. But while I loved camping. Camping in the rain was not fun. So, we called it off; everyone was disappointed. I took the children home.

The next morning, I received calls from Mike and Doug. The rain had stopped. Could we try it again? I called Mr. Boggs he did not like the idea. Also, Heather and Steven had not gotten their work done. He was out. Kelli and Shon called. "Please, Mr. Brauer!" I was a sucker for a "please."

The group would be smaller: Mike, Doug, Kelli, Shon, Danny, Chad, and Carolyn. I went around and picked everybody up Sabbath morning. Rifle Falls State Park was out. It was in a box canyon, and with the rain, the creek was up. We drove out to Colorado National Monument just below Grand Junction. There was a gate across the park entrance since it did not open until May. Thus, our options were running out. We stopped and had a little picnic at one of the roadside stops. I pulled out my maps. We could camp in any Bureau of Land Management area, but there would be no facilities. It would be primitive camping. I proposed that to the group; they were on board with anything. Mike and Doug had both done primitive camping. They assured the group that primitive camping was the real way to camp. Camping at camping sites was for 'Wusses.' So, I found a backroad. We watched for a nice flat area near a creek.

We found a place. I no longer remember where it was. I parked the van, and we unloaded. By then, it was getting to be midafternoon. Everyone set up their tents, and I was impressed with the children's camping skills. I had borrowed a tent from my brother, Ron. They might not have been able to negotiate the big city, the large shopping malls; the girls might not have been experts at make-up or accessorizing like some of the sixth graders I had student taught—who I thought grew up too fast. Still, these kids' parents had brought them up with good values here in the country. I approved of the priorities their parents had instilled in them. True, their families had not been perfect. But as I watched my students setting up their tents, rolling out their sleeping bags, going down to the stream to get water, gathering wood to build a campfire, I thought to myself, when I have children, if I have children, I am going to make sure they camp.

It was still April, and in April in Western Colorado, the days would be pleasant, but the nights could be cold. It was chilly that night. We built a fire and heated water for hot chocolate and sat around roasting marshmallows. Everyone began telling stories. Mike talked about his years in Southern California. It was so different here compared to there; he loved it here. He never wanted to leave Colorado. Doug talked about earlier camping trips they had had when Mr. Caldwell had been here. One year the week after school had ended, they had camped for a week at Arches. That had been nice. Maybe we could do that.

I shrugged.

"Right. You're leaving. I forgot," Doug replied.

"How could you forget?" Kelli was dumbfounded.

"What are you gonna do next year?" Doug tried to recover. Apparently, it was a major faux pas to have a momentary lapse, forgetting that Mr. Brauer was leaving.

"Well, this summer, I am taking General Chemistry at CU. Then back to Union next fall for my pre-med classes. I'm going to try to get into medicine."

"I hate that you're leaving Mr. Brauer," Carolyn said softly. She had been very quiet up until then.

I wanted to stay away from a scene of pathos. I knew Carolyn in particular, was dreading my leaving. Sheila had told me that Carolyn had had a little setback in her counseling sessions recently. I did not want to worsen that. I changed the subject.

"Yeah, well, I have not left yet, so tell me, what are you guys looking forward to once school is out."

That unleashed a torrent ranging from sleeping in, which was very popular, to riding their bicycles, water skiing at Rifle gap reservoir, reading books, which was not as popular, visiting grandparents, travel.

We sat up for what seemed like a long time, adding fallen branches to the fire, occasionally with green needles still on the branch, which caused an outpouring of smoke, and everyone had to move around the circle. It was a night of reflection for me. I would have preferred to have had more of the children. I would have liked to have one or two more parents along to help. I wished we could have camped for two to three days and gone on a long hike. And if given my choice, I would have preferred to be in a developed campsite. I especially loved National Parks. Maybe we could have gone to Dinosaur National Park and camped along the Green River. It was not that far away, but here we were.

I started singing from the repertoire of camp songs that I knew. I knew lots of songs. "You are my sunshine, my only sunshine, you make me happy when skies are grey...." The children all joined in. And we linked up arm to arm swaying back and forth. It was nice. There was something about singing together while seated around that campfire. It was nice. I was glad we had come.

CHAPTER SEVENTY-THREE

DON'T WORRY

While the camping was lovely, poor Kelli continued to struggle. On Monday, I kept having to intervene. She kept instigating trouble. She would not be quiet and would not mind. Frustrated; finally, I moved her desk to the front of the room and pronounced that there would be a wall of silence around her desk. She would stay at her desk. She would not talk and no one else was to talk to her. No one was to go up to her desk. It was very difficult for her.

And it was a difficult day for me as well because despite all the trouble she caused—and she did cause trouble—despite all the times I had to talk her down, if I had a favorite, Kelli was way up there on that list. I understood her, and I could sympathize with her. She would turn and look at me from her desk of silence. On one look, she would be mad, but then a couple of minutes later, I could see genuine repentance and self-recognition. She knew she had brought this on herself. I was tempted when I saw that repentance to halt the wall of silence, but I let it persist all day.

Our play practice went even worse on Monday. And it did not improve on Tuesday. We were scheduled to perform it that night.

When I could not get them to buckle down, I told them we would cancel the play. The banquet was that night. That upset them. They begged me, "Please, Mr. Brauer, we want to do the play." I was against it. I did not want my final legacy to be a monstrously awful play. Mike took up the argument. "Give us a chance, Mr. Brauer." I relented.

I stopped off before the banquet and got a haircut. As I was driving to the church, I saw Carolyn and Kelli walking along the road. I waved at them. Carolyn noticed my haircut and burst into laughter.

At the banquet, the children performed their play. I was expecting disaster, skipped lines, missed cues, blinded in the lights' long pauses, but was astounded at how my kids came through. Once again, when the chips were down, they rose and delivered. I was flabbergasted and so proud of them and just felt that their performance was in some small way a thank you, a 'we won't let you down, Mr. Brauer.' I have always been prone to a little excess emotion, and I admit I had to wipe my eyes. Afterward, many of the parents came up and said how enjoyable it had been, how well-rehearsed the children had been. I smiled and thought if only you knew. The children were congregating around me. They knew they had killed it, and I was dispensing hugs freely. They were happy.

"We did okay, huh, Mr. Brauer?" Mike said as he took in the younger grades all around, getting hugs.

"You guys did. You really did."

Mike nodded as if he didn't have to say, "I told you so."

"Come here, Mike." I laughed, and I gave him a big bear hug.

"That's good enough, Mr. Brauer. That's good enough."

On Thursday, I kept Shon and Danny after school to finish their work. I had designed the schedule to give everybody time to get their work done in school. I kept reminding them during the school day, but they found everything else so much more engaging. Finally, Danny sat down and started to do his work. Shon refused. There was nothing I could do to make him work.

"Well, then sit there and do nothing. I usually spend several hours here each evening getting ready for tomorrow. Frankly, I'd like the company," I said as Shon sat exuding obstinance. It lasted five minutes, maybe ten. And then, with the quiet of the room and knowing that his father would approve of my actions, he set to it. He chugged out the work. There was nothing wrong with Shon's mind. He was a smart kid, but it was hard to be productive when his home life was in such chaos. The two boys would periodically look at the other one and then concentrate on their work. There was nothing to distract them when all the children were gone.

The next week four of the eleven were missing. It was quieter. On quiet days at school, Heather invariably migrated up to my desk, and if I was sitting in my chair, she would scoot me over so she could perch on the seat beside me. Chrissie would come up as well. Shon came forward, and seeing them asked, "What's with Heather and Chrissie always sitting beside you?"

I glanced at my two fourth-grade girls. "I guess they like me." I smiled.

Chrissie was leaning forward, working on her math on my desk. She did not look up but responded in her quiet little voice, "Ron likes him too."

Shon raised his eyebrows in disbelief. That was so uncool. He could not fathom it. Shon's attitude, however, changed the instant we stepped outside. Outside was his domain. The latest fad was basketball. Everybody wanted to be like Magic Johnson or Dr. J. (Julius Erving)

Roy had been growing all year, but Kareem Abdul-Jabbar was more his game style. He got in close and used the backboard. I tried to give him little tips about using his hand and positioning himself. He got more physical. On one occasion, as he was jumping up for a rebound, his elbows crashed into my glasses. They went crashing. That is what happens to glasses when playing basketball. But I was bummed. I didn't want to spend my limited money on glasses. I picked them up. The crash had busted them, so I called the end of recess.

Ron and Steven did not come in. Where were they? A few minutes later, they arrived. They had been up the road looking for Steven's bicycle. In other words, they had left the school property without permission.

"Listen up, everybody. I cannot make it any clearer. You cannot leave the school property without a teacher with you; it is not safe. Miss Ryber and I are responsible for you. I would have thought everybody would have learned that lesson with Kelli getting spanked and Doug getting suspended.

"Steven, Ron, you are suspended. I'm going to call your parents. Get your stuff together."

They sat in silence.

Chrissie argued for Ron. "My mother told us if we got suspended, we would go to public school."

I had to be fair; I must apply the rule evenly. So, yes, I could understand why Steven and Ron wanted to find Steven's bicycle. But the rule applied, without exception.

CHAPTER SEVENTY-FOUR

VEHICLE

On Friday afternoon after school Jerry Smith, Mr. Mitchell's new partner called me up. He had bought a new four-wheel Blazer and asked if I wanted to ride with him as he tried it on one of the nearby four-wheel trails. That sounded great to me. We did not go far, but the whole concept of taking a car over roads that my little Toyota could never traverse was fascinating. I could see the appeal. Steep inclines, go up and over them just by pushing down on the pedal. Western Colorado had many dirt trails that four-wheeling could only access.

Jerry was a clever fellow, and he tended to give good advice. At the end of the evening, he invited me to come up to the Mitchell's. I still went up to their house though not as often.

"Who's up there?"

"Well, you know, of course, Mitch and Tina, Danny, Virginia, and ... David, Ruthie, and Valerie are home."

I had heard that Valerie had an upcoming home leave.

"Not's it okay. I'd rather not." And it was true. I did not want to see her. It would have been awkward and painful. My wound was healing, but if I went back up there and saw her, it would have been like just like tearing open the wound again. I did not want to rip the bandage off. It would be harder to heal a second time, and I did not want to go there. I really did not. I had found a little peace and seeing her would do me no good.

Jerry drove me into my driveway. I started to get out.

"You can at least be friends," he said through the open door.

I stopped and held onto the door. "I hold nothing against Valerie. If she wants to be friends, that's fine." I paused and looked at Jerry for a moment before closing the door. I did not tell Jerry what I had decided: the only way I would go back up to the Mitchell's was if Valerie personally invited me. And it had to be an "I'm sorry. I was wrong" conversation. And I knew that would never happen.

The next day at church, the Mitchell family came in after I was already seated. They sat a couple of rows in front of me. I always sat on the right side, so did they. I should have sat on the left side. I had my usual accompaniment of children. Chad and Wayne were on one side of me, and Chrissie was on the other side. As I sat there, I could not help but look at Valerie. I was struck again at how beautiful she was. She had such full and flowing blonde hair. Her movements were so graceful. And it made such manifest sense to me why I had fallen so quickly, so deeply. I must have unintentionally sighed because I remember Chrissie looking up at me with worry on her face. I gave her a sad little smile and patted her head.

After church, I met Valerie in the hallway. She was coming one way. I was going the other. It occurred to me this would be the time to talk, to clear the air a little.

After our breakup, when she had not invited me to her birthday party, and I had delivered my ultra-short breakup note, Tina had asked me to call her. I had. I had called her at school one evening, and we had talked for a few minutes. I said I was sorry for the manner of my note and that maybe we could just be friends, and who knows, maybe in the future date occasionally. She thought that would be great and was glad I had called. I knew we would never date. The only way we would date would be if she had called me up and had apologized for not inviting me;

maybe there was some valid excuse as to why she had not wanted me going out to eat with her family. Maybe, but I did not think so. And she had had plenty of time to explain things if that was what she had wanted to do. There had been nothing from her end.

We met in the hallway. I smiled and said, "Happy Sabbath," and walked past.

In the afternoon, Jerry invited me to go four-wheeling with him again. He joined the other four-wheelers in the church: the McElvain families, the Cloningers, and the Clifford Sisk family. There were five four-wheelers in the caravan, and we all went up the back of the Book Cliffs. I was intrigued by the seams of coal running through the mudstone mesas on the way up. Dr. Paul McElvain told me that geologists said the coal was in the Pennsylvania epoch sedimentary layer. That was fascinating. He noted that Colorado was still a large coal mining state; I had not realized that.

It was a beautiful spring day, and the air felt so fresh. Little yellow flowers were springing up on the pathways. Everyone in the caravan was careful and considerate with their vehicles. These were careful four-wheelers, not at all reckless. So, up we went, over small boulders in the road, or around them. Finally, in the late afternoon, we stopped at the mountain's crest and looked down on Palisades. I had often viewed this particular mountain with awe from below, but now, here I was on the mesa looking down over the orchard strewn valley below. The cherry trees were in blossom. It was a beatific sight.

As we came down and back into town while driving the Rifle to Rulison backroad, Jerry again invited me to come up to the Mitchell's. Again, he tried to be persuasive. It was tempting; Valerie had looked so beautiful in the morning. I so much enjoyed being around her, but afterward, the pain. The truth is, I did not want to be her friend. It was not possible.

The next day at school, working alone — Virginia did not do her prep in the classroom — I found myself constantly pondering women, not necessarily Valerie or any one in particular, but as a general class of womanhood. I thought of their thin waists, their pretty faces, the levity of their laughs, the way their hair smelled, and I thought about how hard it had been for me with them; how often they had broken my heart. I was probably better off without them, undoubtedly so. Still, it had been nice when I had had a girlfriend. That was very nice. And then I would shake my head and try to concentrate.

In the afternoon, Mrs. Mitchell called to say that she would bring pizza for all the children. I was already planning to go into town to do some grocery shopping, so I stopped by some of the homes and told them they could skip lunch tomorrow. I do not know why I did not call, except I had an aversion to telephones. I had always preferred conversations in person. Anyway, I stopped by the Sisks, the Boggs, and the Hesses. And at the Hesses, I was again so taken by the mood in their house. Judy Hess had a calm demeanor, and her children were so pleasant. They were well behaved. Yes, I had suspended Ron. Maybe I stopped by to reassure Mrs. Hess that I considered Ron a very good student and well-behaved.

CHAPTER SEVENTY-FIVE

BLACK SUNDAY

On Monday before school, as Virginia came in, I could tell she was distraught. My knack, facility, and talent at saying the right words in times of distress had never been my strength. I had good intentions, but my consolations were lacking. She was upset, but I did not know how to approach her.

I got up from my desk and stood in the doorway between the rooms. Virginia had a Kleenex to her eyes. I asked, "What's wrong with you?" I meant it empathetically. It came out completely wrong. She burst into greater tears and waved me out of the room. I thought about trying again but decided against it. I wished my interpersonal skills were better. After Valerie and I had broken up, her comments to me had been comforting. Mine had only made it worse.

She never told me what upset her. I figured it must have had something to do with her fiancée.

But a bigger news story had broken, Black Sunday. The children were all abuzz. Exxon had shuttered all access to the plant. The Colony Development Corporation, the Exxon subsidiary, was going bankrupt, and they had security guards at the gates. They were pulling out. If an employee had equipment still in the facility, they could arrange to have a guarded escort in to get their equipment; otherwise, it was closed. A small number of employees would be left to secure everything safely, but thousands were out of work. During a general recession, Exxon let them go.

Exxon employed some of my student's parents. Almost all of them were indirectly affected. The children said the news had been the only topic of discussion in their houses yesterday. It was an enormous worry.

The whole experiment to get oil out of marble-stone, oil shale, call it what you like, was a bust. The attempt to extract kerogen was not practical. The energy costs to remove it from the rock and then upgrade it to a useable form of petroleum were not fiscally feasible. Exxon was pulling out. Despite the billions in federal subsidies to explore oil reserves in the continental states, the shale experiment was over.

The Grants were already packing, and others were sure to follow. Obviously, the school exploratory committee would have to be revised. Next year there would not be twenty students. My estimate was probably twelve. Twelve students would not need the two teachers the school had committed to.

At the end of the day, when I went home for supper, I met my landlord. He was out back working with the irrigation. We started talking about the news. He told me he had been listening to the news all day. Rifle bank had had a run on cash. The bank had had to close around two p.m. The station announcer also let everyone know that there were no available U-Hauls within a hundred miles of Rifle. They were all rented. The exodus was on.

Mr. McQueary was a fount of knowledge. He had seen the white paper Exxon had posted to the government. He said he had gotten a hold of one of the few that was not in the District of Columbia. Exxon had proposed declaring all northwestern Colorado as a national emergency fuel area. Here, environmental laws would not apply. They outlined building the largest single industrial complex in the world. They would mine for shale on a monumental scale. Over time, the crater they would excavate

377

would be fifty miles in diameter. The shale would have to be ground, processed, and the detritus each year, the waste each year, would be greater than the sum for the entire building of the Panama Canal. Kerogen, it turned out, was the most abundant source of fuel in the world by a margin of ten thousand to one. The problem was kerogen was tar, and it required heavy processing. The only way to make this workable was to do it on this massive scale. Thus, Northwest Colorado would be sacrificed. Meeker, Craig, Rangely, Dinosaur National Park, the White River all sacrificed for the country's sake. Well, maybe they could save Dinosaur National Park.

The country was dangerously dependent on the Arab states and the OPEC cartel for energy. Exxon was by far the largest company in the world, and they planned to salvage the country from this crisis. As they said in their white paper Northwest Colorado was sparsely populated. No one would miss this part of the state. So, they felt it was a very doable plan. As far as the waste, the popcorn rock that remained — and again the waste each year would be more than the total amount of waste in the entire construction of the Panama Canal — they could dump that waste into the canyons of Colorado and Utah. There were a lot of canyons in Colorado and Utah that were ugly, meaningless, and unimportant. No one would care. Not the Grand Canyon, of course, or Arches, but face it, these other canyons were a waste, and Exxon would be doing a service to dump their truckload after truckload into them. This had been Exxon's plan.

I was deeply disturbed. Yes, I knew that money and energy independence were Washington's ruling principles. But how could anyone give an idea like this any credence? To write off all Northwest Colorado, make a desolation of it was entirely out of my comprehension.

"Well, It's the Rulison Project, Operation Plowshare, all over again."

I knew the Rulison Project was the underground nuclear explosion of nineteen-sixty-nine.

"You know I was there."

"At the nuclear explosion?"

"Yes. My friend and I were in the hills above the explosion. We wanted to be witnesses."

"Really?" I was impressed. My estimation for my landlord had just risen. He had gumption. "And what was it like?"

"Well, it was eight thousand feet down. But the earth moved like a wave, just rippling beneath your feet."

"Was there much damage?"

"Not really. The government paid some damage in Parachute, with some cracked foundations." He paused and smiled. "O yes, they paid the local people eight dollars to be out of their house for the day."

"Eight dollars? Wow, so generous."

Mr. McQueary chuckled in appreciation. "Yes, they wanted them out of the house in case there were structure failures."

"I understand; it was a bust."

Chester nodded. "Yes and no. It did clear up gas. There is a large Rulison natural gas field, but there was too much radiation for it to be used."

"Well, fortunately, that ended that."

Again, Chester was equivocal. "Well, yes, it mostly shut it down. I mean, they had been planning on doing one hundred explosions between here and Rifle."

"What! One hundred nuclear explosions."

"Yes, and thousands throughout the Southwest."

I shook my head in absolute amazement. "The hubris of man. It is inestimable."

He agreed. "They did do one more experiment in Rio Blanco County, northwest of Rifle."

I had not heard of that. "And it was a failure as well."

"Fortunately," he replied.

I had a lot to process. One of my fundamental rules was the belief that man, while smart, was also incredibly arrogant and therefore dangerous. If we could do something, we did it. We did not cautiously examine the consequences. O yes, we might pretend to investigate, but if money, power, or prestige were involved, consequences be damned. One had only to look at the rapidly declining whale populations. The only way to halt this destruction was for people to stand up. I tried but knew that I could and should do more.

On the other hand, I was impressed with Mr. McQueary, he had personally gone out to witness the nuclear explosion, and he had taken the time to understand what Exxon had proposed. Good man.

On a completely separate note, in the world of sports, my favorite baseball team the Baltimore Orioles had moved Cal Ripken, Jr. from third base to shortstop and were now playing him regularly. They had moved him from third base to shortstop, and he was tearing up the league. We did not realize it at the time, but he had begun his ironman streak in which he would play every game, two thousand six hundred and thirty-two games in a row. He would not miss a game until nineteen ninety-eight — sixteen years in a row —a record that was highly unlikely ever to be broken.

CHAPTER SEVENTY-SIX

YOU'LL ALWAYS BE MY FRIEND

It was near the end of the day. The school year was ending, less than three weeks away. I was sitting at my desk looking out over the classroom.

"Okay, guys. Tell me what you are going to remember about the year. What was your worst and favorite memory of the year?"

There were a lot of comments about skiing and how much fun that had been.

Kelli raised her hand. "I think you know what my worst memory was, Mr. Brauer." She laughed.

"I can guess."

"What you don't know, however," Kelli was squirming all over her chair. She had a huge grin now. "It didn't hurt one bit. Not even a little."

"Really?" I was quite relieved and then added. "Well, that's not entirely true, Kelli." I paused. "It hurt me a great deal. I am permanently scarred."

She liked that.

Roy raised his hand. "I hated long division. I hope I never have to see another long division problem in my life," Roy moaned. The other fourth-graders agreed.

Mike raised his hand. "Mr. Brauer, I am going to be so glad to be gone from these elementary brats."

"And we're going to be glad to be rid of Mike's eighth-grade superiority," Heather piped up. And on that, there was general agreement.

"It's going to be nice to have a new teacher as well," Doug said.

"I hope I get Miss Ryber," Danny added.

Most everyone liked her. They were glad she was staying. Mike and I looked at each other. It seemed everyone was happy we were leaving.

"I guess they want to win at football again, huh, Mike," I suggested.

'Yeah, that's right," Mike took the joke. "And soccer, and baseball, and football. Let's face it, Mr. Brauer, without the two of us, they might start feeling better about themselves again."

That stirred up a nest of protests. I let it ride for a minute before quieting them.

"Two more weeks, guys. Two more weeks. Let's see if we can have a couple of good ones."

Mike was raising his hand.

"Mike," I called him out.

"Mr. Brauer, I want to add that Carolyn is the only decent girl in the school."

Carolyn blushed and buried her head on the desk.

"You know Mike; if I was going to give out a most improved student, it would be Carolyn. She has worked hard, and it shows."

Carolyn protested, "Stop it, Mr. Brauer. You're going to make me cry."

After school, I grabbed a quick supper and stood out on my driveway. I watched the sun dip below the sandstone cliffs of the mesa. In the yard, the tulips, pink, red, and yellow were closing. I could feel the coolness of the night descending, penetrating, and promoting stillness. Unfortunately, my day was not done. I got in my car and drove to the church.

We practiced the investiture for the Pathfinders. They were all cooperative. On the way home, I brought Shon, Danny, and Steven. They had the windows rolled down and were egging me on to go fast. I got it up to eighty miles an hour on some of the straight stretches. The boys loved it. I felt bad about it. I needed to grow up quit being foolish and reckless. There were a lot of deer in Western Colorado.

After dropping them off at their houses, I pulled into the school driveway. I had a couple of things I needed to do. As I was working on tomorrow's lessons, I thought about the day's comments and how they had cheered that Mike and I were leaving. I knew that had been in jest, but I also realized that they would also move on when I moved on. They had made a deep impression on me, but they would move on. I did not expect there would be many tears on the last day. I looked around the classroom. It was cluttered, a bit of a mess. If I were going to teach another year, I thought to myself, if I were to do one more year, I would really emphasize cleanliness, more orderliness, less of a mess.

On Sabbath, Elder Allan Williamson was over from the conference office. He was the Youth leader for the Rocky Mountain Conference and in charge of Glacier View Camp, youth retreats, and Pathfinders. It kept him on the road a lot, across Wyoming, Colorado, and the Four Corners. I had worked three summers for him. It would be difficult to express my admiration for him entirely. He was a man of integrity. He genuinely liked children and youth and was an excellent boss. When he appointed Deanna Bragaw and me as girls' and boys' directors, he stepped back and gave us room to lead. So, I was pleased that my children performed their roles spotlessly at the investiture part of the service.

Afterward, he found me out in the lobby of the church. We talked. He had incredibly curly blonde hair, and he always had a huge smile. He offered me a job at camp for the summer. We had talked before. I had told him I would not be able to work for him this summer. But it was really gratifying that he would extend the offer this late in the season.

"Well, if you change your mind. I will always have room for people like you."

I liked the fact that he was grace-based. He had not fallen into the radical conservatism that was beginning to creep into the denomination. For example, he always had some Disney films on hand on rainy days at camp. We would gather the children into the auditorium and play them a movie. There were a lot of youth directors who thought that was wrong, including my brother Jim. And there were always some staff members so consumed by guiding the children to Christ in this one-week opportunity that they lost sight of just how much fun it was to be in the mountains and how children ages nine to fourteen should be building up a large reservoir of just pure joy. Elder Williamson was so diplomatic, but he always came down on the side of children having fun in the end. I tried to learn from him.

The next day was the Western Slope Pathfinder fair and Rifle church hosted it on their church grounds. Elder Williamson had left. Mr. Veltman, the Denver South pathfinder club leader, was in charge. They had the largest pathfinder club in the state. I also knew Mr. Veltman from camp. He had volunteered to stand in for Elder Williamson as Camp Director for a couple of weeks last summer. He was a big man, heavy, a central balding pate, and a misplaced opinion of his leadership skills. We got along like a rushing stream above a poorly contracted dam. I tried. I really tried. But gee whiz, how could someone so consistently endorse such wrong ideas. During those two weeks when I had worked with him at camp, he was constantly trying to change the organization of the camp. He wanted to be consulted on any decisions that Deanna and I made. She and I talked about that and decided were not having any part of that, though we tried to be polite to his face.

At the Pathfinder Fair, he had a very hands-on approach. He was the headman. All decisions were unilaterally his; he was the final arbiter. And they were uniformly wrong. Every chance he could, he slanted them in favor of his club. Fortunately, Bill Holderbaum was the Pathfinder director, not me.

The Denver South pathfinders were cocky. They had fancy uniforms, and their marching team even had helmets. Plus, city kids always thought they were so much better than country hicks. And Rifle was definitely Hicksville. Denver was the state capital. Denver had the Denver Broncos, the Denver Nuggets; the children from Denver South went to Mile High Academy, a K-12 school. There was a single grade class with at least twenty students in every class. They had a large indoor gym and a campus that included a full-size football field and two softball diamonds. Denver had Elitch Gardens amusement park and Cinderella City the largest indoor shopping mall. Did Rifle have anything like that? Yeah, they didn't think so.

Furthermore, Denver had at least five Pathfinder Clubs three times the size of the Rifle Club. The Denver South club had ninety members. Tell me again, how many Rifle had? They had brought only the cream of the crop to the fair. They were here to demonstrate best practices, but my kids were not sure about that.

I arrived early and helped Mrs. Mitchell and Phyllis with breakfast. They had a huge grill. I knew how to make pancakes and made pancakes by the baker's dozen and piled them on the plates. Then, the children started passing through the lines.

In addition to the club from Denver, there were clubs from Glenwood Springs, Durango, Farmington, Cortez, Delta, Grand Junction, Montrose. All across Western Colorado. I knew many of the children, and even more of them knew me. My children floated back behind the lines with ownership. Chrissie hung around and helped pour batter on the very large baking surface. I could tell that she really liked that the other children who had known me from camp could see that yes, you may have known my teacher for a week, but I had him for a whole year, and see how he treats me differently than you.

We started getting low on milk, so Tina asked if I could run into town. Sure, of course. I took off the large bib apron Tina had supplied me. As I went to the car, Ron Borden jogged up to the other side and asked if he could come with me. Of course. We drove across the river, and Ron was his usual talkative self. He was in high spirits. We picked up eight gallons of milk and brought them to the car. As we were driving out of the parking lot, we passed a couple of attractive young women.

"Oh, Mr. Brauer, look at them!"

"Yes, indeed they're nice," I added with appreciation as we drove past, and they smiled at the gawking boy.

"They smiled at me," Ron exclaimed. "They were looking at me. Mr. Brauer, we need to turn around them and pick them up."

I laughed. That was funny.

"Ron, do you hear yourself?"

"Mr. Brauer, you have to admit they were fine." Ron could not let it go. He turned around and had his head out of the car, looking at them as we waited at the parking lot entrance waiting to turn left. "Mr. Brauer!" He implored.

I patted him on the back. "You'll find others, Ron."

"Not like that, Mr. Brauer. I swear I'm in love."

We drove back to the church, and he was grinning all over himself. He was enjoying hanging out with me, two bachelors on the prowl. Ron was funny.

The fair began and had several contests. One of the first was a sit-up relay. There were six children, three on each side of the parking lot. One student at a time would do twenty-five sit-ups while his partner sat on his ankles to keep the feet down. When the first student completed the sit-ups, the partner, who had been sitting on his ankles, would stand up, dash the thirty yards across the parking lot, and then do his sit-ups. In our practices over the last few months, we discovered that if we had the partner kneel backward on his partner's ankles, in other words facing the direction they would run, we could cut off two to three seconds on each exchange. When we did the competition, we won by at least twenty seconds. It was not even close.

Mr. Veltman could not abide that. He ruled that the partner must be facing the person doing sit-ups. I argued the case by showing him the instructions in the manual. There was absolutely nothing in the manual concerning the direction the partner must face. He would still not allow it; the children must repeat the competition. My children were justifiably incensed. They correctly pointed out that the marshal was biased. How could the marshal be a director of a competing club?

"Okay, guys. I agree," I said. "But let's shut them up. You're angry. Use that anger. Let's smoke'em, boys!"

Mike, Doug, Ron, Shon, Steven, and Danny went back to their respective sides. They complied with the arbitrary ruling; they sat facing their partner during the sit-up competition. But these were country boys. They were outside playing every day. We regularly ran all winter, and they were all in shape. Doug, Shon, and Steven were in excellent condition; Mike was a machine gun, lean, all fast-twitch muscle. And they were mad. They beat Denver South by a minute on the redo. The Rifle club kept racking up first places through the morning.

A little before noon, there was a choreographed flag competition. This was clearly on the program because the Denver club had emphasized and excelled in this for several years. They had spent a lot of money on their flags. They had a choreographed flag competition. They did well. Our club did respectably. Though the wind came up suddenly during the program—it can do that in Western Colorado—and a gust of wind caught Heather's flag. It sent her tumbling to the ground. I grabbed the flag as the wind tried to carry it to the end of the parking lot. Heather got up and brushed the gravel off her face. Then she ran over to me, laughed, and hugged me. I gave her the flag. The Denver club won that event. They probably deserved it, though I mentioned to Mr. Veltman that there had been no wind when his club had performed. Didn't he think our club should redo the performance?

Through the day, as I watched my children performing, the others who were not performing hung around. Danny chatted. He was still my little shadow. Shon brought a football over to me during the lunch break. He ran a few patterns. He was a gazelle so graceful. Chad tried to imitate Shon and showed that he was well on the way to being an outstanding athlete. Kelli was in a happy mood. She was always in cozy propinquity, continuing to pester me, occasionally tickling me until I hugged her. Roy marveled that I knew so many children from all over. There were always several asking if I would be back at camp next summer. Roy, in particular, wanted to know how I knew so many girls. I put an arm around him. "You'll be okay, Roy. You're going to do well." And Angie, as always, came running and jumping up, confident I would catch her. Sometimes in the classroom, it had been difficult. Families were like that, but now as the year drew close to the end; the feeling inside of me was immeasurable.

CHAPTER SEVENTY-SEVEN

AND DO YOU KNOW ME?

It was the penultimate week, and the latest fad was paper wads. Whenever I turned my back, the twang of rubber bands flicking became a chorus. I did my best to stop it, though on occasion, I would spend a little longer writing on the chalkboard than I strictly needed. When I saw them, I confiscated their rubber bands.

"Mr. Brauer, did you ever shoot paper wads?" Doug asked.

I looked up from my desk and then stood up. "Doug, you've been with me for seven hours Monday through Friday since late last August. I'm very disappointed in you. Is that how little you know of me?"

Doug looked a little embarrassed.

"Come on, Mr. Brauer." Mike joined the conversation. "You must have shot paper wads when you were young."

"Really, Mike, you too?" And then I turned to the class; I had migrated between the desks. "How many of you think I shot paper wads when I was in elementary school?"

I looked around. A few hands went up at first: Danny was the first, then Mike, Doug, and Steven. Then as I stood there, more hands began to creep up, and when Kelli tentatively raised her hand, all the girls followed. I looked around; all my children had their hands up. They all thought I had shot paper wads. I went to the front of the classroom.

"I just want to say… that uh… of course, you're right!" They burst out laughing. "I had three brothers, for goodness' sake. One of my older brothers used to shoot me with a BB gun; of course, I shot paper wads." Then I stopped. "However, I want you to know." And I shook my finger at them. "I do not approve of this. I do not approve. Now I am just going to write a few things on the chalkboard. It will probably take me twenty-five to thirty seconds to write. In that time, I'll be very disappointed if I should discover that you are shooting paper wads. Very disappointed while I am writing with my face to the chalkboard. And I would be even more disappointed if all of you should take advantage of that and shoot at me. Very disappointed."

When I finished writing the assignments on the chalkboard, there was a sizeable pile of paper wads at and around the chalkboard.

At recess, the stream continued to flow through the schoolyard and the children continued to build dams. They never seemed to get tired of that, the boys more so than the girls. On one of those recesses, while I was standing there watching Steven and Doug oversee the building of another Hoover Dam—the younger children had to work under their oversight—Kelli, Carolyn, Heather, and Chrissie came to stand beside me.

They wanted to know my plans for the summer. I outlined them: General Chemistry at Colorado University in two successive sessions. They asked if it would be hard. I thought it would be quite hard and that I had to have an A if I had a chance at medical school.

"Mr. Brauer," Kelli changed the subject. "Will the teachers in high school be as nice as you?" And the others three girls drew closer.

"As nice as me, Kelli?"

She laughed as we both knew that was a reference to the spanking.

I nodded, "But yes, some of my favorite teachers were in high school. I had some really great teachers in high school."

"How come some teachers are so much better than others?" Heather asked.

"That's a really good question, Heather; what do you think?"

Chrissie answered, "I think it is because you like us. I think that is the difference."

"Even when we are bad," Kelli added with a smirk.

"Yeah... well, maybe not so much when you're bad," I joked. Of course, they thought that was funny.

On Tuesday, before the school board meeting, Virginia Ryber informed me she had mailed her resignation to the conference office. She was not returning; that surprised me. That left it all to Nancy Smith. "Whew!" Depending on Rifle's situation, I thought the load could be tough. I knew many of the parents involved with the Exxon project were now scrambling to find ways to stay in Rifle. They liked living on the Western Slope. It appeared there would be a large school next fall. And now, with Virginia announcing she would not be returning, it could be the same chaos as I had stepped into last summer. I felt bad for my students. And I decided that if the conference called me and implored me to stay for another year, I would take that as a sign from God and stay. I would delay my career change for at least one more year. And the thought of another year with my students was wonderful. Furthermore, I hated to leave something before I had mastered it. There were so many skills of teaching that I could work on.

I talked to Ron McElvain at lunch. He had heard about Miss Ryber, and he had already called the conference with the same alarm. What should they do? Mr. Rice had assured Ron that there was a surplus of quality teachers and not to worry about it. There was no need to worry about replacing Virginia.

Really, a surplus of good teachers? In that case, I did not need to sacrifice my life. If they had a surplus, then I was on my way.

Chrissie seemed to be struggling with long division that day. She stayed up by my desk for her whole math time. She wanted help. I showed her errors to her, even though I realized as she quickly understood my directions that she already knew how to do it, and this was just an excuse to be at my desk. I was always okay if children hung around. If they wanted to be close, I was fine with it if that made them happier.

On the other hand, at the end of the year, Roy still felt he was too old to need to listen to a teacher, which had not changed. And when I tried to explain a math problem to Shon, he put his fingers in his ears. I liked Roy and Shon. Roy was still a large ten-year-old, still trying to find his place. And Shon still hated being inside, especially when it was so beautiful outside.

We had a very long board meeting. The members talked and argued about what to do. They did not want to get into a mess like the start of last year. Yes, Exxon was pulling out, but most parents were planning on staying. They were only graduating one eighth-grader, and there were already at least three first graders for the next year. If anything, the school would be larger. Dr. McElvain tried to explain the conference's position, which the board was not buying. They had years of experience at the school. They knew good teachers were hard to recruit in Rifle. The top teachers wanted to be in Denver, at a larger school. There were more than a few looks in my direction, though they refrained from bringing up my desertion. And now Miss Ryber as well. She had lasted less than six months. But in the end, what could they do. They were reliant on the conference. They did want Dr. McElvain to relay their concerns. He said he would, and the pastor also volunteered to contact the conference. I never got the feeling the pastor was sad to see me go. He was more upset about Virginia.

CHAPTER SEVENTY-EIGHT

AND SUDDENLY IT IS OVER

The conference sent out a memo with observations that no child would be putting forth any effort during the last week of school. So they recommended that we do more interactive lessons during the last week of school: have them write stories, playact Bible scenes, read aloud, do math games, art projects, and longer recess; in other words, close the books. Close them, but without telling the students that we were closing them. I thought that was smart.

So, when the children begged to stay out a little longer at recess, I let them persuade me. We ran farther at lunch; we had larger, more epic games of capture the flag. Our worships in the morning went longer. And when the students were engaged in some debate, which at least in my room often was the case, I let it play out longer. I told stories of my school years, usually little jokes.

And in the evening, outside of my house, I tried to be more aware. I tried to take in the moments, hear the stillness of no automobiles, be mindful of the air's freshness, pay attention to the rabbits playing in the strawberry fields, or across the little lane watching the horse chase Mittens up a tree. I took time to examine the intricacy of a spider web between two tulips. This phase, this short phase of my life, was ending.

Mr. McQueary came by to open the irrigation channel to his land. We had a pleasant chat. It had become clear to me that year that he had made his life living around the principles of simplicity and nature. I aspired to that lifestyle. He practiced it, and I had come to value him.

On Wednesday night after school, Bill invited me up to his house to play some basketball. We had a nice sweaty session of twenty-one. I beat him the first game when I hit a hot streak at the free throw lane, dropping seven in a row. He beat me in the second and third games. I had no real answer to his inside power game. Shon and Kelli cheered their dad on, and then he invited me to have another celebratory ice cream sundae. I never refused ice cream.

On Thursday night, it was Mike's eighth-grade graduation. He was our sole eighth-grader. First, the pastor spoke, and then his dad spoke. All the students sang a song. They were all so handsome and pretty in dresses and suits with their hair so nicely combed and arranged. Virginia read a poem. I handed him his diploma and shook his hand. I put out my hands to suggest one more hug if he wanted.

"I'm good with the handshake, Mr. Brauer," he said with his infectious grin. He turned to look at the class sitting in the front row and grabbed his diploma with both hands. He hesitated for a moment on the stage, then turned back to me. "Okay, Mr. Brauer, I know you want to give me one last hug."

"I do, Mike. I do."

We hugged, and I slapped him on the back.

"I'm glad you came, Mike."

He stopped. "And I'm glad you agreed to take me. Twenty-one students in all eight grades. You're one crazy guy. But hey, I might've even learned something from you." He said and then walked off the stage.

They had a little graduation party in the fellowship hall. And they gave Virginia and me a card with a little monetary gift, which was totally unexpected. It was enough money for me to buy a pair of quality Gortex hiking boots. I wore them for years.

The following day was Friday, the last day of school. We had spelling relays, balloon tosses, treasure hunts. Then we did a clean-up. Everyone cleaned out their desks, and I assigned other jobs: the chalkboards, the trash, the bathrooms, the water fountain. We had our last lunch together. It was hot, so we sat outside in the shade. The children were all very excited. Some of the parents began arriving. Now that they were really done, the children were in no hurry to leave. I got up and went inside to throw my lunch bag in the trash.

Carolyn was sitting at her desk. When I came in, she quickly picked her head up.

"Carolyn? Are you okay?"

She nodded. "Yes, yes. I was just checking to make sure I got everything out of my desk."

It was plain she had been crying.

"Are you sad school is over?" I was trying to understand. I had never cried on the last day of school.

She looked at me and sighed and then exclaimed, "I'm mad at you, Mr. Brauer. I'm so mad at you."

"You're mad? Did I do something to hurt you?"

"Yes, of course, you did," she muttered.

Chad came to the door. "Mom is here. She has to get back to the shop. She is in a hurry."

I looked to the door. Carolyn grabbed her bundle and went with her brother.

I was baffled. I did not want it to end this way. I did not want my school year to end with one of my children mad at me for something I had done. Although I had no clue, I followed them. The parking lot was filling up. Wayne and Katie ran up to hug me as their mother packed their school materials in the trunk. Virginia was on the sidewalk saying goodbye. Doyle and Misty were hugging her. Judy Hess drove in, and Chrissie and Angie ran into the classroom. Ron came up the steps.

"Mr. Brauer, you're the best. I know you're going to kill it next year."

He stuck out his hand. I shook it and then rested my hand on his shoulder.

"You too, Ron. Good luck."

Chrissie and Angie ran to me and squeezed me tight. As tight as their little frames could squeeze.

In a few minutes, everyone was gone. On a hot Friday in May, the school had ended. Virginia said she was tired and went back up to the Mitchell's. She would come back on Sunday and Monday to finish up. Her father was coming Monday night and would be taking her and her stuff back to California on Tuesday. She was getting married in the summer.

I sat back down at my desk. I pulled out a notepad and started to write down the things I needed to do to close out the school. I pulled out the memoranda from the conference. There were a lot of items on the list, and without the children, the list looked tedious.

CHAPTER SEVENTY-NINE

FRESH SCARS IN THE ASPEN

The following day I went to church. The children were happy to see me because they thought I had already left. The Mitchell's invited me for lunch. I thanked Tina profusely and excused myself. I told her I had been planning for a long time to take a big hike on the day after school let out. I had new boots.

On the north side of the valley were the Book Cliffs. I have mentioned them several times. They were magnificent, but on the south side the mountain just flowed up in a never-ending triangle of green. The foliage was so dependent on the orientation to the sun. The Book Cliffs faced south and were dry and barren. But the north-facing mountains kept their snow much longer and were verdant and lush. I had often gazed up at these northern mountains as I drove the Rifle-Rulison backroad. There were some white cliffs at the ridge, and I had decided I wanted to climb up and explore. I was not going to follow a trail. I would just walk up. I could see it turned into a spruce and aspen forest at the higher elevations. I aimed to explore it. As John Muir once wrote, "The mountains are calling, and I must go."

Thus, after church, I ate my lunch in my car by the side of a rarely used county road. I parked the car. I laced up my new boots and started up the mountain with a canteen, my Bible, and a light jacket. The weather was pleasant, but some clouds suggested the possibility of an afternoon storm.

I was soon in an extensive scrub oak forest. It was dense, and the leaves were stiff and pointed. My arms quickly became heavily scratched.

I went up, and up, and up. The foliage began to change, and I passed into meadows of lush grass. The fields were soggy. I appreciated the Gortex of my boots since they were keeping my feet dry. Whenever possible, I tried to follow the trails the wildlife had established. The temperature dropped; it was cool and pleasant.

I kept my eye on the prize. I would work up through the aspen and conifer forests and then to the white cliffs. I had no expectations of being able to climb the cliffs. I just wanted to see them up close. Blue spruce trees began to become more common. I entered another field; the grass was longer here. There were a few trickling rivulets I tried to avoid. I kept trying to find the high ground in each plot of land.

I saw a thick-furred canine appear out of a small copse on my right. I wondered for a moment if it was a wolf but decided it was just a large, very thick-coated coyote. He saw me, saw I was no threat, and loped up the hill. He disappeared into the aspen grove. I followed. I was envious of how the altitude had so little effect on him. By this point, I had to take periodic rests.

As I entered the shade of the forest, the ground became nearly covered in snow. At first, I negotiated around the patches, but that soon became impossible. And the depth of the snow increased. I tromped on. The boot's materials had worked well, keeping my feet dry in the soggy ground, but it could do nothing when the snow came over the top and slid down into my shoe.

At this point, I noticed large scratch marks on the trunks of the trees. Some of the scars were old and black, but other fresh scars were still oozing. Bear were marking their territory. I stopped and looked around; Colorado did have grizzlies. It was time to reconsider my plan. The markings were probably not from grizzly. It was more likely a black bear. But black bear in the early spring, especially if I surprised them or got between a mother and her cubs, was not a good idea.

I looked back down the mountain. It had been a long hike. If I started back down now, it would still be late afternoon before I returned to my car. My goal had been to get next to the white cliffs. I had not achieved that goal, but sometimes goals needed to be rethought. So, I changed my plans and turned downhill.

EPILOGUE

"Little Mike", Mike Sisk, is now an orthopedic surgeon in Steamboat Springs. In college, he worked in the rodeo as a bull rider. His stepbrother "Big Mike" works as an emergency room doctor in Rifle, Colorado.

Ron Borden lives in Hilton Head, South Carolina. He studied computer science and is an operations manager.

Doug Sisk lives in Minnesota. He has been teaching high school physics and shop for twenty years. It is only in the last couple of years that he could not beat the high school students at any sport.

Kelli Holderbaum is a dentist in Grand Junction. She still likes to ski whenever she can.

Shon Holderbaum lives in California. He was a world-class athlete until a car struck his bike. He is working hard at rehabilitation.

Danny Mitchell is a small business owner and is very involved in animal rescue.

Steven Boggs has a successful remodeling business in Washington state.

Carolyn Schlisner was told the next year by her teacher that she would never make it in college. Nevertheless, she graduated with honors with a degree in Nursing Home Administration.

Roy Leatherman grew to six foot seven; he was the star of his high school basketball team. He lives in Grand Junction and is a Medical Technician.

Heather Boggs spent a year traveling around the world with her husband and homeschooling her children. She runs a travel business.

Chrissie Hess lives in Tennessee. She is an RN and works in the operating room.

Angie Hess lives in Kentucky. She got a degree as a paralegal and now works as a project manager.

Chad Schlisner has followed his father's trade and works in the carpet business with his brother.

Wayne (Bobo) Leatherman was also a standout basketball in high school. He had straight A's in college until doctors discovered a brain tumor. He survived but was not able to return to school.

Misty Forshee lives in Wyoming. She ranches and is a professional barrel racer.

Doyle Opitz lives in Wyoming.

Kimberley McElvain graduated as a certified middle school science teacher and taught full time, until she had children. She is delighted now to be a full-time mother.

Katie Leatherman lives in Parachute. She is the stepmom of two children.

I could not find information on Cory Grant, Heather Savage, or Justin.

As for me, yes, I was accepted into medical school and graduated from Loma Linda University Medical School in 1987. I practiced in Internal Medicine for 33 years.

And I did run into Nancy's past roommate, Judy. She was working on getting her RN degree and a Master's in Public Health. I called her up the first weekend I arrived in Southern California. Her voice on the telephone was melodic. Mom and Dad, Ron, Nancy, and I were going to the beach, so I invited her to come along.

She was smart, thin, a dark brunette, funny, and had lovely legs. We had a lot in common and hit it off at once, and by that I mean that I liked smart, thin, funny, dark brunettes with lovely legs.

Three months later, I called my parents and told them they needed to talk some sense into me because I was seriously thinking of proposing. My parents had, of course, met her that first weekend in California. They both liked her immensely and did not see the problem.

I proposed. She said, "Yes! Yes! Yes!" We were married that December in Johnstown, Pennsylvania, and it has been a wonderful life.

We had two children, Cassandra Christine and Sashenka Jessica. Cassie followed in my footsteps. She, too, is a Loma Linda doctor. Sasha chose the path I had considered. She graduated from William and Mary School of Law. We raised them beside the Shenandoah River in the shade of the Massanutten, the glades of the Allegheny.

I still think of my students from time to time, and I smile. God, I loved those kids!

CPSIA information can be obtained
at www.ICGtesting.com
Printed in the USA
BVHW041704230822
645291BV00004B/194